PELICAN BOOKS

MAN AND THE VERTEBRATES

VOLUME II

Alfred Sherwood Romer was born in 1894 and is Professor Emeritus of Zoology at Harvard University. For some years he was Director of the Museum of Comparative Zoology, the Museum founded by Louis Agassiz. In 1966 he was President of the American Association for the Advancement of Science. His major interest lies in the study of the vertebrates, the backboned animals, most especially their structural build and the evolutionary and functional conclusions that may be derived from such studies. Although not disdaining living vertebrates, he is especially interested in the tantalizing problems presented by the study of fossil forms, and therefore is as much a paleontologist as an anatomist. Since the fauna of the Permian red-beds of the American south-west represent an interesting stage in vertebrate history, nearly every spring or summer for the past quarter of a century he has scarched for fossil bones among the rattlesnake-infested 'breaks' of the west Texas ranch country. In addition to numerous papers in scientific journals, his publications include *Vertebrate Paleontology* (1933, 1945) and *The Vertebrate Body* (1949).

MAN AND THE VERTEBRATES

A. S. ROMER

VOLUME II

PENGUIN BOOKS

Penguin Books Ltd, Harmondsworth, Middlesex, England
Penguin Books Inc., 7110 Ambassador Road, Baltimore, Maryland 21207, U.S.A.
Penguin Books Australia Ltd, Ringwood, Victoria, Australia

—

First published 1933
Published in Pelican Books 1954
Reprinted 1957, 1960, 1962, 1963, 1966, 1970, 1971

—

—

Made and printed in Great Britain
by C. Nicholls & Company Ltd
Set in Monotype Times

CONTENTS OF VOLUME TWO

The illustrations in the photogravure supplement are reproduced not from original photographs but from the previous edition

CHAPTER 15

Human Origins

THE history of man is, quite naturally, of particular interest to most of us; and, quite naturally, we would wish to inquire into it in greater detail than in the case of other animal lines. This eagerness for details regarding human history is, however, somewhat embarrassing to the paleontologist. As with the primate group in general, ancient remains of man are rare. It seems probable that the centre of our early evolutionary history lay in Asia or Africa, regions which are comparatively poorly explored and which have yielded few remains. The human story is hence very fragmentary and inadequate at the present time. Our knowledge is constantly increasing; many of our most important fossil finds have been discovered within the past decade or two, and, doubtless, with the continued advance of exploration and research other interesting finds will continue to be made. For the present, however, we can merely describe the isolated remains so far discovered and mention the theories as to lines of descent which they suggest.

THE ICE AGE

Human evolution is essentially a Pleistocene story. Advanced manlike apes are known in Miocene and Pliocene rocks, and types transitional to man were presumably in existence in the latter epoch. These are, however, quite unknown as fossils, and we have at present no human remains from before the Pleistocene, which covers (at the most) only the last million years of earth's history.

This epoch was marked by the occurrence of a vast amount of glaciation. Great sheets of ice formed in the northern regions of Europe and North America and, moving southward, covered large portions of those continents with great glaciers, while smaller glacial areas formed about the higher mountain ranges of the Temperate regions. Such conditions (which might easily recur if the average temperature of our present Temperate zones fell but a few degrees) unquestionably exerted a profound influence over the life of the northern continents. As the glaciers moved southward, regions once tropical changed to temperate areas, to pine forests, to barren tundras, and, finally, if in the glaciers' path, became deeply covered with slowly moving masses of ice; with the retreat of the ice cap this sequence was reversed.

PLEISTOCENE ANIMAL LIFE. Under the influence of conditions of this sort, we might expect vast migrations of animals and the extinction of forms unable to adjust themselves to new environmental conditions. We might expect, too, that changed conditions, with a premium placed upon adaptations to meet them, would stimulate evolutionary development. The Ice Age may have been a potent influence in the advance of man.

Among the animals with which our Pleistocene ancestors contended were most of the living forms but, in addition, many types now entirely extinct or much restricted in their distribution. In Eurasia there were great elephants – mammoths – of several types, the woolly mammoth of the north and types adapted to warmer conditions in the south. Rhinoceroses were abundant in Europe, and great herds of horses were present on the steppes which covered much of that Continent. Remains of giant bears and lions are plentiful in Europe cave deposits. The reindeer ranged south to southern France, and, on the other hand, the hippopotamus reached England during the warmer parts of the period.

In North America, too, there were many creatures now extinct. Here, also, were various types of mammoths, as well as the mastodon, a more primitive proboscidian. Camels and horses roamed the American plains. Giant, short-snouted bears, lions, and great sabre-toothed cats were among the most conspicuous of carnivores. Great ground sloths, one as large as an elephant, were numerous, and in the south were present the glyptodonts, giant cousins of the armadillos.

THE GLACIAL AREAS. We must not over-emphasize the extent of the Pleistocene glaciation. It was almost entirely confined to the northern Arctic and Temperate zones, and even here vast regions were untouched. In North America the line of the Ohio and Missouri rivers marks out, roughly, the outer limits of the advance of the glaciers arising in arctic Canada. In Europe, Scandinavia was the centre of a glacial area which covered most of Great Britain, northern Germany, and northern Russia. The Alps formed a smaller centre of activity from which glaciers descended the mountain slopes some distance into the surrounding areas, and other European mountains formed minor centres. Northern Asia appears to have been unglaciated, although with a cold climate, and large areas of Europe and North America were never touched by the ice caps.

THE GLACIAL SEQUENCE. When glaciation was first studied, a century ago, it was thought that there had been a single advance and retreat of the ice. This is now, however, known not to have been the case; there were wide fluctuations in the extent of the glaciated areas, and, between successive advances of the ice, regions in the glacial areas have had climates seemingly warmer than they have today.

In America glacial studies have resulted in the clear distinction of four successive glacial maxima, between which for long periods of time – tens or even hundreds of thousands of years – there were long interglacial periods with temperate to warm climates in the north-eastern United States and southern Canada. In Europe studies of the Alpine glacial areas have furnished considerable evidence that there, too, there were four times of maximum glaciation, with three interglacial periods. These four maxima have been given names derived from Alpine localities in which the deposits formed at that time are well preserved – Gunz, Mindel, Riss, and Würm, names chosen partly because they follow one another in alphabetical as in chronological sequence.

The four-glaciation doctrine is not, however, fully established. There have been many workers who believed that in Europe there were only two glacial maxima and one interglacial period. The other two supposed interglacial periods were, according to this theory, only minor fluctuations within a single major glacial advance. Perhaps a compromise may be made between the two theories, and both ideas may be essentially correct. It may be that there were four glaciations but that they they were grouped two and two. The Gunz and Mindel glaciations may have occurred close together in time in the early Pleistocene, with but a short interval between them. The Riss and Würm may have been similarly associated towards the end of the Pleistocene. A long, warm, major interglacial period may have occurred between the two great times of ice activity. These ideas have been incorporated in the accompanying diagram.

DATING HUMAN REMAINS. Debatable as this subject of the number of glaciations is, it is the only 'time-table' we have for the Pleistocene, and it is important to attempt to tie our knowledge of human history into this glacial sequence. This, however, can be done only in a limited way, and the evidence is none too clear. If human remains were actually found in glacial deposits, their position could be determined with comparative ease; but the edge of a glacier is not the place that man would seek as a comfortable habitation, and such finds are negligible. Finds in caves often occur in stratified fashion, thus giving us a sequence for fossil remains; but these cave deposits usually cover but a limited period of time. The advance and retreat of the ice caps affected climatic conditions over large areas and caused great fluctuations in the flow of streams far from the glaciated areas. These variable conditions resulted in the development of terraces representing old valley levels along stream channels, and the sequence of remains frequently found in such terraces may be determined. Associated with glacial advances and retreats there seem to have been great fluctuations of the coast lines. In a number of regions are found coastal terraces, indicating that the shore once lay at higher levels, sometimes several hundred feet above the present strand.

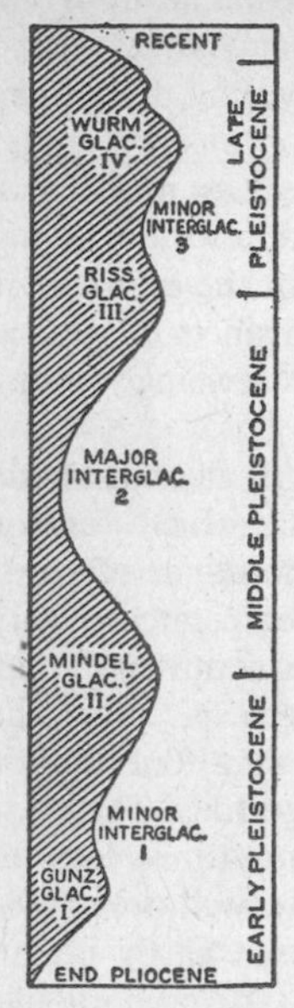

A diagram of Ice Age chronology. The distance from the bottom to the top represents the duration of Pleistocene and Recent times – perhaps a million years. The curved line represents successive advances (curvature to right) and retreats (curvature to left) of the glacial front in Europe and America. There were four such advances, named from Alpine localities and their intervening interglacial stages, the second one perhaps much longer than the others. For convenience the Pleistocene may be divided into Early, Middle, and Late portions, indicated here and as used in subsequent discussion in the text.

In tropical and sub-tropical regions the glaciers cannot, of course, give us direct evidence of the geologic age of human finds. Indirectly, however, they are of aid. Changes in the glaciated regions presumably influenced climatic conditions in far distant regions. In correlation with this, workers in the tropics find strong evidence of alternations of wet, or 'pluvial', periods with dry, 'interpluvials'. It is very probable that the wet stages correspond to glacial conditions farther north, interpluvial times to interglacial periods.

Animal remains found with those of man are of importance. They will tell us whether the times were warm or cold – glacial or interglacial – and the presence or absence of certain forms may afford evidence that we are dealing with early or late Pleistocene times. Plants, too, furnish useful evidence, for they are even more restricted by differences in environment than are animals and hence can reflect the climatic fluctuations which occurred during the Pleistocene. An interesting recent development is due to the discovery that pollen grains may be preserved intact in peat beds for long periods of time and yield valuable information concerning the types of trees present when the peat bog was formed.

Man has long been a toolmaker and tool-user, and stone implements are found in many Pleistocene deposits. The general sequence of the human cultures to which these implements pertain is in many cases well established, and human fossils associated with stone tools can often be assigned to a definite cultural period. But this does not always assure an absolute date, for cultural stages may overlap. The reader of this book lives in an advanced stage of culture; the native Australian is still in the Stone Age. We have no guarantee that greater uniformity existed in the past.

In sum: We may attempt to date human remains by the geologic conditions of the find, by the associated animal and plant remains, and by implements discovered with them. But this evidence is often difficult to correlate with the glacial time-table, and this time-table, in turn, is still not firmly established. Hence dates assigned to earlier human finds must be regarded as only tentative in their nature.

HUMAN CULTURES

Although the skeletal remains of ancient man are our main concern in this chapter, cultural objects are generally found

<table>
<tr><th>Geological Time</th><th>Glacial Sequence</th><th>Rough Estimates of Time in Years since Beginning of Stage</th><th>Cultural Stages</th><th colspan="3">Type of Culture</th></tr>
<tr><td rowspan="4">RECENT</td><td rowspan="4">Postglacial</td><td>1,400 B.C.</td><td>Iron Age</td><td colspan="3" rowspan="2">Use of Metals</td></tr>
<tr><td>3,000 B.C.</td><td>Bronze Age</td></tr>
<tr><td>5,000 B.C.</td><td>Neolithic</td><td colspan="3">Agriculture and animal domestication.</td></tr>
<tr><td>13,000 B.C.</td><td>Mesolithic</td><td colspan="3">Azilian, Tardenoisian, Maglemosian, etc.</td></tr>
<tr><td rowspan="2">UPPER PLEISTOCENE</td><td>Late Würm glaciation (IV)</td><td>40,000</td><td>Upper Paleolithic</td><td colspan="3">Aurignacian, Solutrian, Magdalenian in Europe; related cultures in other areas.</td></tr>
<tr><td>Early Würm glaciation
Third interglacial</td><td>250,000</td><td>Middle Paleolithic</td><td colspan="3">Mousterian culture of Europe and western Asia, Levalloisian (continued), etc.</td></tr>
<tr><td>MIDDLE PLEISTOCENE</td><td>Riss glaciation (III)
Second Interglacial
Mindel glaciation (II)</td><td>800,000</td><td>Lower Paleolithic</td><td>Hand-axe cultures of western and southern Europe, Africa, and east to India: Acheulean, preceded by Abbevillian</td><td>Flake and chopping-tool cultures of northern and central Europe: Clactonian. Levalloisian (part), etc.</td><td>Chopping-tool and flake cultures of south-eastern Asia: Soan, etc.</td></tr>
<tr><td>LOWER PLEISTOCENE</td><td>First Interglacial
Gunz glaciation (I)</td><td>1,000,000</td><td>Pre-Paleolithic</td><td colspan="3">Crude beginnings of use of stone; 'eoliths', etc.</td></tr>
</table>

associated with such fossils, and we should therefore consider, if briefly, cultural as well as physical evolution.

Many of the works of man are made of perishable materials which disintegrate rapidly in the earth. He has, however, always used for his primary tools and weapons harder and more lasting materials – metals in more recent times, stone in earlier days.

FLINT. Among the types of stone available, man early discovered the value of flint as a material for the making of implements. Whereas many types of stone are composed of mixed materials which fracture irregularly and frequently abrade all too readily, flint is a homogeneous, siliceous material which is extremely hard and retains an edge well and yet can be readily chipped by an experienced hand into a variety of useful tools. Flint occurs as nodules in chalk rocks, common in many parts of the world, and hence was available for use by numerous ancient races of man. In the absence of flint other materials were used – quartzite, silicified tuff, hard shales, etc. – but these are generally inferior in their properties and make relatively crude implements.

Two major types of stone tools may be distinguished. In one, common in certain of the oldest recognized cultures, it is the nodule itself which forms the implement; flakes are struck from it until the remaining core has been given the desired shape. The second type, by far the more common, is that in which the flakes rather than the core are the implements.

In many cases the flakes appear to have been struck off the core more or less at random. Such flakes may be useful without further work being done upon them but frequently were retouched, a series of smaller chips being removed along the margins to give more perfect shape and greater usefulness. On the other hand, the shaping was sometimes done before the flake was struck off; the core was prepared by preliminary chipping, so that when the flake was dislodged by a skilfully directed blow, it was already of the desired contour and needed no further work done upon it.

As a result of these methods ancient man was able to manufacture a variety of implements. In some cases we can hardly guess the uses to which they were put, but they appear to include a variety of scrapers, knives, awls, chisels, etc., which experiment shows can do effective work upon such materials as wood and hides.

Below we will characterize briefly the sequence of cultures which the study of such remains shows to have occurred in the process of human development. These stages are termed ages. Following a vague period in which man may have made the first steps in tool-making, they include: (a) the Paleolithic, or Old Stone Age, covering much of the Pleistocene and frequently divided into Lower, Middle, and Upper periods; (2) the Mesolithic Age of the early millenniums of geologically recent times; (3) the Neolithic, or New Stone Age, when man first began to lead a settled rather than a nomadic existence; and (4) the metal ages, Bronze and Iron, which carry the story down to historic times.

EOLITHS. In Middle and Upper Pleistocene deposits we find numerous stone tools which were definitely made by man and which fall into well recognized categories in characteristic

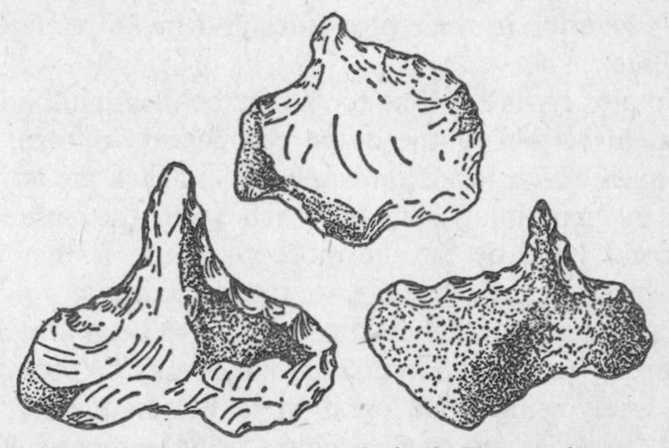

Eoliths from the Pliocene of Kent, England. These and many other finds of Tertiary flints supposed to be of human manufacture are, in many cases at least, probably of natural orgin. (After Harrison)

cultures. But before this level was reached, there must have been stages during which man made his first crude experiments as a toolmaker and tool-user, availing himself of such pieces of flint as came to hand or, at the most, knocking off a few chips to fashion the piece to his hand or to his desires. To flint finds believed to be of this nature, the term 'eoliths', or 'dawn stones', is often applied. But it is obvious that it is a difficult if not impossible task surely to tell such implements from stones chipped or worn through natural causes, and the status of many supposed discoveries of this sort is dubious. Numerous finds of flints from the early Pleistocene have been claimed as man's handiwork. This is, a priori, not unreasonable, and this period may perhaps be termed the Pre-Paleolithic; surely by the beginning of the Pleistocene man's ancestors must have advanced beyond the ape level, and many of these flints give some appearance of having been worked. However, equally convincing eoliths have been described from the Miocene and Pliocene, when it is probable our ancestors were still on the ape level. These are open to considerable suspicion, and scepticism is even stronger concerning still older eoliths from the Oligocene and even the Eocene, when not even a monkey was in existence.

LOWER PALEOLITHIC. In contrast with this dubious situation is that which we encounter when we progress into the middle portion of the Pleistocene. Here man was a maker of

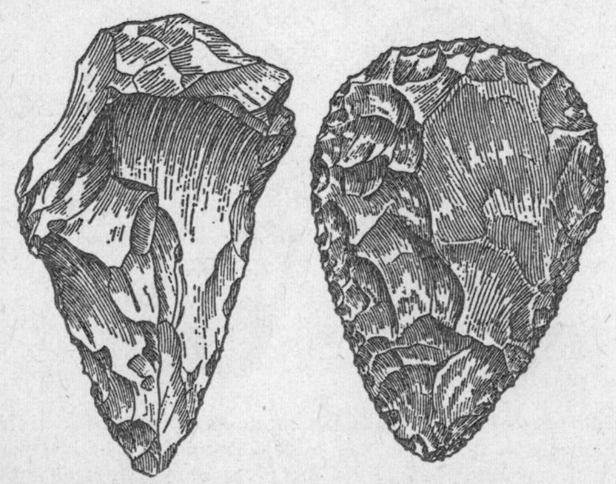

Examples of the hand axe, or *coup de poing*, from Abbevillian (Chellean) (*left*) and Acheulean (*right*) deposits. About ¼ natural size. The Abbevillian types are crudely made; those from the Acheulean are more firmly chipped and thinner and the edges straighter. (After Cole)

stone tools which, although frequently crude, are readily identified and classified by the expert.

The classic Lower Paleolithic cultures are those identified nearly a century ago in the terraces along the Somme River in northern France at Abbeville, St Acheul, and other towns in the Amiens district. In these cultures the characteristic tool was the hand axe, or *coup de poing* (although flakes were used as well). This was a large nodule of flint often weighing several pounds from which chips had been removed to give it an almond-like shape, the rounded end fitting the palm, and a cutting edge extending down either margin. The older phase of this type of culture, in which the hand axe was crudely prepared, is the Abbevillian; * in the succeeding and closely related Acheulean the implement was more carefully fashioned and the cutting edges straighter. Abbevillian and Acheulean types are widespread in Middle Pleistocene deposits in western and southern Europe; beyond this region they have been found as far east as India and south through Africa to the Cape.

But it has been found in recent years that there were other widespread cultural elements in the Lower Paleolithic. In Europe there existed, alongside the hand-axe cultures, others in which the implements were made entirely from flakes, not cores.

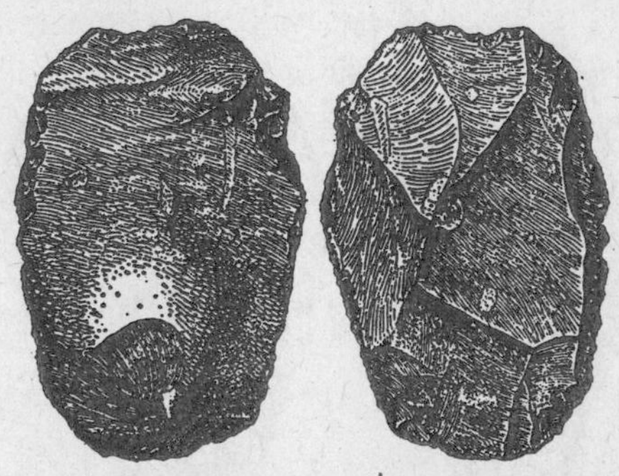

A Levallois-type flake. Large flakes of this sort are characteristic of many horizons of the Lower and Middle Paleolithic. The flint nodule from which they were struck off was first prepared by chipping the surface to the desired contours. After the flake was detached by a sharp blow no further work was done upon it. In consequence one surface (the original inner one) is smooth, except for a swelling (termed the 'bulb of percussion') near the point where the blow was struck. The specimen illustrated was nearly 5 inches long. (From De Mortillet)

Their classification and relationships are by no means settled as yet. We may note the Clactonian culture, characterized by an abundance of small rough flakes, and the Levalloisian, in which the principal type was a large thin flake struck from a carefully prepared core.

* Formerly termed Chellean.

During the past few years there has been emerging knowledge of still another culture complex characteristic of the Middle Pleistocene of south-eastern Asia. In this we find, in addition to flakes, a core tool; this latter is not a hand axe but a crude, massive chopper. Such cultures are present in India (the Soan culture), Burma, China, and Java and are of great interest because they appear to be associated with the early human types of that area – *Sinanthropus* and perhaps *Pithecanthropus* as well.

Apart from the bare knowledge of their tools, we can tell little of the life of men of the early Paleolithic except by inference. Occasional discoveries of hearths indicate that they were users of fire. Clothes, if present, can have been only in the shape of hides. But there is no indication of homes of any sort, probably nothing beyond the use of natural rock shelters and caves or of boughs arranged as a windbreak. They were without agriculture or domestic animals and hence must have been nomadic hunters

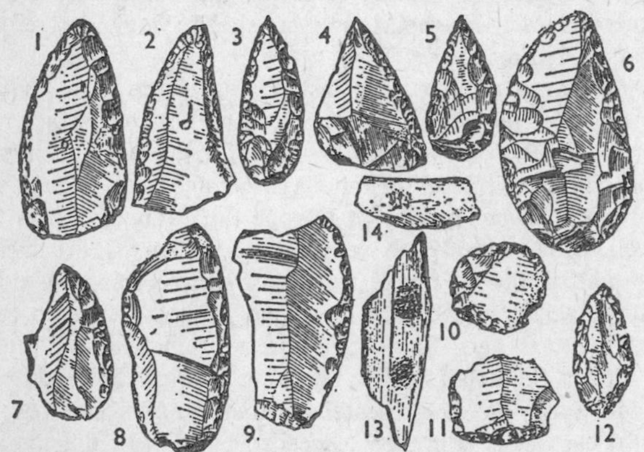

Mousterian implements from the rock shelter of La Ferrassie, France. Most are well-shaped flint flakes with the edges carefully retouched. Bones (13, 14) were used for flaking flints by pressure or as chopping blocks. (After Capitan and Peyrony)

and food-gatherers. All in all, their life, judged by modern standards, must have been on a low plane – and a most disagreeable one.

MIDDLE PALEOLITHIC. Later in the Pleistocene, during much of the last (Würm) glaciation and the warm period preceding it, the characteristic European culture is the Mousterian, which derives its name from the rock shelter of Le Moustier in southern France. In the typical Mousterian the hand axe has disappeared, and we find instead a variety of flake tools which are carefully shaped by retouching. This suggests, as may well be the case, that the Mousterian has been derived from the flake cultures of the Lower Paleolithic. There is no sharp line of demarcation between Lower Paleolithic and this period, and earlier types of implements still persist in the Middle Paleolithic. Even the hand axe is found in some sites of this age (as at La Micoque in France), while the large flakes characteristic of the Levalloisian are frequently encountered with typical Mousterian implements. The Mousterian is common in many parts of Europe and on east into Palestine, west Turkestan, and Siberia, and closely related cultures, together with the Levallois flakes, are widespread in Africa. In many parts of Asia, however, the Mousterian is unknown. In the Middle Paleolithic, in contrast to earlier cultures, the makers of the tools are definitely known; in numerous instances the Mousterian sites have yielded remains of Neanderthal man.

UPPER PALEOLITHIC. The last phases of the Würm glaciation (and hence the very end of the Pleistocene) are characterized by the Upper Paleolithic cultures. Here for the first time we are dealing with implements definitely associated with men of our own species, *Homo sapiens*. In Europe the cultures of this time are well known and have received names based on sites in central and southern France. The major culture was that termed the Aurignacian, which may have had its beginnings as much as 40,000 years ago. Succeeding the Aurignacian we find in many sites a Solutrian layer containing a culture of a different type, which may have represented an invasion of western Europe from the east. This is in turn succeeded by the Magdalenian, an evolution from the Aurignacian. The Aurignacians and Magdalenians seem to have favoured caves and rock shelters as homes; the Solutrians appear to have been nomadic steppe hunters of wild horses.

Flint work in the Upper Paleolithic cultures has as a major feature the production of long slim blades, many suitable for knives, struck from a prepared core. A characteristic type is that known as a graver (or burin), in which the end of the blade was used as a knife-point. The Solutrian was characterized by large

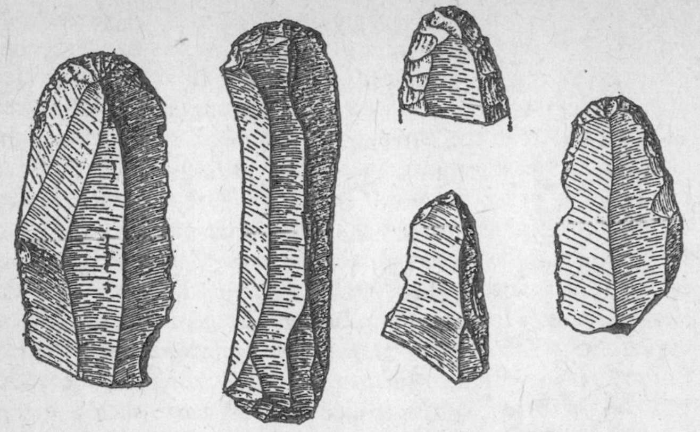

Upper Paleolithic scrapers from the cavern of Font-de-Gaume. Long blades of flint, simply but effectively worked, are characteristic of the Aurignacian and Magdalenian. (After Capitan, Breuil, and Peyrony)

'laurel-leaf' and 'willow-leaf' blades. These were carefully shaped by the removal of small flakes through pressure rather than hammer blows.

New cultural features made their appearance in the Upper Paleolithic. Bone, previously little used, is extensively employed, particularly in the Magdalenian. An interesting item is the discovery of bone needles. A novel feature is a marked development of art, particularly in the Magdalenian. Many engraved and carved bones and statuettes have been discovered, for example, and especially striking are the engravings and paintings which adorn the walls of a number of caverns in southern France and the Pyrenees.

Although our present knowledge of them is limited, similar Upper Paleolithic cultures were widespread in Asia and Africa, in India and China to the east and Kenya to the south. In some cases these appear to be closely comparable to the European Aurignacian; in others local terms have been given, as in north Africa, where Upper Paleolithic cultures termed the 'Capsian' and 'Oranian' are notable for the abundance of tiny flakes termed 'microliths'.

MESOLITHIC. It was once believed that from the typical Old Stone Age man advanced at once into the settled, essentially 'civilized' Neolithic stage. But in recent decades it has been increasingly realized that there existed transitional cultures, now classed as the Mesolithic, or Middle Stone Age. The Old Stone Age, for the most part, can be considered as having come to an end with the final stages of retreat of the glaciers, somewhere of the order of 13,000 years before Christ; the Mesolithic may have, on the average, lasted through the next 10,000 years.

A Solutrian laurel-leaf blade. This cultural stage is characterized by finely worked flints. The desired form was attained by the removal by pressure flaking of small chips over the entire surface. (After Cole)

Mesolithic man lived under climatic conditions which had changed greatly from those known by his predecessors. In much of Europe, with the retreat of the ice, there ensued a forest stage with a damp climate, and many of the animals which man once hunted had vanished from the scene. Farther from the erstwhile glacial regions there also appear to have been climatic shifts, and great regions of the Sahara and central Asia, earlier well watered, appear to have become progressively drier and less adapted for human life.

Mesolithic man was still a wandering hunter and food-gatherer like his predecessors; although the dog appears as a camp follower, there were no other domestic animals and no agriculture. Many of the flints found in Mesolithic camp sites are microliths – small chips in triangular and other geometric shapes. In Europe, Azilian, Tardenoisian, and Maglemosian are among the more familiar names given to cultures of this age. Mesolithic cultures of various sorts appear to have been widespread also in both Asia and Africa, bridging the gap between the Old Stone Age and Neolithic times. Although most groups in the Old World have passed beyond this level, Mesolithic or even Upper Paleolithic conditions persisted in outlying regions (such as Australia, for example), and it seems certain that the early invaders of the Americas were in a Mesolithic (or even late Paleolithic) cultural stage.

NEOLITHIC. The initiation of the Neolithic marks the greatest revolution that has occurred in human cultural evolution. The age gains its name from the relatively unimportant fact that stone implements, although retained, were modified in type. Somewhat more important was the development of pottery, which improved facilities for food storage (because of the indestructibility of pot fragments, this has been invaluable to the archeologist in identifying cultural groups through ceramic variations).

The major developments of the Neolithic, however, were in two other fields: the development of agriculture and the domestication of animals. Man thereby gained control over his food sources, could cease to be a wandering hunter, and could live in settled communities with all the implications for future social and economic advances that such a life implies. Among agricultural products, edible grasses, from which our modern grains have arisen, were prominent from the first. Of animals the pig, cow, sheep, and goat were early domesticated; the ass and, later, the horse were added as beasts of burden and transport. While there are many uncertainties, it appears that the wild progenitors of many of these plants and animals were present in a belt of country extending from Egypt east through Mesopotamia to northwestern India, and the valleys of the great rivers of this area – the Nile, the Tigris, the Euphrates, and the Indus – may well have been major centres of origin of the Neolithic mode of life. The time of origin cannot be definitely set. Certainly, however, the Neolithic was well established in the Near East by 4000 B.C., and from that time on this new culture appears to have spread rapidly over vast areas of the Old World.

INTRODUCTION OF METALS. Having exploited the animal and vegetable resources about him, Neolithic man was not slow to explore the possiblities of the mineral world. Copper objects soon appear in Neolithic materials. This metal by itself, however, is too weak to form good tools. It was soon found that alloys with other metals gave a much harder product. Particularly useful was bronze, a copper-tin alloy, and by about 3000 B.C. a Bronze Age had begun in the Near East, with this metal supplanting stone in the more important tools and weapons. From this centre bronze spread widely over Europe and Asia so that this metal was common in most of Europe by 2000 B.C. and had extended east to China by about 1400 B.C.

Later – again apparently in the Near East – man mastered the methods of preparation of a second, more difficult but still more useful metal – iron. Beginning about 1400 B.C., the use of iron spread rapidly, and within a relatively few centuries iron had supplanted bronze in great areas of Eurasia and is today the dominant toolmaking material of the great majority of Old World peoples.

In Africa, however, bronze did not penetrate far south, and iron was introduced but slowly and to a limited degree. In consequence, many peoples of that continent are still in an essentially Neolithic stage, and the same is true of many areas of Asia. America was still more backward, for the Indians had barely begun the use of copper at the time of discovery and were thus far behind the Old World.

PRIMITIVE MAN IN ASIA

For the late phases of the human evolutionary story, much of the evidence is derived from finds in Europe and the general Mediterranean region. For the earlier part of the story, however, the European data are, as yet, unsatisfactory. From the Middle Pleistocene deposits of Asia, on the other hand, have come two famous and closely related types, *Pithecanthropus* and *Sinanthropus*, which furnish valuable knowledge regarding the most primitive stage of human evolution of which we have certain knowledge.

THE JAVA 'APE MAN'. In the late eighties Dr Eugene Dubois, of the Dutch army medical service, went to the East Indies with the announced intention of finding primitive man. Many have made such announcements; the surprising thing is that Dubois did actually find what he was looking for. Remains of extinct animals had been discovered in deposits of volcanic ash on the banks of the Solo River in eastern Java. Dubois set to work, in 1892, to excavate such a bone bed near the village of Trinil. Soon, among the mammal remains, he came upon a tooth of human appearance. Close by was found a skullcap and later, and some distance away, in the same excavation, a thigh bone (femur) and two other teeth. Dubois returned to Europe, gave a scientific description of the fragments, which he named *Pithecanthropus erectus*, the 'erect ape man', and turned the remains over to a Dutch museum. With this, additions to our knowledge of this Java man ceased for three decades. A German

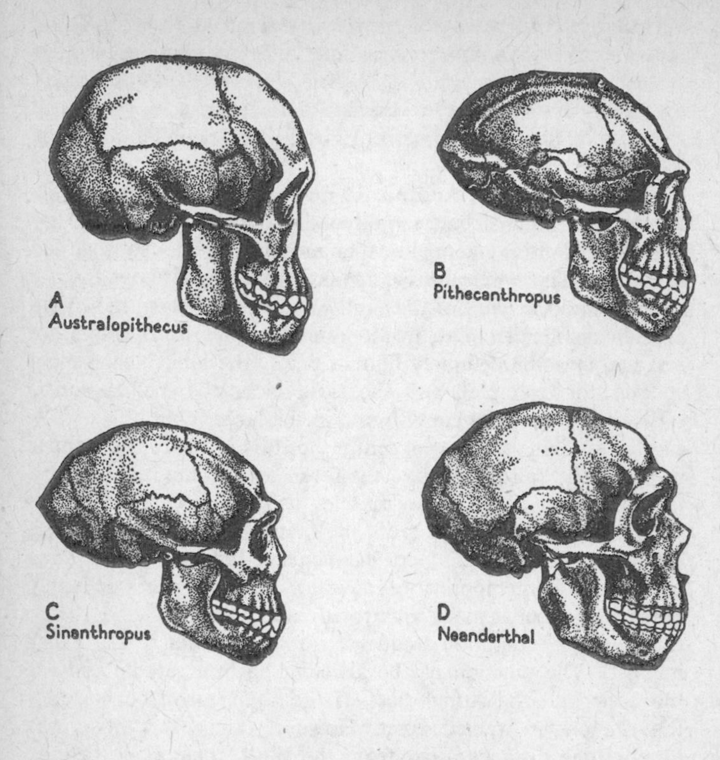

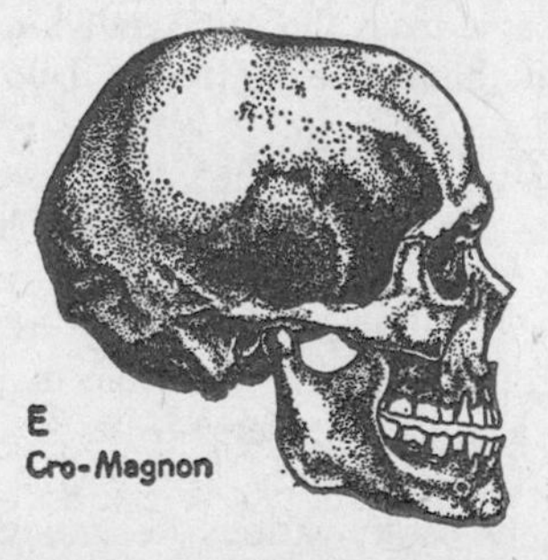

A comparative series of skulls of fossil apes and men. (*A*, after Dart and Broom, *B*, *D*, *E*, after McGregor, *C*, after Weidenreich)

scientific expeditions made vast excavations at the Trinil site, found numerous animal bones, but failed to find the slightest further trace of *Pithecanthropus*. And, for some reason difficult to understand, even the original find itself was during all this time kept hidden from both the public and the scientists.

The nature of the skullcap, as described by Dubois, was so unusual that much debate and discussion ensued. It was obviously far more primitive and apelike than anything previously regarded as human. There were heavy, apelike brow ridges above the eye sockets, and the vault of the skull was extremely low, indicating a brain far smaller than in modern man. But brow ridges are retained in some definitely human types (the later Neanderthal species, for example), and the skull lacks the median longitudinal crest (sagittal crest) found in the larger apes. (The skullcap has a slight ridge in the centre, but this is due to the manner in which the paired bones of the forehead became fused, not to the attachment of heavy jaw muscles, as in the ape crest.)

Nothing could be said, from the first remains, about the face and jaws, and the teeth were inconclusive (and in fact two may belong to a contemporary orangutan). The femur was definitely human (a peculiar bony outgrowth near its upper end is due to a diseased condition frequent in man and not of particular interest). The position of the articular surfaces at the ends of the bone and the straightness of the shaft prove conclusively that its owner walked erect. However, since this bone was found some distance away from the skull, there is no definite proof that it came from the same individual, and some writers are inclined to think that the femur belonged to some other form of man.

In summing up this evidence, Dubois himself was at first inclined to consider that the creature was halfway between man and ape – the 'missing link' of popular terminology – a form with many apelike features but walking erect in human fashion. From this point of view the scientific name is an appropriate one. As to its age, its discoverer believed it to be Pliocene and hence of remarkable antiquity.

There were, however, various dissenting opinions. As to its geological position, it soon became apparent that it was rather later than at first appeared; that it was Pleistocene, not Pliocene, and not even early Pleistocene at that. It comes from beds at about the middle of the Pleistocene – about 500,000 years ago according to some current estimates. As to its evolutionary status, a majority of students were inclined to believe that, although unquestionably primitive, *Pithecanthropus* was man rather than ape. But, on the other hand, one authority claimed that it was nothing but a gigantic gibbon, for the contours of the gibbon skull are similar (although on a much smaller scale), and the gibbon, too, can walk erect.

The last two decades have seen a great increase in our knowledge of *Pithecanthropus*. In 1923 the original remains were made available for study, and it was disclosed for the first time that the interior of the skull had been excavated, thus affording valuable data on the brain. Dubois further revealed that he had other materials which were from the same beds (although from other localities) and hence may well have belonged to *Pithecanthropus*. These materials included four other femora and a partial lower jaw. Still more recently, from 1936 to 1939, paleontological work in Java by von Koenigswald has unearthed a number of new finds of this ape man. All are from the valley of the same Solo River, but from other localities, and most from Sangiran, farther upstream. At this last place were found remains of three more skullcaps, one very well preserved, a lower jaw, and an upper jaw which gives much information, previously lacking, concerning the face. From Modjokerto was obtained a child's skull in somewhat older beds; this was at first thought to be of a different type but is now recognized to be a young *Pithecanthropus*.

If we check over this list of material now available, it is seen that we know little except the skull and jaws. These, however, are fairly adequately represented, and from these structures the expert can extract many valuable data as to the nature and relationships of Java man.

As has been said, the braincase was extremely low and the brow ridges enormous. It is, further, rather narrow compared to its length, a feature common to most early human forms. The breadth/length ratio is one universally used in the study of human skulls. Those in which the breadth is less than 75 per cent of the length are termed dolichocephalic – long-headed; if the percentage is above 80, brachycephalic, or round-headed;

intermediate figures indicate a mesocephalic condition. The average index of the three skullcaps measured is 75.

From the contours of the interior of the braincase there can be made an endocranial cast. This mirrors the folds of the tissues wrapping the brain and hence gives valuable clues as to brain shape and size. A study of such a cast of the type skull shows that the brain cavity of *Pithecanthropus* had a capacity of about 940 cubic centimetres; in the case of the other good skullcap, the estimate is lower, 835 cubic centimetres. The endocranial capacity of a modern male European is about 1,500 cubic centimetres; that of some primitive existing races averages about 1,200; few great ape brains exceed 600. *Pithecanthropus*, from these figures, was thus about midway between the great apes and living men in the size of his brain. These figures of brain size are rather smaller than is the case in any other group of fossil men. However, early human types tend to show a considerable difference between sexes in brain capacity, the female being the smaller, and a study of the materials suggests that the two good skullcaps belonged to early Javan ladies. In brain, *Pithecanthropus* may be rather on the human side of the ape man 'divide'. That this is the case is shown by the brain contours seen in the cast. These indicate an arrangement of the 'grey matter' in an essentially human rather than a simian pattern. The development of areas related to speech and its reception suggests that *Pithecanthropus* had at least the rudiments of language.

The upper-jaw specimen shows that *Pithecanthropus*, like certain other related types, differed markedly from modern man in a more projecting and broader face, with a large and probably flattened nose. The teeth are rather large and show some apelike features of the molar pattern but, on the whole, are human rather than apelike. The 'wisdom tooth', small in many later fossil and living men, is not yet reduced. In apes a gap exists in the upper tooth row into which fits the projecting canine of the lower jaw. In the only upper-jaw specimen of *Pithecanthropus* this gap is present. Apparently this is a male; the female presumably had a smaller and more normal human canine, and this simian feature has not been reported in any other human type.

If the evidence now at hand concerning *Pithecanthropus* be summed up, it is clear that this ape man was a man and not an ape. Nevertheless, he was a man of a very low and seemingly primitive sort and had retained many archaic features absent or reduced in most other known fossil men. We may postpone further discussion of his position in human evolution until we have examined the closely related *Sinanthropus*.

PEKING MAN. In the early 1920s a Swedish scientific mission in China investigated a series of caves in the limestone hills near Choukoutien, some thirty-seven miles south-west of Peking, China. These contained an enormous mass of deposits which included bones of a variety of animals, many of which are extinct. This fauna is now known to indicate definitely a Middle Pleistocene age for the associated materials.

Included in the finds were two teeth which were either simian or human and attracted the interest of Dr Davidson Black, anatomist at the medical school in Peking. Study of a third tooth, found in 1927, convinced him that it was human but of a primitive sort. On this slender basis he established a new genus and species of man, *Sinanthropus pekingensis*, and undertook further investigation of the site.

His seemingly rash conclusions were, happily, verified. In 1929, a well-preserved skullcap of a very primitive sort was unearthed. Adequate funds were procured for extensive excavations, and, in the course of a decade, under Dr Black and, after his untimely death, Dr Franz Weidenreich, there has come to light a whole series of remains belonging to about three dozen individuals including both sexes and both young and adults. There is little postcranial material, although there are fragments of most of the principal leg bones, and hence we have very little idea of the general bodily build. No skull is complete, but between the various specimens nearly the entire cranial structure is known.

The braincase is quite similar in its proportions to that of *Pithecanthropus*, with large continuous supraorbital ridges and a very low retreating forehead. The skull is long and narrow posteriorly, the bones much thickened. The face, too, is quite similar to that of *Pithecanthropus*, and the jaws show a similar chinless, primitive, and yet essentially human structure. The brain size is, however, rather greater than in the Java man, for the endocranial capacities reported are 915, 1,050, 1,1,00, and 1,200 cubic centimetres.

Several points of interest can be deduced regarding the life of Peking man. He was already a tool-user, for a number of implements have been found in the cave. These are of the crude chopper and flake types, which we have noted earlier to be characteristic of the Lower Paleolithic period in eastern Asia. He was, further, a fire-user, for a number of hearths are found.

Still another characteristic – not so pleasant – is suggested by the nature of the fossil finds themselves. The remains consist, we have noted, almost entirely of skulls. These were not burials, as far as can be determined from the conditions under which they were found, and in every instance the braincase had been broken open from below. It seems highly probable that the brains, and probably the missing bodies, were used as food. By whom? There are no traces there of any other creature capable of doing this except Peking man himself. He may thus be reasonably accused of cannibalism.

RELATIONSHIPS OF *PITHECANTHROPUS* AND *SINANTHROPUS*

When the first braincase of Peking man was discovered, it seemed fairly sure that this type and *Pithecanthropus* were related, and this impression has grown continually stronger as more material of both forms has become available. Recently the major workers on both forms have agreed that the two are exceedingly close to each other and represent little more than racial variants of a single human type. There are a few differences, but these are entirely of a minor nature. The two are so close that they obviously belong to the same genus (despite the customary use of two different generic terms) and rather surely to the same species; the differences are no more marked than those between human races at the present time.

That these early Asiatic finds belong to a very primitive human type is obvious. We no longer believe, as Dubois did originally, that the Java man is half way between ape and man. He is definitely on the human side of the boundary, and markedly advanced over the 'man-apes' of the *Australopithecus* group. On the other hand, *Pithecanthropus–Sinanthropus*, apart from the australopithecines, represents a lower stage of true human type than that represented in any other adequately known human fossil.

We may say a word here about the lavish use of generic and specific terms by students of human history. Every animal carries a double name, that of the species of which it is a member and, prefixed to it, a generic name, denoting a group of related forms of which the species is a member. Thus the domestic dog is *Canis familiaris*; the wolf, related to the dog but clearly distinct, is included in the 'dog' genus *Canis*, but placed in a separate species, as *Canis latrans*.

What terminology should be applied to human types, recent and fossil? How to define a species is a complex problem, about which whole books can be (and have been) written. But one common definition of a species is that of a population of individuals that can interbreed with one another, and generally do. This is the situation with modern man; we may have personal preferences as to our mates, but white, yellow, and black races can breed together – and often do. All modern men, then, are one species, *Homo sapiens*.

But what about fossil human types, for which an abundance of generic and specific terms have been invented? Common sense suggests that most of them do not merit retention. We pointed out above that '*Pithecanthropus*' and '*Sinanthropus*' are not markedly distinct from each other; their differences, one from the other, are no greater than those present between the races of the single modern human species living in eastern Asia today. And as to genus? These 'old-timers' are more primitive than modern men, but they are distinctly human, and truly human, and properly to be considered as members of the genus *Homo*, although as a distinct ancestral species, *Homo erectus*.

What was the range of the '*Pithecanthropus–Sinanthropus*' type, which we have agreed to call *Homo erectus*? Apart from the specific problem of European history (treated below), there is increasing evidence that the same type of man was widespread. Arambourg a few years ago discovered in Algeria several jaws which are reasonably attributable to this species, and a similar jaw has been discovered in Morocco. Of further interest is the very recent report by Leakey of fragmentary remains from East Africa which he believes to belong, like '*Pithecanthropus*', to the genus *Homo*, but possibly more primitive in nature, and older in date, overlapping the survivors of the *Australopithecus* group.

EUROPEAN MEN OF THE OLDER PLEISTOCENE

Since most workers on human history have been Europeans or

are of European descent, it is but natural that the remains of ancient man from that continent have been carefully searched for and studied intensively. As we shall see, however, early fossil human materials from this small (if interesting) area are few in number and in part dubious in nature.

THE HEIDELBERG JAW. Near the little village of Mauer, not far from Heidelberg, is a large sand deposit formed in an old oxbow of the Neckar River at a rather early stage of the Pleistocene – according to the latest studies, possibly the first interglacial stage. This has been intensively worked for commercial purposes and was found to contain numerous animal bones, including, for example, ancient elephants, rhinoceroses, and lions. In consequence, a careful watch has been kept on the pit for decades. In all this time only one human bone has been found; but this one is a specimen of great interest, the so-called Heidelberg jaw, excavated in 1907 at a point about 80 feet below the surface. The most striking impression given by this specimen is its large size and heavy build. There is no chin prominence, and hence at first sight the jaw appears somewhat apelike; but the teeth and dental arch are definitely human, and the tooth row itself is no larger than in some modern types. The canine does not project at all above the other teeth, and the wear on the molars shows that the chewing motion was of a human rather than apelike sort. An unusual feature is the great width of the ascending ramus (the upper part of the jaw behind the tooth row) and the shallowness of the notch at its top.

The essentially human character of this ancient type finds expression in the fact that it is commonly assigned to our own genus, although to a different species, as *Homo heidelbergensis*.

It has long been recognized that, except for the broad ascending ramus and its rather unusual size, the jaw can be compared in many respects with that of Neanderthal man, who later occupied this territory. On the other hand, except for its rather heavier build, the jaw is not markedly different from that characteristic of the men of the *Pithecanthropus* group, who were roughly contemporaneous. Both of these comparisons may well be valid. Heidelberg man may have been a European variant of the early stock better known in Asia and may well have evolved onward into the typical Neanderthaloids. But until (if ever) the skull is discovered, we cannot be positive of these conclusions.

PILTDOWN MAN. A perplexing problem, only recently solved in unexpected fashion, was long posed by the remains unearthed at the manor of Piltdown, in Sussex, England. In 1911 a small gravel pit there was being worked for road material. In their digging, the men discovered what they described as a brown coconut which they found difficult to break. Discovery of a fragment of it on the dump by Charles Dawson, a respected local solicitor and amateur paleontologist, led to his recognition of the coconut as a human braincase. He instituted a vigorous search for the rest of the skull and was successful in finding several large pieces; others had undoubtedly been spread upon the roads and completely destroyed. The skull was obviously a fossil 'document' of some importance, for the Piltdown gravels are of Pleistocene vintage. It has been claimed that they date far back into the early Pleistocene. Recent research indicates that the skull is not more than 50,000 or so years old; but even so, this is a respectable antiquity, and the skull is well worthy of careful study.

If the workmen had only saved the 'coconut' intact, much mental energy would have been saved. The pieces that were recovered include a fairly large proportion of the top and sides of the braincase. But, unfortunately, few of them fit together, and the proper construction of the skull has proved a difficult task; opinions as to the proper orientation of the fragments have been by no means unanimous.

The bones are quite thick – twice as thick as in a normal modern man – and in this respect a comparison with the Peking man seems obvious. But in other respects the Piltdown skull is much farther advanced. The forehead and the vault of the skull are much higher and essentially modern in their contours. The superorbital ridges are quite undeveloped, as in modern man and in contrast with even such a late Pleistocene type as Neanderthal man. We are dealing with a much larger-brained form than those previously considered. The general consensus at the present time would place the figure in the neighbourhood of 1,350 cubic centimetres, well within the limits of modern races. The skull as a whole is essentially modern in type except for the unusual thickness of the bones, and if found under different circumstances, might have been considered as merely a somewhat abnormal specimen pertaining to our own species.

But quite another aspect was given to the situation when, two years after the original discovery, a partial primate jaw was uncovered in the gravels close to the place where the skull had been found – uncovered by Dawson in Smith Woodward's presence. It was similar in colour and seeming general nature to the skull, and in the absence of any other remains of primates, human or otherwise, in the gravels, seemed surely to be associated with the skull. But whereas the skull, as we have seen, was of 'modern' type, the jaw was more primitive in nature than in any fossil human form, much more apelike than in *Pithecanthropus* or the Peking man. In fact, as is shown in the accompanying figure, it is structurally identical with that of a chimpanzee.

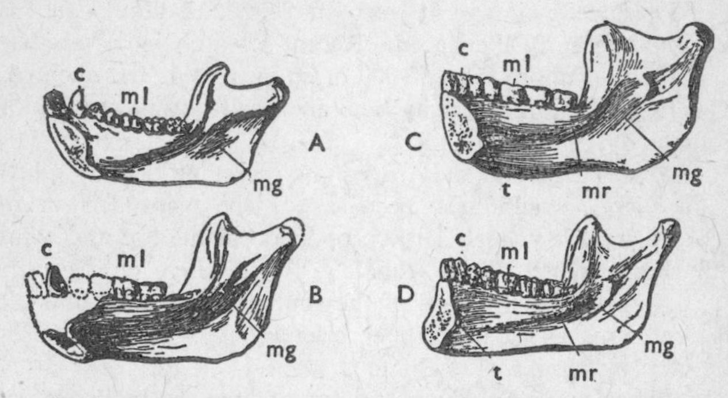

Inside of the lower jaw of various forms *A*, chimpanzee; *B*, Piltdown jaw; *C*, Heidelberg jaw; *D*, modern man. A chin tubercle (*t*), present in modern man, is absent in apes and the Piltdown jaw; this last has an apelike shelf at the point of union of the two jaws halves (the symphysis). In modern man there is a ridge (mylohyoid ridge, *mr*), absent in *A* and *B*. A groove (*mg*), which in modern man runs back into the hole where a nerve enters the jaw, is separate from the opening in the chimpanzee and Piltdown jaw. *c*, canine; *ml*, first molar. (From Smith Woodward)

What could this mean? If the association of skull and jaw be accepted, we have a type with advanced skull development, but a 'retarded' jaw, and since such a combination is unknown in other fossil human finds, we must conclude that Piltdown man has evolved upward from an ape stage independently of other human types. This is difficult to believe, and hence a fair proportion of students of fossil human types claimed that the jaw was that of an ape which just happened to be buried in the gravels close to the truly human skull. But nowhere else in the entire Pleistocene of Europe has there ever been found any trace of a fossil ape, and hence this interpretation, too, was difficult to accept.

The true solution is a third alternative, not even suspected until very recently – namely, that although the skull is an authentic and interesting specimen, the jaw (and several other minor finds) was deliberately 'faked', and 'planted' in the gravels!

Suspicion of this first arose when, recently, the teeth in the jawbone were carefully examined. The crowns showed evidence of having been ground down. This happens as a result of natural wear in any mature or old individual, but here the supposed 'wear' was of a type that could hardly have occurred in life; close examination of the worn surfaces strongly suggested that the teeth surfaces had been artificially abraded. With this suspicion in mind, the jaw was subjected to other tests by a group of responsible scientists (Drs J. S. Weiner, K. P. Oakley, and W. E. Le Gros Clark). When tested for fluorine content, the jaw proved to have no more of this element than any modern bone, whereas the skull has the somewhat higher amount expected in a specimen of reasonable antiquity. Still further, it was discovered that the brownish colour of the jaw, matching that of the skull, was not natural, but due to clever staining with potassium bichromate and iron. The jaw had been deliberately 'faked' – and faked so carefully that the fact had not been suspected for a third of a century.

With the elimination of this controversial jaw from the material to be considered, our story of human evolution is much less subject to confusion than had long been the case. But the interesting question remains – who perpetrated the fraud? Certainly not Sir Arthur Smith Woodward, the major scientific worker on the Piltdown material. Apart from the fact that all who knew him will vouch for his unimpeachable integrity and sincerity, it is unthinkable that any person of his high scientific standing would (no matter how unscrupulous) have dared to risk his reputation by such a fraud. The culprit must have been a person of intelligence and scientific knowledge, as well as one with ready access to the discovery site. The local labourers concerned can be ruled out, and by elimination the finger of suspicion seems to point to Dawson. Can this respected solicitor and friend of scientists have been tempted to enhance his earned reputation further by 'gilding the lily'? Probably we shall never know the answer.

THE SWANSCOMBE FRAGMENT. The occipital bone of a human skull, perfectly preserved, was found in 1936 in one of the terraces of the lower Thames Valley at Swanscombe (Kent). The following year renewed search brought to light an equally well-preserved parietal. Nothing further has been found of this individual. Despite its fragmentary nature, this find is of the utmost importance because it is the only specimen from Europe that can be positively associated with a Lower Paleolithic industry. The 100-foot terrace deposit in which it was found was formed during the great interglacial stage of the Middle Pleistocene; and in the undisturbed layer with the human remains were typical Acheulean implements.

But while we have here the one and only definitely known user of the Lower Paleolithic hand axe, our knowledge of him is distressingly limited. The occipital is a bone which includes the posterior part of the braincase; the parietal covers much of the roof. We have then considerable data as to the back part of the skull. The bones are rather thick but in other respects are modern in type, with rounded contours contrasting strongly with those seen in paleoanthropic forms. We have even sufficient data to make a reasonable estimate of the brain capacity (about 1,350 cubic centimetres). But of the rest of this man we know nothing. Were his brow ridges large or small, his face and jaw 'modern' or simian? We cannot say. The Swanscombe fragments suggest that the makers of Abbevillian and Acheulean implements may have been men of neanthropic type but do not prove the point.

FURTHER REPORTS OF EARLY NEANTHROPIC MEN. A number of other finds from various areas of Europe, and from Africa as well, have been reported from time to time which have tended to confirm this thesis that the modern type of man was in existence in Middle Pleistocene days rather than a form which appeared only at the end of the Ice Age. On the whole, however, no great weight has been placed on such reports by most authorities, because the skeletal remains concerned have been either fragmentary or of dubious age or both. Of these perplexing finds we will cite as typical the case of the Galley Hill skeleton.

Galley Hill is near Swanscombe, mentioned above, and the site is the same 100-foot terrace containing Acheulean deposits. In gravels of this age, in 1888, a workman and local amateur scientists excavated a nearly complete human skeleton, including most of the skull and jaws, except for the bones of the face, and much of the body as well. The whole structure is typically neanthropic, including a jaw of modern type; in fact there is nothing to distinguish this Galley Hill man from *Homo sapiens*. If this skeleton had been found in a later deposit, its authenticity would not have been doubted. But when claimed to come from a horizon this early, it runs counter to the evolutionary beliefs of many workers, and hence a loophole was sought. This was found in the fact that the disinterment was done by amateurs. Several scientists who made careful inquiry later were satisfied as to the authenticity of the find. But there are strong doubts about this specimen. The current majority opinion is against the Galley Hill find as a true 'antique'; the skeleton is quite likely an intrusive burial rather than 'native' to these old gravels.

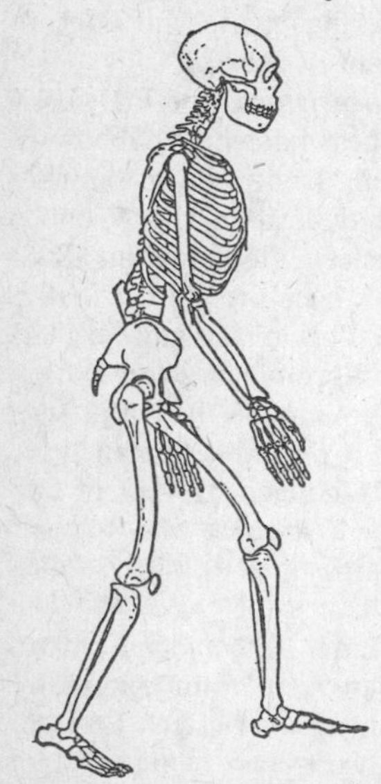

The skeleton of Neanderthal man. (After Boule and Weinert)

To list the various other cases of this same sort would be not only exhaustive but exhausting. The evidence suggests that a highly developed man was present in the Old World far back in the Pleistocene, but the point is not proved. However, where there is so much smoke, there may be some fire. More incontrovertible facts are needed.

With this we conclude our survey of the records of earliest man in Europe. It is a blurred and confusing picture. Heidelberg, Piltdown, supposed neanthropic man; each find supplies us not so much with facts as with problems for which we have no adequate solution.

THE NEANDERTHAL PHASE OF PLEISTOCENE HISTORY

The middle Paleolithic cultural period occupies a vast extent of time in the later part of the Ice Age, including the last interglacial stage and the earlier part of the final (Würm) glaciation. In Europe and Western Asia this was the era at which the Mousterian stone industries flourished; the maker of these implements is known to have been Neanderthal man, who appears to have been at the time the sole resident of Europe.

Neanderthal man, *Homo neanderthalensis*, was the first fossil type to be discovered and is still the best known of subhuman species. The first recognized specimen, from which the race takes its name, was found in a cave deposit in the Neander Valley near the Ruhr district in western Germany in 1856. Although a complete skeleton may have been present originally, little was preserved except the skullcap. This immediately excited interest because of the low forehead and prominent brow ridges, but, in the absence of anything else comparable, its status was debated. Some rightly recognized it as a primitive human type, but others claimed that it was merely a congenital idiot of our own species or (according to one eminent scientist who appears to have been a Russophobe) the remains of a Russian soldier killed in the Napoleonic wars!

NEANDERTHAL DISTRIBUTION. Later other and more complete remains of this type of man were found in many localities. Numerous finds have been made in western Europe, particularly in France. To the south-west, two skulls of this species have been found at Gibraltar, and a fragment of a jaw recently discovered across the straits in Tangier shows that the race reached the shores of Africa at this one spot at least. The Neanderthal type was long unreported from Italy, but in the 1930s three characteristic skulls were found in the general Rome district. Farther east the rock shelter of Krapina in Croatia has yielded skeletal remains of a considerable number of Neanderthal individuals (there are suggestions of cannibalism at this locality). To the south-east recent discoveries have shown Neanderthal man (including remarkable variants from the general type) to have inhabited Palestine. Farther to the north-east this race was present in Russia, and in 1938 a Neanderthal child's skull was discovered in a cave in western Siberia once occupied by a group of Mousterian goat hunters.

Neanderthal man thus occupied a considerable territory. As yet, however, he is not known from any part of Africa except its northern coast, nor from central or eastern Asia. His absence may, of course, be only apparent, and new finds may presently extend this range. We have noted, however, that he is, where known, associated with Mousterian culture. The Mousterian appears to be absent in Africa and much of Asia, although other Middle Paleolithic cultures may be present. We have no strong reason to believe that the other cultures were made by Neanderthal man, and it may well be that known finds do actually outline the territory he occupied.

TYPICAL NEANDERTHAL STRUCTURE. Most of the specimens of this race conform closely to a single type, best described in a classic monograph by the French paleontologist, Marcellin Boule, based on a well-preserved skeleton from the rock shelter of La-Chapelle-aux-Saints in southern France. At first glance one is impressed by the somewhat apelike appearance of the skull. The head is massive, with heavy supraorbital ridges, a receding forehead, and a low vault to the braincase. This, however, does not indicate that the brain was small, for the braincase juts out strongly posteriorly, with a marked projection which contrasts sharply with the rounded contours of modern man in this region. The brain, thus, is large, with an average capacity in typical males of about 1,550 cubic centimetres, a figure as large, or larger, than that found in the highest of living races. Sexual differences are marked, for females average about 200 cubic centimetres less. Although this brain is of modern size, its proportions are, as would be expected, quite different from that of *Homo sapiens*. The frontal region of the brain hemispheres, which is thought to be important in the development of the highest mental faculties, is relatively small.

Details of the ear region and the heavy arch at the side of the skull are also quite different from those of neanthropic man. The face is very long and large in proportion to the braincase, the jaws projecting, the eye sockets large and rounded in form, the nose opening broad. The cheek bones of modern man have a characteristic hollow (fossa) excavated above the canine teeth; this is lacking in the Neanderthal type. The size of the face is related to the fact that the teeth are in general large and powerful, the dental arch being much larger than in typical modern men. The patterns of the molar teeth retain some apelike features, but the dentition is on the whole essentially human in character, and there is none of the ape projection of the canines. The jaw, as one would expect, is also massively built but essentially human, lacking apelike features seen in the Piltdown mandible. There is, however, no chin projection in typical members of this group, the front edge of the jaw falling away vertically below the anterior teeth.

In contrast with other primitive types of man, the skeleton of Neanderthal man is nearly completely known. This was a race of short stature; the average height of males seems to have been about five feet four inches; the females may have been about six inches shorter. Although short, the body was powerfully built, the chest barrel-shaped. The forearm and lower leg were proportionately much shorter than in modern man. The carriage is thought by some authors to have been somewhat stooped, the head inclined somewhat forward on the short neck, the knees habitually slightly bent. The ankle joints indicate that the squatting pose was frequently assumed.

EARLY NEANDERTHALERS. These typical Neanderthal men are known mainly from deposits laid down in the earlier part of the Würm glaciation. A few specimens are considerably earlier – from the preceding Riss-Würm interglacial. Some of these appear to be typical members of the group, but others appear to depart from the general structural pattern in various features. The specimens from Italy are found with a fauna characterisitic of a warm climate and hence may come from this interglacial stage. The Krapina finds mentioned above may also be of this age. Although the remains are fragmentary, they appear to represent a subrace characterized by a more slender build and smaller brains than the typical Neanderthal man. Specimens from the Ilm River Valley near Weimar in Germany include two typical jaws and a skull which appears to have a little higher vault to the braincase than is generally true of this race.

Most interesting of specimens from the Riss-Würm interglacial is a skull found in 1933 at Steinheim, Germany. This has a brain capacity of only 1,100 cubic centimetres, a remarkably low figure even for a female and well down towards the *Pithecanthropus* level. On the other hand, the face has less of a snoutlike appearance than most later Neanderthals, and the back of the braincase has more rounded, neanthropic contours than is usually the case.

THE MOUNT CARMEL RACE. In Palestine, following the finding of a Neanderthal skull near Galilee, excavations made during 1929–35 in caves on Mount Carmel revealed a series of twelve or more skeletons of people who dwelt there in Upper Pleistocene times and are associated with a typical Middle Paleolithic culture of flints of Mousterian and Levallois types. These remains have been carefully studied by McCown, one of their discoverers, and Sir Arthur Keith, and show a most interesting series of variations in structure. Their describers agree that all are to be classed with the Neanderthal group. But while a few individuals, including a woman from a cave called Mugharet-et-Tabun, are typical members of that group, the others, mostly from a second cave, Mugharet-es-Skuhil, show to a variable degree numerous neanthropic features which are suggestive of *Homo sapiens* rather than *H. neanderthalensis*. Typical Neanderthalers are short; at Mount Carmel the men tend to be tall, for they have heights of 5 feet 7 inches to 5 feet 10 inches, and even the females are of moderate height. The face is not as large as in Neanderthals; the skull vault is not as flattened; the supraorbital ridges, while fairly prominent, are not as continuous; and the forehead is moderately full rather than receding. In Neanderthal man, we have noted, the occiput projects backward with a rather vertically compressed shape; here the contours tend to be more rounded, halfway towards modern conditions. The face is not as long as in typical Neanderthals, and there is little of the prognathism, the forward projection of the front teeth, seen in that form. In Neanderthal man the eye sockets are very large and round; here they are wide but not high. The nasal opening, primitively broad, is rather variable in these finds but sometimes approaches the narrower type of modern man. The teeth, rather large in typical Neanderthal men, are variable in size, although the pattern of the molars remains primitive. In the jaw the angular region at the lower back corner is rather more developed than in the ordinary members of this race, while an obvious and striking feature is the fact that there tends to be more or less of a projecting chin as in modern man. In the postcranial skeleton the posture is rather closer to that of modern man than that of the typical Neanderthal, the distal segments of the legs are long rather than short, and the structure of the backbone is intermediate between Neanderthal and modern types. The brain capacity of the typical Neanderthal woman of Tabun is 1,271 cubic centimetres; of the women of the Skuhl group, 1,300 and 1,350 cubic centimetres; of the men, 1,518–87 cubic centimetres. While these figures are such as might be found in either Neanderthal individuals or large-brained modern men, the brain shape, including a better development of the frontal region, is closer to the modern type.

We have, thus, at Mount Carmel a group of people who exhibit, to a variable degree, a mixture of features characteristic of Neanderthal man and of *Homo sapiens*, particularly of the general Cro-Magnon type which was soon to appear in Europe. In summarizing the evidence, McCown and Keith point out that of twenty-five important features which they list, the Mount Carmel individuals are Neanderthaloid in but three, intermediate in fourteen, modern in eight. In a long series of features of lesser importance, the figures again favour modern man by a 'vote' of forty-six to sixteen. They point out, however, that too much reliance should not be based mere statistics and that in really basic body pattern Mount Carmel man is still fundamentally a Neanderthal type, although with many neanthropic features.

NEANDERTHAL RELATIONSHIPS. Before discussing the possible implications of these recent Palestinian finds, let us consider the general evolutionary position of the Neanderthal species. As to its origin, there is general agreement. Neanderthal man obviously had nothing to do with the poorly known neanthropic men who may have lived in the European region in Lower Paleolithic days. On the other hand, it is obvious that there are many points of agreement with the Java-Peking types of earlier times in eastern Asia. *Pithecanthropus* may well have been Neanderthal man's ancestor, and, as has been suggested, the Heidelberg jaw may represent a forerunner from the eastern group into the territory in which Neanderthal man later flourished. While Neanderthal man is obviously a more advanced and larger-brained form, the basic paleoanthropic skull pattern remains unchanged, and such a line of descent is quite reasonable.

In Europe Neanderthal man disappears, apparently rather suddenly, towards the end of the Pleistocene and is succeeded by Cro-Magnon and related forms of our own species. What were the relationships between these successive groups?

A number of alternatives are possible. One theory maintains rather flatly that there are no blood relationships; that Neanderthal man was wiped out; that he was perhaps harried and exterminated by invading groups of *Homo sapiens*, who had come from an entirely different line of ancestors. A second theory is that, on the contrary, modern man has actually evolved from the Neanderthal type and that this evolution took place on the spot, in Europe. To support this it is pointed out that various Upper Paleolithic European specimens (Predmost, etc.) show certain features suggestive of the Neanderthal type, such as rather massively built skulls and brow ridges more pronounced than is usual in *Homo sapiens*. But this appears none too probable. It seems clear that the seeming Neanderthaloid features of these Upper Paleolithic men are but minor elements in their make-up; these individuals are very definitely neanthropic men who have a few archaic features; there is no European transitional type.

Compromise is possible between these two extreme views. One such is the suggestion that, although Neanderthal man as present in Europe is not the direct ancestor of the modern species, nevertheless the two may have had a common ancestor in some other area, Asia perhaps. From this centre Neanderthal man may have invaded Europe, while in the original homeland the ancestral stock progressed onward to the modern type and then, in a subsequent western migration, swept over the earlier Neanderthal population.

The evidence of the interesting 'intermediate' types from Mount Carmel should, one would think, help to settle this issue. But, as a matter of fact, they do not; their presence can be reconciled with any one of these three theories.

If one believes that neanthropic man represents a new invader of Europe and was not a descendant of Neanderthal man, the Mount Carmel people may be considered as due to interbreeding of the dominant race with its lowly predecessors. For comparison, in Tasmania in recent times the native population has been succeeded by Europeans and virtually exterminated; but a fair number of half-breeds exist. Just so modern man may have supplanted Neanderthal man but may have interbred to some extent. To this 'dash' of Neanderthal blood, some suggest, is due the rugged build of the Upper Paleolithic people of Europe and the occasional primitive features noted in their skulls.

If, on the other hand, one believes that Neanderthal man evolved locally into *Homo sapiens*, one can point out that Palestine is not so far from the supposed evolutionary centre in Europe and claim the Mount Carmel people as individuals actually in the process of rapid evolution from one form into the other.

The third alternative – that Neanderthal and modern man in Europe are related but not directly descended one from the other and represent two successive waves of invasion from another evolutionary centre – is the one adopted by the describers of the Palestine material. They suggest that after Neanderthal man had entered Europe the unknown Asiatic or African stock from which he came progressed onward towards a neanthropic type. The Mount Carmelites are examples of these transitional forms which had wandered from their unknown homeland into Palestine. Later, when the evolution to modern conditions had been completed, the end products of this series migrated into Europe as definitive Upper Paleolithic members of *Homo sapiens*. Thus, from this point of view, Mount Carmel man and Neanderthal man are not direct ancestors of later Europeans. They are not 'father' and 'grandfather' but 'uncle' and 'great uncle'.

SOLO MAN. We may conclude this section with a description of two other types of men which are not Neanderthals in the proper sense of the term but yet exhibit a number of comparable paleoanthropic features and may be of like antiquity.

From the banks of the Solo River in Java, where *Pithecanthropus* was discovered, have come the remains of a second human type, described as *Homo soloensis*. The materials representing this form come from the neighbourhood of Ngandong, only a few miles from Trinil. Despite the geographical nearness of the two sites, the two human types are clearly separated chronologically, for the Ngandong deposits are apparently from a late period of the Pleistocene, roughly the age of Neanderthal man in Europe.

Of Solo man there have been found eleven partial skulls. In all of them the base of the skull had been removed, suggesting, as in other cases noted, a cannibalistic fondness for brain food; and face, jaws, and teeth are as yet unknown. The brain was rather small, for a male skull has a capacity of only 1,316 cubic centimetres, and several females average but 1,175 cubic centimetres. The forehead was low, the brow ridges heavy – paleoanthropic features suggestive of Neanderthal relationships or of a descent (as in the case of that form) from the much earlier *Pithecanthropus* type. But the contours of the rest of the braincase and a number of diagnostic technical features are not at all those found in these archaic human types but are, on the contrary, much more like modern man; so much so that some are inclined to believe that, after all, Solo man may not deserve recognition as a separate species but should be considered as a primitive type of *Homo sapiens*. If so, how are we to account for the suggestively massive brow ridges and low forehead? As in the case of the Mount Carmel finds, there are alternative suggestions. It may be that Solo man represents an evolutionary progression upward from *Pithecanthropus* to a modern level in eastern Asia. On the other hand, we may have a blended type in which, as some believe to be true in Palestine, there is a mixture of races, an infusion of paleoanthropic blood into an early neanthropic race. As to descendants, it is suggested that Solo man may have given rise, through forms considered in a later section, to the living Australoids.

RHODESIAN MAN. It is generally agreed that Solo man presents close similarities to the unique Rhodesian skull, which may be considered at this point, although its geologic age is uncertain.

At Broken Hill, Rhodesia, valuable ore deposits were present in a hill which has, in consequence, gradually disappeared in the course of mining operations. A long cave passing through much of the hill contained many bones of animals so heavily impregnated with minerals that they were fed to the smelters. Fortunately a human skull was rescued, together with a few other fragments of bones of doubtful association and lesser interest. The skull is uncrushed and almost perfect and represents an unusual human type, with a number of primitive and specialized features. At first sight one tends to compare this bestial form with Neanderthal man because of such features as the heavy brow ridges and the low forehead. The face is enormously developed and the palate as well, features which are specializations not known to be developed to such a degree in other known fossil types. But the contours of the braincase and other details of the skull show none of the diagnostic characters of Neanderthal man. The brain was small, with a capacity of only 1,300 cubic centimetres, strikingly low for such a large skull. We have no data from which to estimate the age of the skull, but the similarity of its braincase to that of Solo man suggests that it may well be late Pleistocene. Again, as in the case of Solo man, it is difficult to place this skull in proper evolutionary position. It has been given a separate specific name, as *Homo rhodesiensis*, but it may equally well be regarded as a primitive type of *Homo sapiens*. The problem of its ancestry is exactly the same as in the case of Solo man. As to possible descendants, there is a fairly general belief that Rhodesian man may be related, through other extinct types considered later, to the ancestors of the living Bushmen.

MODERN MAN

Towards the close of the glacial period, during the latter part of the Würm glaciation and the phases of the final retreat of ice, man of our own species entered Europe. Succeeding the Mousterian implements we find, in numerous deposits, a layer containing new industries, those of the Upper Paleolithic, with flint blades and numerous bone implements replacing the flake tools of Neanderthal man and with evidence of contemporary activity in art and other fields which indicates that the newcomer was a man of wider intellectual horizons and activities than his predecessor. This new European, we know from numerous associated skeletal finds, was, as Cro-Magnon man and related types, a representative of our own species, *Homo sapiens*.

Whence he came is a question to which we have as yet no satisfactory answer. Unless we accept the hypothesis – on the whole rather unlikely – that he evolved on the spot from Neanderthal man, his coming must represent a migration from an earlier homeland. But whether this homeland was Asia or Africa cannot at present be determined. Nor can we be dogmatic as to his exact pedigree. Quite surely his ancestry traces back in a general way to members of the *Pithecanthropus–Sinanthropus* stock. As we have just seen, forms advanced from this stage reached a Neanderthal-level in evolution in various parts of the Old World during the latter part of the Pleistocene. Further evolutionary advances toward and to the *Homo sapiens* level may have taken place amongst a variety of races, partially (but surely not wholly) isolated from each other, in African and Asiatic areas.

CRO-MAGNON MAN. The Upper Paleolithic stage in Europe may have begun as early perhaps as 40,000 B.C. and persisted until approximately 13,000 B.C. It is customary to refer the human finds of this age to the Cro-Magnon race, which takes its name from a French rock shelter where characteristic skeletons of this type were discovered. Remains of this sort are particularly abundant in the caves of France but are found widely distributed in various regions of western and central Europe; about one hundred individuals are known.

The head is rather large and massively built, features which some suggest are due to a dash of Neanderthal blood in the Cro-Magnon race. In general, however, one can state with confidence that paleoanthropic features are absent. The great brow ridges are lacking, the forehead and skull vault are high, the occiput rounded, the face reduced to modern proportions, the nose narrow and prominent, the chin highly developed, and in every respect Upper Paleolithic men were on a high plane of development. The skulls are almost always dolichocephalic, with cranial indices generally ranging from sixty-five to seventy-six (an exception, however, is one brachycephalic skull). These large heads contained large brains, averaging in males 1,700 or 1,800 cubic centimetres; again, however, sexual differences are marked, and the females were smaller-brained. As racial peculiarities we find that the face was short but broad and the eye sockets correspondingly wide but low.

This was a tall race, on the whole, many males being six feet or so in height. In the body as in the skull, build and proportions are modern, without any trace of Neanderthaloid characters.

Some degree of variation existed, of course, among these ancient men. The Predmost type, for example, is that of a group of mammoth-hunters of ancient Moravia, in which the face was rather long, the chin rather less prominent, the supraorbital ridges more than normally developed – features which give a slight Neanderthaloid aspect to their skulls. Skeletons from Chancelade in France and Obercassel in Germany, which date from a rather late stage in the Upper Paleolithic, show more rounded orbits, longer faces and shorter bodies, and a general appearance which has suggested to some workers a comparison with the Eskimos. A skeleton from Combe Capelle in France is that of an individual with both skull and body rather smaller than usual in the Cro-Magnon type. A burial in the caves of Grimaldi on the Riviera contains two skeletons, probably a mother and her adolescent son. Here, as in the last instance, body and head are relatively small. The general proportions, projecting teeth, and rather broad noses have suggested to some writers Negroid affinities, although this belief is disputed.

Variations do exist, but, on the whole, they are not marked. A recent objective metrical study of the entire series of known Upper Paleolithic residents of Europe shows that, all in all, there are no greater variations than one finds today in a relatively pure racial group.

With the withdrawal of the ice and related changes in climates, plants, and animals, the Upper Paleolithic culture came to an end, and presently new racial types appeared in Europe. What was the fate of the Cro-Magnon race? The details are obscure, but, as suggested in the next chapter, their blood may still flow in the veins of many modern inhabitants of western Europe.

AFRICA. We have thus far concentrated our attention on the appearance of *Homo sapiens* in Europe and have done so because our knowledge of his early history there is much more adequate than it is in other areas. In recent decades, however, many new finds of ancient representatives of our species have come to light in various parts of Asia and Africa. While the story is none too clear as yet, we may briefly mention some of the more interesting discoveries of this nature.

In northern Africa, finds in Algeria indicate that Upper Paleolithic races of that region were fairly similar to their Cro-Magnon contemporaries across the Mediterranean. Not too dissimilar, also, are certain Upper Paleolithic finds from East Africa, including a series of skeletons from Gamble's Cave in Kenya and another individual from Oldowai in Tanganyika (the latter was once believed to be still older). In many regards these men are comparable to the Cro-Magnon race, but they are rather more slenderly built, with longer and narrower faces and rounder eye sockets. They appear to be rather similar in type to the basic stock of brunette 'whites' which form the modern Mediterranean race (in a broad sense of that term).

Africa today is the great centre of the Negro race, and there are some evidences of ancient members of that stock. A skull from Asselar, in the southern Sahara, which cannot be accurately dated geologically but appears to be of respectable antiquity, shows Negroid features, and the same is said to be true of other skulls from East Africa.

Workers in South Africa have accumulated considerable fossil evidence which suggests that the Bushman is a descendant of ancient inhabitants of that region. Among others a skull from Boskop in the Transvaal appears to represent an ancestor of this interesting race, although one with a larger body and larger brain than in his physically degenerate descendants. A still more archaic-looking skull from Florisbad in the Transvaal is thought to be a connecting link between the Rhodesian type and these Bushman ancestors.

ASIA. Upper Paleolithic cultures, rather comparable to those of Europe, stretch away eastward through northern Asia, and their makers may have been not too dissimilar to the Upper Paleolithic men of Europe. In China the very caves of Choukoutien have in their upper and later layers skull remains of this age which, while varied in details, are of a 'high' human type.

We have no evidence of any sort regarding the early history of the Mongoloid peoples, now so important in Asia; possibly they may have developed at a relatively late date. Deeply regrettable is the lack of knowledge of Upper Paleolithic times in central Asia and in Iran and India. These areas have probably been of the greatest importance in the early history of our species, but we do not have the slightest scrap of a bone from these regions.

The native Australian is rather generally considered to be an archaic type of our species which has reached his present home by a migration down the East Indian island chain. Several fossil 'documents' appear to record this migration. In Java still another type of some interest is Wadjak man, represented by two skulls. The age is uncertain but may be late Pleistocene.

This man definitely pertains to the modern species but is rather primitive, with somewhat prominent supraorbital ridges and a massive skull build. Wadjak man may have descended from the Solo man mentioned in the last section; on the other hand, it is generally agreed that he may be a primitive Australoid. Other early Australians are found in Australia itself; skulls excavated at Talgai (Queensland) and Cohuna (Victoria) have unusually massive faces, enormous palates, and large teeth, but are in most respects very similar to the living Australians.

AMERICA. Despite a considerable amount of investigation, we have failed to find in America any story of early human evolution comparable to that of the Old World. Apparently primates had become extinct in North America early in the Tertiary, before they had even attained the monkey stage, and manlike apes are unknown in the Western Hemisphere. Some years ago teeth were found in the late Tertiary of western Nebraska which appeared to be rather manlike and were given the name of *Hesperopithecus*, the 'western ape'. But further research disclosed that they were merely rather aberrant teeth of a fossil peccary, a member of the pig family; teeth are one of the features in which man and swine show embarrassing similarities. In South America a patriotic paleontologist, ambitious to show the evolutionary importance of his country, once described a series of 'protohomos' supposed to show the evolution of man from ape in Argentina. But these remains, on critical examination, appear to be far from convincing evidence. They include, among other specimens, part of the skeleton of an ordinary South American monkey and a bone dredged out of the Buenos Aires harbour, which we may suspect to be a souvenir of a sailor fallen overboard after a large evening in that gay city. The earlier stages in human history, it would seem, were already past before man reached the western world.

The time of his arrival, however, is a problem of current interest. There is an increasing body of evidence that when Columbus and later voyagers arrived to discover the Indians in possession, man was far from being a newcomer and may have been here for many thousands of years. As we have noted, the Ice Age fauna of the Americas was a far different and richer assemblage of animals than those now living. For many decades there have been repeated finds which suggest that man had entered this hemisphere before the Pleistocene fauna had become extinct and was a contemporary here of native American camels, ground sloths, mastodon and mammoth, and fossil species of bison.

But even so this need not mean any remote antiquity. At one time it was thought that many of these extinct animals had died out rather early in the Ice Age. This is no longer believed to be the case, and it is not improbable that the older fauna survived to a late date. Camels, proboscidians, and sloths may have lingered on in North America well after the retreat of the last glaciation and have been present in this country until ten to twenty thousand years ago.

If man had been an inhabitant of America during any great extent of the Ice Age, we would expect to find flint implements comparable to those of the Lower or Middle Paleolithic of the Old World. This is not the case. The oldest types of flint implements known at present are best represented by the Folsom type of point, named after the New Mexican locality where it was first discovered, but since found widespread in the western U.S.A. This presumably was used as a spearhead and is readily recognized by a groove channelled down either side. This type of implement and others found associated with it differ from any used by recent Indians in the West. But this is not in itself any proof of great antiquity, and such a flint might have been produced by a people in the Mesolithic cultural stage not so many thousands of years ago.

Few skeletal remains are known in North America which can lay claim to any great antiquity, and none appears to be in any way primitive. The 'Minnesota lady', for example, is the skeleton of a maiden found in a supposed Ice Age deposit in that state. The skeleton indicates that she had a powerful jaw (a feature upon which we shall not comment further) but in all other regards appears to be similar to members of recent Indian tribes of that region.

All the evidence so far cited is thus inconclusive in nature. Careful geological work may eventually give us better dating. The 'Minnesota lady' is claimed to have come from a deposit laid down in a Pleistocene lake, about 20,000 B.C., but the skeleton was excavated during a road-repair job, and we cannot be sure that she actually came from these lake beds. Geological investigations of sites where Folsom implements are present suggest dates of from 15,000 to 25,000 years – that is, very late glacial to early post-glacial times.

To sum up, the evidence on the whole indicates that man reached America only as a full-fledged *Homo sapiens*; that the first invaders had attained a Mesolithic (or possibly very late Paleolithic) cultural stage; that they arrived before the extinction of the numerous Pleistocene mammals; that the time of arrival was at the end of the last glaciation or early in the final recession of the ice, at a time to be estimated at 15,000 to 25,000 B.C.

How did man reach America? Probably not by any lengthy sea voyage, for although a stray canoe or so might have reached America by sea, there is not the slightest trace of racial similarity between the Indians and the inhabitants of the Pacific islands to the west or Africa to the east. Presumably migrations were mainly by land, via the Bering Strait route from Asia. The crossing there today is a short one, a trip which would not be too difficult for any coast-dwelling primitive people which could make a crude craft of some sort. Further, geologists have pointed out that sea levels fluctuated greatly during the Pleistocene; a drop of little over 100 feet would turn the strait into dry land.

Once across, penetration of the continent would have been accomplished without too much difficulty. Even during the peak of the glaciation it seems that considerable portions of Alaska and British Columbia were free of ice; there existed down the west flank of the Rockies a corridor through which a hardy folk could have passed to reach the more hospitable lands to the south. We can picture the peopling of America as occurring by the passage into Alaska of successive waves of Asiatics who drifted slowly southward and spread out to populate the temperate and tropical regions.

CHAPTER 16

Human Races

IN our last chapter we discussed the position of our own species, *Homo sapiens*, in the human family; here we shall make some attempt to differentiate between the various racial types comprising this species.

RACIAL DETERMINATION

POSSIBLE NONPHYSICAL CRITERIA. Upon what basis can we discriminate between one race and another? One obvious suggestion would be to use nationality as a basis. An Englishman, a Frenchman, a German, are all definite types to us, and we associate these types with definite governmental units. But we have only to look to Europe to see that national and racial boundaries need not coincide; many of the troubles of that troubled Continent have been, and still are, due to the inclusion of alien populations within national boundaries.

Language is another possibility. Man tends to retain the speech of his fathers even in a foreign land; various types of language show clear evidences of relationship and common descent. Cannot the evolution of languages be correlated with the history of the peoples who speak them?

Language may afford a clue as to racial affinities but often a treacherous one. Chief Two-Guns-White-Calf and a Calypso singer may speak English, but they are obviously unrelated racially to the English people among whom this language originated. In modern Europe there are numerous areas where a change in language has been made or attempted without any change in the racial make-up of the population, and there are many instances where the conquest of a country has resulted in the replacement of the native language by that of numerically insignificant conquerors. A century ago it was discovered that almost all the languages of Europe and those of Persia and much of India were descendants of a common tongue, of which Sanskrit is a little-changed relic. On the basis of this discovery was erected a theory of common descent of the peoples who speak Indo-European languages. But we now realize that this language stock is native to only a small proportion, at the most, of those who now utilize it; it may have been carried by migrations and conquests, but the Indo-European languages have spread far more vigorously than the people who have carried them.

Can culture be used as a basis for studying racial history? We tend as a rule to be conservative in our customs, our beliefs, the types of material objects which we fashion for ourselves. But here again we must be wary, for cultural traits often spread widely by adoption or are superimposed by conquest. The American Indian of pilgrim days travelled on foot and fought with bow and arrows, but the horse and rifle, both taken over from Europeans, were major elements in the life of the Indian of the covered-wagon era. The Mexican peon is a Christian, but the blood in his veins is almost identical with that of his predecessors who worshipped Quetzalcoatl.

Nationality, language, cultural traits, and cultural objects – all these may afford suggestions as to racial affinities or origins; but they are to be used with caution. The only definite and fairly positive knowledge which we can obtain regarding the pedigree of an individual or a group is from a study of its physical characteristics.

RACIAL MIXTURES. When we discuss the relationships of other animals we do so in terms of species or larger units. These groups are generally clear; species seldom breed with one another and are usually separated by clearly defined structural differences.

But in the attempt to study human races we are dealing with quite another type of problem. All living men are seemingly members of a single species. Members of all human groups can breed with one another and frequently do so; in the Hawaiian Islands, for example, may be found almost every conceivable type of cross between the major racial groups of the Orient and Occident.

Such wide racial intermixtures are facilitated, it is true, by the development of modern communication methods, but crossing between races must obviously have been a common occurrence throughout human history. Intermediate border groups have probably been common at all times, and every war or conquest has naturally resulted in a mixing of the strains of conqueror and conquered. We would think, for example, of the offspring of an Englishman and a Frenchwoman as products of a mixture of two races. But what is the English race? Within historic times we know of three invasions which have added new strains to the pre-existing population, and there is good evidence that a number of similar invasions have taken place in late prehistoric times. The history of the French 'race' is a similarly complex story.

Probably there is not, and never has been, a really pure race. When we attempt to establish a racial type, we attempt to set up a series of characteristics commonly found in the people of a certain area or of a certain caste; few will exactly meet our specifications in all respects. A pure racial type is a man-made ideal, seldom perfectly realized.

MIGRATIONS. It would be difficult enough to deal with racial problems were peoples stationary. But our problems are further confused by the fact that movements of peoples appear to have been common throughout human history.

The overseas movements of the European peoples are only the most recent and striking of human migrations. Throughout the historic period, wave after wave of peoples have swept into western Europe from the east – Celts, Germans, Huns and Avars, Turks – and archaeology reveals similar prehistoric events. A great southern migration of Negroes into South Africa was in progress when England took over that region. The Chinese people have spread southward over a vast area during the time covered by their written history. Many migrations of American Indian tribes can be definitely plotted.

These are but a few of the more striking of known migrations of peoples. Mankind has been, and still is, in motion. Groups once strangers have come into juxtaposition or have fused; related types have been isolated from one another and their affinities obscured or rendered doubtful.

Can we trace any general pattern in these migrations? The movements of a people may be due to a variety of causes; they are, in physical terms, a 'resultant of forces'. Better lands ahead to hunt in, to till, or to plunder; powerful enemies behind; a need for more territory for increased numbers; these and many other factors may make for migration.

In the evolutionary history of mammals we find that the

main, early centre of group dispersal appears to have lain in the northern land areas and particularly in Asia (although other continents, particularly North America, have acted as minor centres). From that continent appear to have radiated many mammalian groups to migrate eastward via Alaska to the Americas, southward to Australia or Africa, westward into Europe. In agreement with these findings is the fact that the most primitive of living mammals are found in comparatively isolated areas, farthest from their original Asiatic homes, whence they have been pushed by more advanced types. Australia is the home of the most primitive of existing mammal faunas; archaic ungulate types persisted in South America long after their extinction elsewhere; the modern African fauna is a survival of that of Eurasia two epochs ago.

The distribution of modern human races and the known history of human migrations suggest that the geographical story of man has been similar to that of many other mammalian types. A majority of known migrations have emanated from an Asiatic centre; and some of the seemingly most primitive of human races are found in the Australian region and Africa. Whether or not Asia is the original home of man cannot be said with certainty; but Asia has surely been a major centre of human dispersal.

PHYSICAL CRITERIA OF RACE. Attempts to characterize racial groups should not be made merely upon casual and random observations but upon careful study of numerous individuals, such studies being of a quantitative nature as far as possible. Many features may be observed or measured on the living; numerous standard types of measurement may be made upon the skeletons. Naturally, skeletal measurements alone are available for prehistoric peoples, and even for well-known historic races accurate data as to the soft parts, such as hair, skin, pigment, etc., is usually woefully inadequate.

We must, of course, use some caution in drawing conclusions regarding racial evolution from physical data. Environmental factors, particularly, may cause changes in the development of an individual to such an extent that we might incline to place him in a racial category rather different from that to which he belongs. We are all familiar, for example, with the fact that hardships in youth, particularly poor diet, may make for restricted and abnormal growth. On the other hand, studies of American college fathers and their sons indicate that the younger generation is distinctly taller – by an inch or so – on the average. This does not indicate that there is any change in inherited factors but is due, we fondly believe, to more intelligent upbringing and better diets, which have given an environment more favourable for growth. Measurements of the children of Italian immigrants indicate that their head shapes are rather different from those of their parents. It has been suggested that in such a case the new environment has resulted in a permanent hereditary change in this character. There is, however, a reasonable alternative explanation. In their native land the inhabitants of each region mate only with their near neighbours, and stable local types develop. In the New World, however, Calabrian may wed Milanese, Sicilian may wed Roman; new combinations are formed, and it is not unexpected that measurements would vary in such mixtures. All in all, it seems probable that physical traits are generally stable; environment may cause individual variations but can exert little direct influence on a racial type.

COMPLEXION. Skin colour is the most conspicuous of racial traits and in earlier days was used almost exclusively as a basis for major racial distinctions. The pigment in all human skins is the same. It consists of dark brown granules of a substance called melanin, embedded in cells of the skin. If abundantly present the pigment gives a black effect. Smaller amounts give brown or yellowish effects. If little pigment is present a 'white' appearance results, while a plentiful blood supply to the skin gives a ruddy tinge. The Negroes are, of course, notable for high amounts of pigment; the Australians also tend towards a black; brownish to olive or yellowish complexions characterize the greater part of the remaining races, while blond tendencies are most noticeable in northern Europe.

To be distinguished from ordinary blonds are instances of albinism, in which individuals have a congenital lack of pigment. An unusual example of this is the case of a group of 'white Indians' in Panama among whom there is a strong albinistic strain, although they are closely related to the copper-skinned Indians of the same region. It is frequently assumed that skin colour is affected by the environment – people living in the tropics tending to take on a heavier pigmentation. This may be to some extent true; but the Albino Indians just cited are an extreme example of the fact that colour and environment are not necessarily related.

Primates generally have a considerable amount of skin pigment, and hence it is reasonable to assume that primitive man was 'dark-complexioned'. But whether the pigmentation was primitively as heavy as in the modern Negro seems somewhat doubtful; and there is, of course, no evidence on this point regarding older races.

EYES present important characteristics. The varying eye colours depend upon the pigmentation of the delicate iris, the diaphragm covering the margins of the lens. Some pigment always present in the deeper layers of the iris reflects a purplish tint. In blue-eyed persons there is no other pigment in the iris. If, however, pigment is present more superficially, the blue is masked, and other colours appear. A slight amount of dark pigment will produce a grey or hazel colour if the blue is not completely masked; heavier concentrations of pigment tend to give yellowish, brown, or black shades. In most races brown to black eyes dominate; blue eyes are in general characteristic only of northern Europeans or those who have interbred with them.

The upper eyelid frequently bears a fold which may project downward and, when the eye is widely open, covers the free, lash-bearing margin of the lid to a greater or lesser degree. Such a fold may occur at the inner corner of the eye (apparently an infantile character) or at the middle or the outer margin (regions in which folds tend to be more pronounced in old age). In the more characteristic Mongoloids of north-eastern Asia this fold may extend clear across the eye.

THE FACE. Noses vary greatly in length, in breadth, and in profile. Breadth of nose was, as we have seen, characteristic of early human types, and breadth and shortness is today characteristic of Negroes and Australians. Mongoloids tend to be rather intermediate in nose shape, with a concave profile, while western Asia and Europe are regions where high, narrow, and long noses predominate. In narrow-nosed types the contour is frequently convex, with the peak either high up the nose, as in the 'eagle beak', frequently seen in Europe, particularly northern Europe, or with a general pronounced convexity, as in the Armenoid type common in Asia Minor and in somewhat modified form in the Balkans. Curiously, a somewhat similar nose form is found among the Oceanic Negroes, and many North American Indians are hawk-nosed. Lips, in general, give little basis for racial characterization. In Negroes, however, we find an exceptional condition in rather thick and out-turned lips.

The proportions of the face are frequently characteristic of racial groups. In a child the face is always relatively short and broad; in adults these proportions are sometimes retained, but in many cases the depth of the facial region of the skull and of the jaw increases to give long 'horse-faced 'types. The short face seen, for example, in many Negroes and Australians is perhaps primitive; long faces tend to be common, on the other hand, in north-western Europe. In some broad-faced races the cheek bones jut out prominently; this is a characteristic Mongoloid feature. Also useful in classification are features of the face as seen in side view. Prognathism is a term used to characterize a forward-jutting of the jaws such as is seen, in our own species, most commonly in Negroes and Australians, in contrast with the more vertical plane of the face in, for example, Europeans. We have noted variations in chin projection in the older evolutionary story. Similar but less pronounced variations are present among existing races.

HAIR. Perhaps the most useful bases for racial classification lie in the characters of the hair. As regards form, one extreme type is that found in Mongoloid races, where the hair is very coarse and straight. In Alpine 'whites' and Negroids the hair is coarse to medium in texture, while fine hair is characteristic of Mediterranean peoples. In marked contrast to the straight hair of Mongoloids is that found in typical Negroids, markedly coiled in tiny spirals, giving a woolly appearance. In the Negroid type the root portions of the hairs beneath the skin are curved to begin with, and the shafts are flattened, comparable to a ribbon of tooth paste, allowing curling to take place readily. In the Mongoloid type the roots are straight and the hairs have a round cross-section, making twisting difficult. Between these two types there are many intermediates. In many Negroids the hair is longer and less tightly coiled than in extreme forms; 'kinky' or 'frizzly' are here more appropriate terms. Many peoples, such as Europeans and Polynesians, for example, have wavy hair. Here the hair tends to be long, moderately fine, and with an oval cross-section which allows some degree of twisting. Although hair is not preserved in prehistoric remains, the present distribution of hair types suggests that considerable curling may have been characteristic of early man.

There is great diversity in the amount of hair present in various races. In both Negroids and Mongolians there is little beard or body hair. On the other hand, wavy-haired races tend to have relatively heavy beards and much body hair. The 'aboriginal' Ainus of Japan have the reputation of being the hairiest of living races. Among Western peoples the short-headed types, 'Alpines', in a broad sense, tend to have heavier beards and more abundant body hair than long-headed races.

Hair colour is, for the most part, dependent upon the amount of melanin (similar to that of the skin) present in the hairs; hair and skin colours are typically correlated. The pigment is very abundant in Negroes and Mongoloids, giving a black colour; little pigment is present in blond northern Europeans; an intermediate condition yields brown hair. In addition to the melanin a second, red-gold, pigment is sometimes present; if the melanin is reduced in amount red hair may result. In many light-haired races the amount of black pigment in the hair tends to increase with age, so that blond or red-haired children tend to have more brownish and darker hair as adults.

STATURE unquestionably differs greatly from one racial group to another. However, it must be used with caution for racial discrimination, for it is obvious that there are great individual variations within groups, and we have noted that nurture may be responsible for marked individual variations in height. We must, in addition, discount the sporadic appearance of gigantism, cretinism, and other abnormalities due to improper functioning of the secretions of the pituitary and thyroid glands.

The adult male may be taken as a standard for measurement. Average human stature on this basis would be in the neighbourhood of five feet five inches. The shortest groups of mankind are the Negroid Pygmies, in which a five-foot stature is about the maximum, and many individuals may be half a foot or more short of this. Short stature, although not so extreme, is common in the general Malay region; the Bushmen and Hottentots of South Africa, the Ainus of Japan, the Lapps of northern Europe, the Eskimos, and a few Indian tribes are also markedly short.

On the other hand, height averages of about five feet seven inches or higher are found in a number of regions, notably in various types in north-western Europe and the Balkan mountains, a number of tribes of central and south-eastern Africa, some Indian groups of eastern North America, and a few other scattered regions.

SKULL PROPORTIONS. The cephalic index, the ratio of breadth to length of the braincase, is a universally used measurement discussed in the last chapter. Extinct human types, we have noted, were almost all dolichocephalic; very probably brachycephaly is a comparatively late human development. In Europe broadheads were rare until quite late prehistoric times; in America there is much evidence that long-headed folk preceded the more typical brachycephalic Indians. Among existing Old World races we find that dolichocephaly is prevalent in Africa and Australia and the 'fringes' of Europe and Asia; brachycephalic skulls are dominant in all the more central portions of Eurasia, suggesting a newer development.

But while this index measurement is of interest, there are many other features of the braincase to be kept in mind. Absolute size of the head, slope of the forehead, height of the cranial vault, are all items of interest. Further, broad skulls are not always well rounded; the brachycephalic people of south-eastern Europe and Asia Minor tend to have flattened occiputs and angular skull contours. The capacity of the braincase interior is a measurement to which we have referred earlier. As noted, this figure is of interest and appears to show racial variants but cannot be used as an index to mentality. European male capacities average about 1,500 cubic centimetres; some small-bodied races average 300 cubic centimetres less without obvious harm to the intellect.

BLOOD GROUPS. When, long ago, attempts were first made to give blood transfusions, it was discovered that the blood was not the same in all men and that frequently after the introduction of blood from another person that new red blood cells tended to stick together in clumps (agglutinate) in the host, with disastrous results. Research has given us the reasons for this effect. In many cases the red blood cells of an individual contain one or both of a pair of complex chemical structures which are arbitrarily called A and B. There are thus in any human group four possible types of individuals, which (if absence be designated by O) can be called O, A, B, and AB. The blood plasma of the individual becomes, so to speak, 'accustomed' to A or B if present in his red blood cells. But if either or both are absent in the donor individual, his plasma tends to attack and agglutinate red cells containing such substances. In consequence, we find that plasma from an AB individual can be transfused freely into anyone, since his plasma is 'accustomed' to both possible substances; that plasma from individuals of Groups A or B will attack red cells containing the other type of material; and that the plasma from Group O will, of course, agglutinate red cells of all the three other groups of individuals.

The recognition of substances A and B is of interest not only to the physician but also to students of heredity and evolution. These substances are inherited by normal genetic processes. And, further, it is found that the percentages of A and B present in individuals vary greatly in different areas and races. Tests of the blood have been made in many thousands of persons from all regions of the world.

The A material is, on the average, present in 20–25 per cent of individuals in the Old World. In parts of Australia, however, it may be present in as much as 40 per cent of the natives. In the Americas substance A is apparently very rare in natives of South America and much of the southern and eastern regions of North America. In the Indians of Canada and the Rockies, however, much higher percentages are present, and the Blood and Blackfeet Indians have this factor present in more than half the individuals. Substance B is, in the Old World, present in many areas in 15–20 per cent of individuals, with the highest percentages mainly in central Asia and central Africa. In certain peripheral groups, however, including the Australians, the Bushmen of South Africa, and people on the western fringes of Europe, B is quite rare. And in American Indians, except for one or two dubious records, B is almost unreported.

Such items of distribution of blood groups as those noted above are interesting and suggestive. Blood groups appear to give one more clue to aid in unravelling the snarls of racial relationships and histories.

CLASSIFICATION OF RACES. No general agreement exists among students of race as to the criterion which should be used as the major feature in racial distinctions; skull shape, hair texture, and colour all have their advocates. The schoolbooks of our grandparents used skin colour as the major factor and divided mankind into the whites of Europe, the blacks of the Old World tropics, and the yellow peoples of Asia, to the

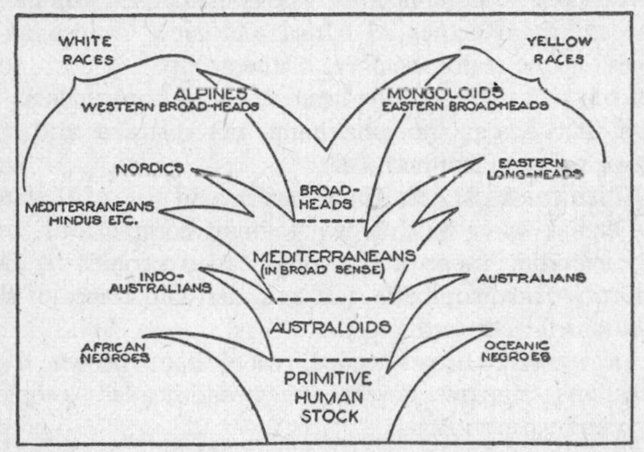

A provisional phylogeny of human races. It is assumed that the various Negroid types were early, although highly specialized, branches of the primitive stem of *Homo sapiens* and that the Australoids, including Australians and 'pre-Dravidians' of India, were also early developments. From the Australoid level little advance was needed to attain a brunette, wavy-haired, long-headed type which may have been ancestral to the remainder of humanity; such a type may be termed Mediterranean, in a very broad sense of that term. Eastern members of this group have been more or less submerged by Mongoloids; western representatives are the Mediterraneans and related races, probably including the Nordics as modified descendants.

A final stage in human evolution has been a trend towards round-headed types. In the East the roundheads have developed into typical Mongoloids, which have 'swamped' earlier races in much of Asia and the America. In the West the roundheads are the Alpines and related forms who, mixing with Mediterraneans and Nordics, are a component of the 'white' or 'Caucasoid' group of the European area.

It is, of course, impossible in a simple diagram to indicate the complicated racial mixtures that have undoubtedly occurred throughout human history.

last of which were usually added the 'red' Indians of America and the brown peoples of south-eastern Asia and the Pacific islands. This classification gives a fairly neat geographical arrangement, but it tends to obscure the facts of migration and presents an unduly simplified picture. We shall here use a somewhat different (although quite tentative) arrangement, as in the accompanying diagram, and attempt to take into account factors of racial migration and evolution. In this, skull proportions and hair characteristics are used as major diagnostic features, with skin colour and shape of nose as additional aids:

I. NEGROIDS: Long-headed, woolly hair, dark complexions, flat noses; the Negroes of Africa and New Guinea and the Pygmies are the major members of the group.

II. AUSTRALOIDS: Long-headed, wavy hair, dark complexion, flat noses; the inhabitants of Australia and certain primitive tribes of southern Asia.

III. MEDITERRANEANS (in a very broad use of that term): Long-headed, wavy hair, brown to light complexions, narrow noses; including most of the long-headed peoples of Europe and north Africa, southern Asia to India, and traces of similar populations farther to the east.

IV. ALPINES: Broad-headed, wavy hair, brown to light complexions, narrow noses; the broad-headed peoples of Europe and western Asia.

V. MONGOLOIDS: Broad-headed, straight hair, 'yellow' or 'red' complexions, noses of intermediate type; most of the peoples of eastern Asia and America.

This classification differs from the 'orthodox' in one major respect – the fact that, in emphasizing the late appearance of brachycephalic men, the western broadheads are more widely separated from the long-headed whites than is customary. The groups given may, however, be united to suit varying tastes. For those who wish to classify by colour, I and II may be united as blacks, III and IV as whites, or Caucasoids, V as the 'yellows'. For those who prefer a classification on the basis of hair, I is the woolly type; II, III, and IV are the wavy type; and V is the straight-haired type. On the basis of skull shape, I, II, and III are longheads, IV and V are shortheads.

Our present knowledge of human history suggests that long heads, curly hair, dark complexions, and flat noses were primitive human characteristics and that short skulls, straight hair, light complexions, and thin noses are more specialized (although by no means necessarily 'higher') features. We shall treat of the various racial groups in this general order, from primitive to specialized.

NEGROIDS

The characteristics of the typical Negroid are familiar: the hair is black, short, coarse, and of a kinky or woolly texture, and there is little hair on the face or body; the skin is black, the eyes dark. The face protrudes markedly (prognathism), and the lips are thick and out-turned. In typical members of the group the skull is long, the nose short and broad, the stature medium to high.

AFRICAN NEGROES. The major homeland of the Negroids today is Africa south of the Sahara, where, except for the Hottentots and Bushmen mentioned later, they are the only native races. The Negroes are a flourishing group and are not only successful in the African environment but, as has been proved, can withstand transplantation to new regions. Culturally the Negroes, before being directly influenced by white civilizations, had progressed far beyond the Paleolithic level and had for the most part reached a full Neolithic type of culture, with well-developed agriculture, domestic animals, weaving, pottery, and even the knowledge of metals. In a number of cases social development had progressed to the organization of powerful tribal structures, but there were few stable or highly organized communities except in isolated cases such as the city-building Fulas of the Niger region and perhaps the unknown builders of Zimbabwe in Rhodesia. Among the typical Negroes of Africa (and for the moment neglecting the Pygmies), a number of subgroups may be distinguished. The belt of grasslands running from the Nile westward to the Atlantic along the western 'bulge' of Africa is the home of the Sudan Negro, characterized by great height and powerful build. Many of the tribes in this northern region show distinct traces of the infusion of blood from 'Mediterranean' whites. South of these grasslands is the region of the tropical rain forests, including much of the Congo and a strip to the north-west along the coast. The forest Negro is a comparatively broad-headed, short-legged, stocky type, which contrasts rather widely with his northern neighbours. From this and the preceding group came most of the slaves imported into America. Somewhat intermediate in character are the Bantu-speaking inhabitants of eastern and southern Africa, from the great lakes south to Cape Colony. These sturdy and frequently warlike peoples include such well-known tribes as the Zulus and the various Kaffirs. Centring in southern Abyssinia is a series of tribes in which there appears to be a considerable admixture of Mediterranean blood from their neighbours to the north. In consequence, we find less kinky hair, lighter skin, and higher and narrower noses.

OCEANIC NEGROES. A second area occupied by Negroes lies far from Africa, in Melanesia, an island group which begins at the west with New Guinea (or Papua) and extends on eastward to the Fiji Islands. In Melanesia the populations are exclusively Negroid, mainly types termed Oceanic Negroes. In almost all major features these Negroids are exceedingly similar to their presumed African relatives; however, the jaws tend to be rather less projecting, the lips not as much thickened, the hair less kinky, and (curiously) there is frequently a strongly hooked nose like the Armenoid type rather than that characteristic of other Negroes. These Oceanic Negroes are none too well known, for they are, in general, decidedly unfriendly and have a reputation for treachery and bloodthirstiness. They are frequently divided into Papuans and Melanesians, the former mainly inhabiting the interior of New Guinea and the other larger islands, the latter, the coasts of the large islands as well as the entirety of many smaller ones. This division is linguistic, the Melanesians speaking languages related to others found in that part of the world, while Papuan is distinct. It seems, however, that the distinction is in part at least a physical one as well. The Papuans are more purely Negroid; it has been suggested that they may represent pygmy Negroes, of the sort discussed in the next section, who have gained a more normal stature through admixture of blood from some taller people (such as the Australians). The Melanesians may contain still other admixtures of blood, for their Negroid characters are less pronounced.

PYGMIES. Still more discontinuous in geographical distribution are the pygmy Negroids, for whom the term 'Negritos' is frequently used. These little people are of extremely short stature, with unusually flat and broad noses, and with a tendency toward brachycephalic skulls. Otherwise, however, they exhibit typical Negro features. They are found only in a limited number of much-restricted areas, including parts of the deep Congo forests, the Andaman Islands in the Bay of Bengal, and spots in the interior of the Malay Peninsula, New Guinea, and the Philippines. They have a relatively crude culture and can obviously do little to protect themselves against aggressive neighbours; the few areas in which they dwell appear to be essentially isolated hiding-places. Their extremely scattered distribution has suggested to many authors that they represent survivors of a human stage still farther down the evolutionary line than that of the typical Negroes. There is at present, however, no fossil evidence that man ever went through a pygmy human stage in his evolution, and the history of the Negritos is a mystery.

TASMANIANS. We may here discuss several other races which, although not definitely Negroes, show many similar primitive characters – the Tasmanians, for example. This race when first found by white men somewhat over a century ago was confined to the island of Tasmania and numbered only a few thousand. Proving troublesome to the settlers, most of the natives were hunted down and exterminated. They have survived only in the shape of a few score of individuals of mixed white and Tasmanian blood. Their extinction is an anthropological calamity, for the Tasmanians were a very primitive and interesting group. Culturally they appear to have been in a Paleolithic stage. They had no pottery, no weaving, no domestic animals, practised no agriculture, and even their stone tools were of a very crude type. In many regards they were physically similar to Negroes, including such features as the very broad, flat, short nose, and the woolly or frizzly hair. On the other hand, the skin, while dark, was not as black as in pronounced Negroid types; the skull was not as markedly dolichocephalic, and, in at least the fact that facial and body hair was more abundant, they showed a less specialized condition than that of typical Negroes. Possibly the Tasmanians represented a type still closer than the Negroes to the primitive human stock; it is to be regretted that our knowledge of them is so limited. It is very likely that the Tasmanian type once inhabited all Australia and was driven out of the main continental area by the later arrival of the modern Australian natives.

BUSHMEN AND HOTTENTOTS. The Bushmen of South Africa are a vanishing race of which only some 25,000 survive in the Kalahari desert region of South Africa. Culturally they are quite primitive, being still in a hunting, food-collecting stage analogous to that of the Upper Paleolithic or Mesolithic peoples of prehistorc Europe. They are very short in stature, with an average height well under five feet. In many regards they resemble the Negroes, for the hair is black and exceptionally kinky, and the nose broad and flat. In other respects however they depart considerably from the Negroid type. The skin has very little pigment and is rather yellowish; the eye form is rather suggestive of the Mongolian type; the cheek bones are prominent; and a racial peculiarity is the pronounced steatopygia, an excessive development of fat on the buttocks.

The Hottentots, also of South Africa, are much more numerous and, as cattle-herders, culturally more progressive. They show Bushman features but to a less pronounced degree. While there is no accord on the matter, the majority of workers believe that the Hottentots represent a Bushman stock with a considerable admixture of blood from the whites of north-eastern Africa.

Archaeological finds indicate that the Bushmen are surely old inhabitants of southern Africa and that they once occupied a much larger area than that in which they are found today. Their antecedents are unknown and are matters for speculation; we have noted earlier some fossil skulls showing Bushman-like features. Paintings and engravings on rock made by the Bushmen are suggestive of those found in north Africa and Spain in late Paleolithic or Mesolithic times, but there is no evidence of bodily similarity between Bushmen and ancient men of those regions. The low stature brings to mind the Pygmies, but there are no other marked similarities. The complexion and eye shape suggest Mongolian relationships, but geographical considerations render this quite unlikely.

We have considered under the general category of Negroids a variety of primitive peoples – African Negroes, Oceanic Negroes, Negritos, Tasmanians, Bushmen, and Hottentots. No one of these, perhaps, is to be considered as directly representative of the most primitive stage of our species. But taken together we may not be far from the truth in considering this assemblage of races as representative of a series of early branches from the main line of evolution of *Homo sapiens*.

NEGROID DISTRIBUTION. The present distribution of the

Negroids offers an interesting problem. They are found in two separate areas – Africa, on the one hand, and south-eastern Asia and Australasia, on the other. How has this discontinuous distribution come about? One suggestion is that one of the two areas – Africa, let us say – was the homeland, whence a migration took place by sea to the other. But pure Negroids are almost never ambitious seafarers. The most reasonable explanation at present is one which draws suggestions from the history of lower mammalian groups. Among mammals there are in Africa or the East Indies today many forms once present in Eurasia but now extinct there. Perhaps the Negroids were, at an early stage of human history, present in continental Asia, migrated thence both east and west to their present territories, but became supplanted by other races in their original home. If this were true one might reasonably expect to find some trace, at least, of Negroid blood in southern Asia. Apparently this is the case, for anthropologists have noted Negroid characters among the more obscure peoples of India, Burma, Assam, Persia, and Arabia, perhaps the last vestiges of an ancient Negroid population.

AUSTRALOIDS

The natives of Australia are a group of great interest to the anthropologists. They were in complete possession of that continent when it was first settled, apparently having invaded it from the north at some remote time. They drove the still older Tasmanians before them but probably interbred to some extent with their predecessors and show traces of Negroid blood. Today there remain about 60,000 pure 'blackfellows', mainly concentrated along the northern coasts. The Australians have an elaborate social organization; as far as material culture goes, however, they are in a very primitive stage. They are hunters and food-gatherers, without permanent shelters. They are ignorant of metals, but their stone work is on a higher level than that of the Tasmanians. There is no agriculture, and domestic animals are unknown, except for the dingo, which, although now partly reverted to the wild, was probably introduced by them.

There are considerable variations among living Australian natives, presumably due to the admixture of Tasmanian and Negroid blood. Physically they are a 'low' type. The brow ridges are more prominent than in any other existing race and seem rather reminiscent of Neanderthal conditions. The forehead is low, the brain frequently small, the chin weak. A character in which they are less specialized than the Negroes lies in the more abundant hairy covering. Many presumably primitive features are shared with the Negroids; the skull is pronouncedly dolichocephalic, the jaws noticeably prognathic; the nose is very broad and flat. On the other hand, they approach the white and yellow races more closely in certain features. The lips lack the swollen appearance of the Negroids; hair and skin, while dark, are typically brown rather than the black of the more extreme Negroids. Most important of presumed advances is the fact that the hair lacks the pronounced kinking seen in Negroids and is merely wavy or somewhat curly, after the fashion of many races of Europe and southern Asia.

If one adheres to the older geographical concept of a threefold classification of races into black, white, and yellow, the Australian is an embarrassing anomaly who does not 'fit' and can be accounted for only on the assumption that he represents a cross between Negroids and whites in which the white element has 'toned down' the Negro coloration and hair curl. An evolutionary explanation, however, seems well in accord with the known facts. It may be that on the Asiatic continent the main human stock evolved beyond the stage at which the Negroids branched off and attained the characteristics seen in the Australian type. A migratory wave of these peoples spread southward to Australia and survived there in isolation, while their representatives elsewhere became submerged by the development of more progressive human types. Such an explanation would be closely in accord with the known facts of evolution in other animal groups; we have noted that Australia is a refuge for many archaic mammals whose relatives are almost entirely extinct in other regions.

If this explanation be true, it is not unreasonable to expect that there would be some trace, at least, of the former presence of Australoids in Asia. This appears to be the case. Some survivors who may be termed Indo-Australians are found in a number of regions in southern Asia, particularly in central and southern India. There, among the more isolated hill tribes, such as the Bhils, etc., and the Veddahs of Ceylon, we find types which exhibit almost exactly the features of the Australian native. These 'Pre-Dravidians' may well represent isolated mainland survivors of this ancient human stock. There are also traces of such peoples in south Arabia. And it is even possible that some Australoid blood was present in the earliest human invaders of the Americas.

MEDITERRANEANS AND RELATED STOCKS

We have now, through a consideration of the Negroid and Australoid groups, accounted for the peopling of the more southerly regions of the Old World, including most of Africa and Australasia. These racial groups, however, have left little imprint on Asia, Europe, or the Americas. These areas are occupied by groups generally lumped as 'white' and 'yellow', which, while diverse in character, are certainly more specialized than either of the major evolutionary stages so far discussed. If we attempt to find their 'lowest common denominator', a type of man from which the remainder of mankind could have evolved, we find that in all probability he should possess essentially some such set of characters as follows: As in Australians, the head might be persistently long, the hair wavy and brown to black in colour, the face and body at least moderately hairy, the eyes brown. On the other hand, we should expect a more advanced condition in a lighter brown skin and a narrower and higher nose than that of typical Negroids and Australoids.

We have no difficulty in finding a series of races which fill this bill of particulars; they are, and long have been, among the most numerous and important peoples of the world. Extending from Spain and Morocco eastward along both sides of the Mediterranean, through Arabia and Persia to India, we find race after race of brown, long-headed peoples who closely fit the diagnosis given above. The western members of the group are generally termed Mediterraneans, and it is not inappropriate to apply this term to the series as a whole. Few major changes are needed, as has been noted, to derive them from ancestral Australoids, and it is reasonable to assume that they represent a third progressive step in the advance of *Homo sapiens* in an Asiatic homeland. Here, however, we have reached a group late enough in appearance to be still represented close to its area of origin.

MEDITERRANEANS OF INDIA. Northern India is a region which has been subject to repeated racial invasions and in which many racial types and mixtures are to be found; peninsular India has been much less subjected to external influences. In this region there are, as we have noted, surviving vestiges of Negroid and Australoid groups. The dominant type, however, the typical Hindu, is a more advanced one, with the essential Mediterranean features. Presumably they represent the Mediterranean close to his native home.

A curious offshoot of the native Indians is that nomadic group known as the Gypsies, or Romanys. Despite the implications in their usual name, these swarthy people appear to be descended from pariah tribes of India which have wandered westward to appear in Europe during the Middle Ages and attach themselves to western peoples. Their racial type appears to be fundamentally that of the Indian Mediterraneans, although an admixture of western blood appears to be present; their speech is basically a Sanskrit modification, although there are many loans from western languages.

FAR EAST MEDITERRANEANS. The westward expansion of the Mediterraneans is readily followed and will be discussed shortly. What of their history to the east? Most of central and eastern Asia is today occupied by the Mongoloids, peoples which differ markedly from the Mediterraneans in such features as their round skulls and straight hair. But, despite their present dominance, there are many indications that they are late-comers and were preceded in many eastern regions by an earlier wave of brown, long-headed, wavy-haired Mediterraneans.

India is surrounded on the north and east by Mongoloid groups, but traces of the earlier presence of brunette Mediterraneans in these areas seem to be shown by mixed types found in Burma and east into Indo-China. The inhabitants of these regions, although classed as yellows, show Mongoloid features in a much less marked manner than is the case farther north; probably they represent a blend with earlier Mediterraneans. Farther south, in the Malay peninsula and the East Indies, the characteristic Malay populations, while dominantly Mongoloid, show some indications of mixture with a preceding Mediterranean 'wave'. In various isolated groups in the East Indies (such as the Murut people of Borneo) these Mediterraneans have survived in relatively pure form. They tend to retain their primitive long heads and wavy hair, although showing some Mongoloid features and perhaps some Negroid admixture. To these peoples the term Indonesian is applied. As would be expected, these survivors are inland dwellers, with the more Mongoloid Malays occupying the coasts.

POLYNESIANS. We have, then, many indications of an early eastward 'push' of the Mediterraneans into south-eastern Asia and beyond this into the East Indies. But this was by no means the end of their migrations in this direction.

The numerous island groups scattered over the open Pacific from Hawaii to New Zealand are known collectively as Polynesia, and their inhabitants form the Polynesian race. These tall, fine-looking people are expert seamen, as they must be to have reached their isolated homes, and, although many cultural elements which we find in 'civilized' groups are absent, these lacunae are mainly explicable in terms of the peculiar environment under which they live. It is certain that they reached these islands from the west, probably in a series of waves, of which some are of quite recent date. It is generally believed that their starting-point lay in the East Indies. Proof of this is afforded by the fact that a few Polynesians are still present on some of the East Indian islands.

Some racial admixture appears to be present in the Polynesians. In their southern members, particularly the Maoris, there are some suggestions that a Negroid strain was picked up during the outward journey from Asia. There are most distinct indications of Mongoloid blood, for the cheek bones tend to be prominent, the head shape, although variable, is often brachycephalic, and body hair is scant. But in most features, such as the brown and wavy hair, brown skin, and brown eyes, it seems apparent that the Polynesians are essentially a far-flung eastern branch of the Mediterranean stock.

THE AINUS. The Mediterraneans, in the broad sense of a primitive, long-headed, wavy-haired, brunette white stock, spread in early days to the north-east as well. Most of the northern half of eastern Asia is filled with typical Mongoloids. But there are long-headed strains among various Siberian tribes to the far north-east, which suggests the early presence there of Mediterraneans. More positive evidence is found in Japan, where the

Ainus are an archaic race of strong affinities with this type. Now few in number and restricted to parts of the northern island of Yezo (Hokkaido), where they are 'preserved', the Ainus appear to have once occupied all of Japan. The skulls tend to be dolichocephalic, the hair wavy and abundant (unusually so), the eyes brown, the skin a light brown. These are features which suggest a relationship to the brunette Mediterraneans and are in marked contrast with those of their Asiatic neighbours. There is, however, some suggestion of a bit of Mongolian blood in the prevalence of black hair and rather thick-set bodies and prominent cheek bones.

AMERICAN LONGHEADS. We have every reason to believe that long-headed brunettes essentially Mediterranean passed still farther to the north-east to become early, perhaps the earliest, inhabitants of the Americas. The Indians are usually classified as a subdivision of the Mongoloids, and rightly so, it seems, as regards the majority of the population. But there are Indians and Indians. In many regions there are groups which show few if any of the characters of typical Mongoloids and tend to have long heads, cheek bones less prominent than in typical Mongols, and other features suggesting the basic Mediterranean type. The earliest known Indians of the South-west, the basket-makers who preceded the present tribe of that region, are known to have been markedly dolichocephalic; longheads are abundant among the Indians of the Amazon basin, and the Yahgans of far Tierra del Fuego are apparently of this type. Even in North America the eastern Indians, now nearly extinct, lacked a full Mongoloid development.

Presumably the peopling of the Americas did not consist of a single migration but of a series of successive waves of invasion. The last immigrants were definitely Mongoloid; the earlier ones, however, appear to have been essentially Mediterraneans (and there may even have been some still earlier comers representing Australoid or Negroid types). As would be expected, traces of these earlier settlers are to be found today mainly in areas far off the beaten track of later migrations.

EUROPEAN UPPER PALEOLITHIC SURVIVORS. In the last chapter we noted the presence in the Upper Paleolithic of Europe of men of our own species – mainly long-headed individuals – who show little of either Negroid or Mongoloid features and hence might well be considered white. Were they early forerunners of a western migration of Mediterraneans? Probably not in any direct sense. A few of them were rather similar to the Mediterraneans, but most, including the typical Cro-Magnards, were quite tall, rather rugged specimens, contrasting sharply in many respects with the typical Mediterraneans, who are relatively small and less robust. One possible explanation of their nature calls upon the evidence from Palestine which suggests an interbreeding between Neanderthal man and *Homo sapiens.* Possibly the Upper Paleolithic men of western Europe do represent a blend between early westward-travelling Mediterraneans and Neanderthals, with the *sapiens* strain dominant, the Neanderthal mixture giving a touch of crudity to the skeleton.

Concerning the later history of Cro-Magnon man and his contemporaries, there is much speculation and little knowledge. A touch of this blood may persist in northern Africa, where Upper Paleolithic populations were numerous, and in the Canary Islands off the western shore of that continent the people show many features suggesting partial derivation from this ancient stock. It seems reasonable to believe, however, that most of this population would have tended to drift northward as the Ice Age came to a close. In the following Mesolithic cultural period remains which are suggestive of Upper Paleolithic types are found farther north along the European coast, as far as southern Scandinavia, and it is highly probably that a strain of Paleolithic blood may persist today in some northern regions. This is especially the case in the British Isles (particularly Ireland), northern Germany, and the Atlantic coast of Scandinavia, regions where otherwise the Nordic type is dominant. Some of these 'suspects', particularly in Norway, differ little from their Nordic neighbours except in a more massive build. Others, especially in north Germany, tend towards darker hair and rounder heads, the latter perhaps inherited from the (relatively rare) brachycephalic members of the Upper Paleolithic races.

WESTERN MIGRATION OF THE MEDITERRANEANS. Whatever the nature of the Upper Paleolithic peoples, the true Mediterraneans spread westward at an early date, and widely. As early as Mesolithic times these southern whites were present over a vast territory. They were present then in Palestine. In

Africa Mediterraneans which appear to be of this age are found not only in Egypt but far to the south, near the headwaters of the Nile. To the west Mediterraneans had reached the shores of the Atlantic in Portugal. By Neolithic days they were in possession of the entire Mediterranean region and had spread far to the north. People who appear from their skeletons to have been Mediterraneans inhabited the Danube basin and, in a somewhat taller phase, the plains farther north from the Rhone to southern Russia. Farther east, as well, the Mediterraneans appear to have pushed north into the Eurasian steppes, for Neolithic skeletons from Turkestan are of Mediterranean types. The Mediterraneans thus constitute the oldest known population of the Near East and were apparently the main factor in the peopling of Europe and northern Africa.

The contributions of the Mediterranean peoples to the evolution of culture cannot be overestimated. We have noted that Neolithic culture appears to have originated in the Near East; this was an area inhabited by typical Mediterraneans. They appear, further, to have been the peoples who carried this culture to Europe and westward along the Mediterranean and northward by various routes to the Danube and the northern plains – for almost everywhere the villages of the Neolithic settlers reveal skeletons of this type.

Linguistically, however, they are of lesser historical importance. Many of them now speak Indo-European languages akin to those of other European peoples. But this group of languages is not native to the Mediterranean world. Many Mediterraneans today speak Semitic languages, such as Arabic and Hebrew, or related 'Hamitic' African tongues, such as ancient Egyptian (and its modern Coptic derivative), and Berber. In addition, however, it is strongly suspected that the older Mediterraneans possessed still other languages, most traces of which have been lost.

PRESENT DISTRIBUTION OF MEDITERRANEANS. Today a great racial group of darker, long-headed, southern whites occupies a long strip of territory extending west from India to the Atlantic. An eastern group, Irano-Afghans, rather tall and hook-nosed, occupies the plateaus and mountains of Persia and Afghanistan and extends northward into part of western Turkestan. In Arabia are found typical Mediterraneans rather shorter in stature; the basic Jewish stock was of this type. Quite similar are the native Egyptians. To the south the general region of Ethiopia is characterized by races frequently termed 'Hamites', which are essentially Mediterraneans but with a Negro admixture in many cases. In northern Africa west of Egypt the Mediterranean type also prevails but in a rather taller phase. Shorter men, however, reappear in Spain, which is a nearly pure Mediterranean country, with bodily features closely comparable to those seen in Arabia.

North of the Mediterranean Sea the area once occupied by this race has been much restricted because of racial changes and the great increase, in relatively late times, of round-headed types. In Asia Minor the original population appears to have consisted of Mediterraneans with rather prominent noses, but they have been swamped in great measure by brachycephalics. In Greece, however, there is still, as in classical times, a very large proportion of Mediterranean blood, and a pronounced Mediterranean strain is to be found from here northward through the eastern Balkans to the Russian coasts of the Black Sea.

Farther west the original Mediterranean population of Italy is still strongly represented in Sicily and the south of the peninsula; as we progress northward, however, brachycephalic types increase in proportion, and there is little trace of Mediterraneans in northern Italy. This race has left a strong impression on the populations of central and southern France, but the French are mainly brachycephalic.

In central and northern Europe this stock has almost completely disappeared, in its original form at least. In Great Britain the Neolithic population was mainly one of Mediterranean longheads, and there are still marked traces of them in the population of Wales and the west coast of Scotland. Otherwise Mediterraneans in northern Europe are non-existent.

EARLY NORDICS. The Mediterranean blood does survive in the north, but in a modified form, in the Nordics. Typical members of this race, found in its purest form in Scandinavia and the east Baltic shores, are different in many respects from the typical Mediterraneans. They are tall, with light skin, hair which tends to be blond, and eyes which are blue or grey, in contrast to the brown of the Mediterraneans. But like that group they are essentially dolichocephalic, and there are no reasons why they cannot have evolved by a 'bleaching-out' of early Mediterranean migrants to the North.

The prehistoric archaeology of Europe furnishes much evidence which is in agreement with this theory, although of course the evidence from skeletons cannot tell us anything of pigmentation. We have noted that the Neolithic Mediterreaneans sent strong colonies north into central Europe to the Danube basin and into Germany and the Russian plain. The date of these settlements cannot be definitely fixed but presumably may have been about three thousand years before Christ. A thousand years or so later bronze begins to be found in these areas. During the next millennium, the Bronze Age in this region, there were some cultural shifts and evidences of migrations, but essentially the same people seemed to have remained there. When the Iron Age arrived, about 1000 B.C., historical evidence abundantly shows that the northern Europeans were Nordics, with the blond features, blond hair, and blond eyes of the modern Nordic. They were not, however, immigrants, as far as we can tell, but the descendants of the browner Neolithic Mediterraneans, who had arrived there several thousand years before. Here, in central and northern Europe, it appears, occurred the loss of pigment which is characteristic of the Nordic group.

Best-known centres of this early Iron Age Nordic race were southern Germany and the Danube basin. But even in early days the Nordics occupied a much larger territory. To the west the Rhine Valley appears to have been their approximate boundary. They spread far to the north, into Scandinavia, where southern Sweden became an important Nordic focus. Eastward, the steppes of south Russia appear to have been Nordic country in Iron Age days. There is also good evidence of the early presence of northern blonds in southern Siberia and western Turkestan – country now inhabited by Asiatics – and there is even evidence of Nordic penetration far to the east into the Tarim basin of central Asia.

These early Nordics were not particularly progressive culturally. They adopted the use of iron with avidity and used it energetically (if perhaps somewhat bloodily). They were capable of agricultural pursuits but were never city-builders. They seem, on the contrary, to have been a rather restless race, and many, the more eastern groups particularly, were essentially nomadic, with the horse an important element in their activities.

In another respect, however, the Nordics played an important role in later European culture, namely, as language-bearers. Today a great majority of Europeans, as well as their overseas colonists and the people of Iran and large parts of India, speak languages of the Indo-European group. This great variety of tongues – from Gaelic and English on the west to Sanskrit and its modern derivatives in India – shows many fundamental similarities which indicate that they had a common origin. There was at one time a tendency to assume that all speakers of these languages were racially similar, members of an 'Aryan' race (the name is derived from that of the Sanskrit-speaking invaders of India), but this thesis can no longer be maintained.

We can, however, reach with considerable certainty some idea of the region in which this language group originated, using historical and linguistic evidence. Quite surely the area was somewhere between eastern Germany and southern Russia. This region, as we have just seen, is the centre of the prehistoric Nordics. We are thus justified in believing that these long-headed northern blonds were the originators as well as the disseminators of Indo-European tongues.

Although the early Nordics were too barbarous to have left us written records, archaeology and historic accounts by more southern peoples can give us some idea of the distribution of the various Nordic groups a thousand years or so before Christ. At that time much of the Danube region was occupied by Nordics, generally termed Illyrians and Thracians, rather poorly known but important as the peoples who were probably responsible, through invasion, for the introduction of both Indo-European languages and a blond ruling caste into Italy and Greece. The western Nordic territory, roughly western Germany today, was occupied by the Celts. To the north, in southern Scandinavia, was the early Germanic centre. South-east of this, in Poland and towards the Ukraine, were Nordics who spoke ancestral Slavic and tongues from which have descended Baltic languages, such as Lithuanian.

Farther east, in the steppes of south Russia and western Asia, there are relatively few data, either archaeological or historical, as to the early nomadic Nordics of these regions, but some general facts can be made out. In early Greek days the southern Russian plain was occupied by the Scythians – trouser-wearing, horse-riding nomads who were early users of the covered wagon. They were apparently blond Nordics who later fused with other peoples and made little historical impression. To the east of them, into Asia, stretched other horse-nomads, still more poorly known, who were apparently speakers of tongues now found in Iran and India.

NORDIC MIGRATIONS. These Nordics appear to have been rather restless and aggressive peoples. About them, mainly to the south, were wealthier and seemingly less warlike nations. Given these circumstances, it is not unnatural that much of Nordic history has been one of movement, war, and invasion, from early times down to the Viking raids of the early Middle Ages.

Some of the movements are essentially prehistoric, although often recorded by tradition. Eastern tribal movements were early. The Aryans moved south into India, as the Sanskrit records indicate, at about 1200 B.C.; the Persians' southern movement into Iran appears to have been of about the same date, and the fact that an Indo-European language appears in the records of the Hittite empire indicates an early wave of Nordics into Asia Minor. Farther west, too, there were early southern movements. As noted above, Nordics made their appearance in Greece and Italy in prehistoric times, and the Hyksos and 'sea-peoples' who annoyed the Egyptians equally early were not improbably far-flung Nordics.

Centuries later the Celts 'erupted'. This group, then centred in south-western Germany, was apparently not purely Nordic – a shade browner, a bit more round-headed than the true type. By about 500 B.C. they appear to have reached a flourishing condition and began to expand. This expansion went in various directions – east as far as Asia Minor, where Galicia received its name from Gaulish invaders, south into Italy to conquer the Po Valley and sack Rome. Mainly, however, they moved westward, where the Gauls dominated France in Caesar's day, and on into the British Isles, which had become essentially a Celtic land when invaded by the Romans.

Then followed the tribal wanderings of the German peoples, most of which took place in the full light of history. As has been said, the early Germans centred in southern Sweden. From that area came several prominent groups which broke into the Roman Empire – the Burgundians, the Goths, who wandered far to the south and west, and the Vandals, who even reached Africa. Other German tribes followed the westward movements of the Celts to make Germany German for the first time. To the west the Franks extended into Gaul to give their name to modern France. Anglo-Saxons, Germans from the North Sea Coast, crossed to Great Britain. And for many centuries afterwards the Vikings from the Scandinavian fjords plied the seas, making their greatest influence on the British Isles, but wandering south to Africa and the Mediterranean and on the west venturing to Iceland, Greenland, and even 'Vinland'.

Last of all Nordic dispersals was that of the Slavs. This, however, had a curious history. The Slavs were originally Nordics who appear to have had their homes in the forests and marshes lying north-east of the Carpathians in south-eastern Poland and the adjacent part of the Ukraine. There they remained – obscure and relatively undisturbed – until most of the great racial movements were over. Then, beginning about A.D. 500, began an expansion which carried Slavic languages far and wide. To the south such languages are spoken in much of the Balkans. To the west the Slavs reached Bohemia and at one time penetrated Germany as far west as Berlin. To the north-east they spread over modern Russia, and today Slav-speaking immigrants are playing an increasingly important part in northern Asia.

But this has been a conquest of language, not of race. As we have noted, the Slavs were originally long-headed Nordics. Today relatively few speakers of Slavic tongues are longheads. The primitive Slav blood has been submerged by brachycephalic races.

The present distribution of Nordics is far more limited than our recital of their conquests would suggest. Today their main centre is close to the original Germanic home. In pure form they are mainly concentrated in eastern Norway, central and southern Sweden, Finland, and the little Baltic States, while the Low Countries and Great Britain also show a large percentage of Nordic types. Outside of these districts Nordic blood tends to be rare. In coastal Norway, Denmark, and northern Germany the

Nordic strain is clearly to be seen in the predominantly blond types encountered, but we are dealing with a blended people with more brachycephalic skulls – the squareheads of popular terminology. There are still fair amounts of Nordic blood present in central Russia, Saxony, Austria, and parts of Switzerland and northern France. Elsewhere, however, in all the Mediterranean region and in Asia, the Nordic is almost non-existent.

The Nordic has been of interest linguistically and as a fighter but is not particularly remarkable in other fields of activity. Despite this, there tended to grow up a great cult of worship of the Nordic, the essence of which is seen in Hilaire Belloc's verses:

> Behold, my child, the Nordic man,
> And be as like him as you can:
> His legs are long – his mind is slow,
> His hair is lank and made of tow.
>
> And here we have the Alpine race.
> Oh! What a broad and brutal face.
> His skin is of a dirty yellow;
> He is a most unpleasant fellow.
>
> The most degrading of them all
> Mediterranean we call.
> His hair is crisp and even curls,
> And he is saucy with the girls.

It is amusing that the centre of this Nordic worship has been Germany, in which, as we have seen, true Nordics are relatively rare. It may be noted, however, that emphasis in recent years has changed from Nordic to Aryan. Since this shift is from a racial term to one associated instead with speech or culture, we need not, as biologists, be further concerned with it here.

ALPINES

The races so far considered have been, almost without exception, long-headed. A final major event in the evolution of man would seem to have been the appearance of brachycephalic skulls. That this event was a relatively late one is suggested on grounds both of distribution and of archaeology. A map of the distribution of head shapes in the Old World today shows that broadheads are overwhelmingly preponderant in central and eastern Asia and in eastern and central Europe; the longheads dominate in the 'pendant' southern continents of Africa and Australia but in Eurasia are found only about the peripheries of that continental mass. This strongly suggests that brachycephaly is a new strain, the bearers of which have spread until the longheads have been forced out into marginal regions. Archaeologically our evidence is meagre, apart from Europe, but the record there seems to agree with this conclusion. Roundheads, as we have seen, are very rare there in the Upper Paleolithic, not common until quite late in prehistoric times, and have but recently attained their present dominance.

The roundheads are generally regarded as sharply divided into two groups. The western European members are usually regarded as whites, closely related to Mediterraneans and Nordics; the eastern brachycephalics, on the other hand, are the typical Mongoloids. We find, however, that along the borders of Asia and Europe there are types of roundheads which are essentially 'neutral', which do not appear to be mixtures, and yet are hard to classify as either Europeans or as true Mongoloids. The brachycephalic group may thus have developed as a unit, with the western whites and the eastern Mongoloids merely representing two extremes from a common mean. Nevertheless the histories of these two types have been in the main discrete, and we may for convenience treat of them separately, beginning with the western roundheads, to whom the term 'Alpine', in a broad sense, is generally applied. The name is due to an interesting fact of distribution. Excluding for the time being the Russian area, most of the European broadheads tend to cluster along a line running from France east along the Alps, down the chains of the Balkans, and on east into the mountains of Asia Minor. These roundheads have thus been situated during historic times in an east-to-west zone between the Mediterraneans and the Nordics on the other side of the Alps. Even if originally a 'pure' race, it is obvious that, in close apposition with other types to the north and south, they might readily have mixed with them, and taken on characters of their neighbours. This apparently has occurred, and there is little we can say of features common to all Alpines, except for the brachycephalic condition and the probability that they have been, in general, types of moderately brown pigmentation.

ALPINES OF WESTERN EUROPE. A large proportion of the population of France is essentially Alpine. The typical Frenchman of this type is a short sturdy individual, with a broad face and short nose, a round head, and a moderately brown complexion. Such types are found farther east along the range of the Alpines, but relatively rarely. Most of the rest of this region is occupied by roundheads whose physical make-up appears to have been modified in various regards through the influence of neighbouring populations. One such group is prominent north of the Alps in Bavaria, Bohemia, and the Saxon region of Germany, where a prominent type among the inhabitants is a round-headed blond. Presumably these people represent a cross between the Alpines and the Nordics which once peopled this region. This race may be termed 'Noric', after the name of an old Roman province in this region, Noricum.

DINARICS. More important is a section of the Alpine peoples in which the centre of distribution lies in the eastern Alps – from east Switzerland through the Tyrol and south through Yugoslavia to Albania. These mountaineers are the Dinarics – tall and rather brownish men with prominent faces and noses. They appear to carry a considerable amount of Mediterranean blood. Beyond the mountains they extend to the north-east, where they are prominent in the Hungarian region, while to the south they are the major stock in the Po Valley and have introduced a considerable brachycephalic strain into Italy as a whole.

ARMENOIDS. Eastward beyond the Bosphorus there are strong Dinaric influences in the dominantly brown and round-headed populations of Asia Minor and Syria. Here, however, we find an admixture of a further related brachycephalic racial type, the Armenoid, so called because it is found in its purest state in the territory of that harried race, the Armenians. The Armenoids are similar to their Dinaric relatives but tend to be a bit darker and with a still more prominent face and the large convex nose common in the Levant. Beyond Armenia ceases the Alpine occupation of the highland chain; but there appear to be traces of typical Alpines still farther east, in Turkestan.

ALPINE ORIGINS. The origin of these Alpines is a question to which we have as yet no thoroughly satisfactory solution. Archaeology, as far as the facts go, indicates that roundheads were rare in these regions in early prehistoric times, with a continued and accelerated increase in their numbers in later periods of history. Can they simply have evolved on the spot by a gradual change of head shape in the old Mediterranean populations? Possibly, but it is difficult to see why such a shift should have occurred only in this one region. The striplike distribution, combined with the enormous increases in Alpine numbers in later times, suggests great invasions of brachycephalics from the east along the mountain belt. But the evidence shows no indication of major movements of this sort. Possibly the truth may lie between these extremes. There may have been a certain amount of east-to-west migration from time to time, bringing in a relatively modest amount of roundheads who frequently interbred with their neighbours, particularly the Mediterraneans. It is possible – although incapable of proof – that the great increase in numbers of brachycephalics has been due not to great original numbers but to greater fecundity and to a dominance of round-headedness in racial crosses.

EAST EUROPEAN ROUNDHEADS. But the Alpines of the Alpine strip just discussed are not the only round-headed peoples of Europe. In north-western Europe, in the general Nordic area, we have already noted the present of brachycephalic types which, it has been suggested, may represent the survival of very early roundheads. More important is the situation in eastern Europe. There, particularly in Poland and most of Russia, we find the peasants to be a nearly uniform type of individual. They are round-headed, short, and stocky, as are many Alpines. But they tend to have broad faces, low short noses, hair which tends to be straight and coarse – rather suggestive of more eastern peoples. And finally, as in Nordics, skin, eyes, and hair tend to be light in colour. No generally accepted term for this race exists. One usually thinks of them as the characteristic Slavs; but this is a linguistic rather than a racial term, and we have already noted that the original Slav-speakers were Nordics. East European is a more non-committal and perhaps useful term.

The characters of this race suggest that it has been formed by a fusion of two types. One presumably was that of the Nordics, who formerly inhabited much of this region and supplied both blond complexion and language. The second was presumably a brachycephalic race with characters not as markedly European as in Alpines and hence very probably from some more easterly homeland.

TURANIANS. Along the boundaries of Asia and Europe, particularly in west Turkestan between the Caspian and the mountains of central Asia, there are found today various racial groups to which the terms Turanians or Turco-Tartars are often applied. These are round-headed people, typically with short broad bodies, broad faces, reduced noses, and straight hair as in Mongoloids. But the more marked Mongoloid features are absent, and the general brown pigmentation suggests comparison rather with western brachycephalics. It may be that in some cases this type has resulted from a cross between Mongoloids and Alpines, but certain, at least, of these people do not suggest a mixed heritage. Not improbably we are dealing here with a central, halfway group of roundheads in the centre of the area of origin of brachycephalic men who have never possessed the more specialized features of either eastern or western varieties of the roundheads.

One may reasonably believe that the people who have contributed the brachycephalic element to the eastern European race were members of this general group who spread westward. In this general category, too, may be placed the little Lapps of northern Scandinavia, who are known to have reached their Arctic home as the result of a long migration from the western Asiatic steppes.

MONGOLOIDS

The vast majority of the inhabitants of eastern Asia and of the Americas (before European settlement) are generally grouped as Mongoloids, including the yellow and red faces of popular classification. In its most characteristic development the Mongoloid physical type is readily recognizable. The skull is brachycephalic, the face broad, with prominent cheek bones, the nose small, the body stockily built. The skin has a yellowish tinge, which may verge on brown; the eyes are dark in colour. Hair is long and abundant on the head, but beard and body hair is poorly developed, and the hair tends to be notably coarse and straight. A specialization frequently seen is that of the eye-opening, which is a slanting slit with a characteristic fold covering the upper eyelid.

As has been noted, the geographic distribution suggests that the Mongoloids are a relatively recent group; but we have little archaeological evidence as yet concerning their racial history, and their classification into sub-groups is still imperfectly worked out.

Mongolia and eastern Siberia are regions in which Mongoloid characters are seen most highly developed. We have noted that in earlier days the western Asiatic steppes appear to have been largely populated by blond Nordics. Today much of this territory has been taken over by Mongoloids. Like the more westerly white nomads, the steppe Mongoloids took to horseback and made forays not only south into China but westward; the Huns and the Mongols are names familiar as western invaders. In west-central Asia Mongoloids have replaced European types to a considerable degree, but, except for a minor Mongoloid element in Russia, these orientals have had little influence on the population of the Western world.

Most of the peoples of eastern Asia are to be classified as Mongoloids, but the more characteristic features of this group become less prominent as one goes southward through China. There are, as was noted earlier, many peoples in south-eastern Asia who are difficult to classify and seem to partake of both Mediterranean and Mongoloid characteristics. Possibly they may represent mixtures of the two; but equally possibly it may be that they have come from ancestors in which the full complement of Mongoloid features has never developed. In this region the Mongoloid type is best developed in the Malays of the East Indies, who differ from their northern relatives in their still shorter stature and browner skin. Variants of this type extend along the islands fringing the eastern coast of Asia, to the Philippines and Formosa; the Japanese are fairly recent arrivals in their islands and appear to have a large amount of Malay blood, and the same may be true of the Koreans.

In the sphere of cultural achievements the Asiatic Mongoloids have been exceeded only by the Mediterraneans; for while this group includes many a tribe of hunters, fishers, and pastoral nomads, the Chinese and other southern groups advanced far in civilization, and recent decades have shown eastern Asiatics to be readily capable of adapting modern technology to their own needs.

AMERICAN INDIANS. It was suggested earlier that Mediterraneans may have been early invaders of the Americas. However that may be, the great majority of the native American population is of Mongoloid descent. In most American Indians many of the characters are those of the true Mongoloid, such as the brachycephalic head, prominent cheek bones, the colour, form, and distribution of the hair. There are, however, some differences from the Mongoloid pattern; the skin has more of a brownish or reddish tint; the nose, in sharp contrast to the typical Mongoloid, is frequently high bridged and convex, and there is seldom any marked trace of the Mongolian fold of the eyelid.

It is probable that the Mongoloid invasion included a number of successive waves travelling down from Alaska, spreading out over the two Americas, and blending with earlier migrants. In agreement with this, we have seen that traces of older stocks are most frequently off the main migrational tracks, while, on the other hand, certain Indian stocks of North America show physical and even linguistic similarities to some of the Siberian Mongoloids, which indicate that they are quite recent arrivals.

Our usual conceptions of Indian build are based on the type seen in the western tribes of pioneer days, the 'noble redskin' as portrayed on the nickel – tall, powerful, copper-coloured, with craggy features and prominent nose. But from this there are variants so numerous that we shall mention only a few. In Central America, for example, the descendants of the Indians who were responsible for Mayan culture are much shorter in stature, the features much less rugged. The forest Indians of South America tend to differ still more; the skin tends to be darker, the nose short; the head tends to retain a dolichocephalic contour; the hair sometimes is persistently wavy rather than straight.

Although many groups of Indians, such as Mayas, Aztecs, and Incas, had reached a moderately high degree of civilization before being harassed by Europeans, it seems fairly sure that relatively little cultural equipment was brought into this hemisphere by the various Indians in migrations. Except for the dog, such few animals as were domesticated were American forms, and so also were the domestic plants (many of them promptly adopted into European culture). This suggests that the settlers had been derived from Mesolithic or even Upper Paleolithic ancestors; however, it may be pointed out that little in the way of advanced culture could have survived long tribal journeys through the sub-arctic regions of Siberia and Alaska.

ESKIMOS. Rather sharply marked off from the normal Indian types are the Eskimos, who, with their typical Arctic culture, are widespread along the northern lands from north-eastern Asia to Greenland. Physically they are closer to the Old World Mongoloids than the typical Indians, but have one notable peculiarity – a remarkably narrow head. Their history is not well known, but there appear to be some close relatives among northern Siberian tribes. Perhaps they represent a blend of Mongoloid with some older long-headed group; it is of interest that some Upper Paleolithic skulls have been compared with those of Eskimos.

CHAPTER 17

The Human Body: Skin, Nervous System

WE are all more or less aware that we have bodies. Most of us have had at least in secondary school some sort of course, usually labelled 'anatomy' or 'physiology', in which the rudiments of its structure are set forth (although in general most of the time is often spent in impressing upon us the evils of tobacco and alcohol). We know that we have various internal organs, but (apart from a pious hope that they may continue to operate to our satisfaction) they are not of particular interest to us.

This tacit acceptance of our bodies leads to a curious result in the restrictions of our mental processes. We may ignore our bodies, but our minds cannot readily grasp the idea that any other highly organized being could be built otherwise. Romances of life on Mars or in the moon in the wood-pulp magazines, for example, usually picture the imaginary creatures of these other worlds as fairly similar to men, with a similar complement of limbs, eyes, ears, nose, etc. When man thinks of a supernatural being, be it a brownie or a Zeus, he smugly assumes that such a being must be manlike in build.

But this state of mind leaves us far from the truth. After all, the human body is far from perfect; it is not an ideal structure built for man as man. We have a long and complicated history behind us. This history has left its imprint deeply upon us. The ordinary recital of proofs of evolution points out such things as the appendix or the rudimentary muscles of the ears as indications of man's descent from other animal types. But this is a curiously superficial point of view. In reality, man's whole being is irrevocably bound up with his family history. The main plan of his organization was already laid down in the early chordate stage, aeons ago. The long aquatic life of his early vertebrate ancestors has left irremovable imprints upon his body. The pattern of his limbs is still reminiscent of the Paleozoic days when his ancestors first left the water for the land. Brains, heart, and many other features own much to the many millions of years which his early mammalian forebears spent in obscurity under the threat of the dinosaurs. Every portion of his body still bears the imprint of changes brought about in the arboreal life of his primate ancestry.

In the following pages we shall give a brief account of some of the more interesting structures in our bodies. We shall discuss processes, but relatively briefly, and leave the detail of functions for the physiologist. In great measure we shall take the point of view of the historian. For the history of human culture or science or art we have established great museums. But for the history of our most precious possession, our bodies, they are themselves museums, living witnesses to their historic past.

GENERAL CHARACTERISTICS

In our consideration of the body of man, let us first mention some of our more general characteristics.

SIZE. We are among the larger animals of the world. Some of our vertebrate relatives are larger, but even among back-boned animals we are not far from the top. A very few fishes, crocodiles, some giant tortoises, whales, sea cows, elephants, a few carnivores, and some dozens of hoofed animal types – these are our only superiors in bulk.

Size is a useful feature. It renders us safe from attack from a great majority of possible animal foes. Modern man can defend himself against large enemies by his inventions; but in the early days of ground-dwelling the size of our sub-human ancestors must have been a great advantage. Size, too, results in an increase in physiological efficiency. Animals waste much energy by loss of heat through the surface of the body. This is especially troublesome in warm-blooded animals where a high body temperature must be maintained. With increasing size the amount of heat lost is greatly reduced proportionately, for while the bulk of the body increases by the cube of any dimension, the surfaces of the body increase only by the square. A tiny shrew, we noted, in keeping up its bodily fires eats more than its own weight of food in a day. Our needs are much less.

But large size brings up many other problems. Support is one of these. It is of interest that few invertebrate types are of any great size, and the large invertebrates are water dwellers in a medium where problems of support are of comparatively little importance. Man's size is presumably a feature which would have been impossible of attainment were it not that he is a vertebrate with a hard internal bony skeleton better adapted for support than the external armour of most invertebrates.

SYMMETRY. Man is a bilaterally symmetrical animal, one side of the body being essentially a mirror image of the other. This type of symmetry is, as we have seen, associated with the active mode of life of most chordates. The original chordate, and, indeed, all of man's ancestors until comparatively recent geologic times had the main lengthwise axis of the body in a horizontal position. In man, with the assumption of the erect posture, this axis has been shifted to a vertical position. And, in addition, the gradual increase of limb size in land forms has tended to alter still further the general aspect of bodily proportions. A fish is mainly body; a man is (we exaggerate) mostly limbs.

Our symmetry is not, of course, a perfect one; many of our internal organs are placed somewhat asymmetrically. A curious human feature is our greater dependence upon one side or the other of the body; we are 'right-handed' or, occasionally, 'left-handed'. Actual measurements show a greater development of the bones and muscles of the limbs on the side most used. Our bodies connect with our brains in criss-cross fashion, and we find that, in correlation with bodily use, one side of our brain (usually the left) is larger than the other. Even in fossil human types we can measure the development of this functional asymmetry of brain and bone.

SKIN

To take up in detail the various human structures, we may not inappropriately begin in superficial fashion with the skin. It is through the surface of his body that man gains his main contacts with the outer world; the skin is a source of protection from the world and the medium through which his knowledge of the world comes.

This outer layer was the seat of the sensory and nervous structures in primitive animals. In man these structures have in great measure been removed from the actual skin and will be considered later. But in their development the nervous system and sense organs still demonstrate their origin from the surface of the body (cf. chap. 20). Even with the removal of these important organs, the skin still has many useful functions to perform. It must protect us, if it can, against enemies large and small, against heat and cold, too much moisture, or too much dryness.

ARMOUR. In primitive vertebrates, as we have seen, there developed, in the deeper layers of the skin, bones and bony scales as a protection against larger enemies. These structures have for the most part disappeared in land types. The bony scales soon vanished. In the skull and shoulder region the bony plates have been retained as part of the skull and the collarbone. These have, however, sunk beneath the skin and have allied themselves with the internal skeletal elements and may best be considered elsewhere.

In reptiles horny scales derived from the superficial part of the skin succeeded the older bony scales. These have, again, disappeared in man as in most mammals. Only on our finger tips have we retained remnants of this scale covering. The fingers of primitive mammals retained claws as a grasping device. Man and his primate relatives, however, have taken to the use of the hand as a whole for a grasping organ, and the claws have flattened down to become, as nails, merely finger guards.

EPIDERMIS. Despite this lack of actual armour, the human skin – fifteen square feet of it – is an effective protective device. Of especial importance is its superficial portion, the epidermis. In its deepest part the epidermis contains an actively growing layer from which cells are constantly divided off on the side towards the surface of the body. As they are pushed outward, these cells gradually pass from a living to a dead condition, become granular and horny, and, finally, reaching the surface, rubbed off or gradually shed. In addition to affording constant renewals for these surface layers, the deep layers of the epidermis must be prepared to grow laterally as well and promptly close over any gaps caused by wounds.

SKIN GLANDS. From the epidermis, too, are formed a number of specialized structures. Small glands (sebaceous glands) secrete an oily material which tends to keep skin and hair in good condition. Of vital importance are the sweat glands – small, twisted tubules which grow inward from the surface of the body; Oliver Wendell Holmes aptly compares them with 'fairies' intestines'. They play an efficient role in the prevention of overheating by taking water from the body and discharging it to evaporate on the skin.

A type of skin gland which is so characteristic of man and other mammals that it has given its name to the group is that of the milk glands. Very likely they are derivatives of the sebaceous glands. In many animals they are situated in two rows down the underside of the chest and belly. They sometimes number as many as two dozen, but four to eight are commoner figures. Supernumerary nipples are sometimes present in man. In some groups the teats are concentrated under the abdomen. In man and other primates they are situated on the chest. It has been suggested that this is an adaptation related to arboreal life, the youngster clinging upright to the mother's chest when travelling.

HAIR. Both of the warm-blooded vertebrate groups have an additional superficial protective layer outside the surface of the skin – in birds, feathers; in mammals, hair. Hair seems very probably to have arisen in early mammals in relation to the need for heat conservation. In a normal mammal with a thick hairy covering there is great deal of 'dead air' enclosed between the hairs; this forms an excellent insulating device, closely analogous to the use of rock wool in a dwelling. In man, probably an inhabitant of warm countries to begin with, the hairy covering has been in great measure lost, and we must (for better or worse) use artificial means instead of our own fur to clothe ourselves against cold weather. The 'back to nature' nudist movement may be all very well in the summer time, but it is hardly practical in a northern winter.

Hair is thin in higher primates generally, and in man, except for a few areas – the head, the pubic region, and beneath the arms – it is generally but a thin down and is absent altogether on palms and soles. The beard is probably a peculiar human regional over-development of hair, for our ape cousins have no such structure, and the beard is light in many human races.

The hairs of our body are not in general erect but slanting and trace out patterns over the various parts of the body. In some regions, notably the crown of the head, are growth centres from which radiate little whirlpools of hair. Attached to each hair is a tiny muscle. Human hairs are generally beyond the reach of our will, the nerves to them belonging to the autonomic system. 'Goose flesh' is an appearance caused by an extreme contraction of these little hair muscles.

In most mammals which walk on the ground there are several hard, thick skin pads on the bottoms of both front and hind feet. Normally there are pads on the palm and sole, others between the bases of the toes, and pads on the tip of each toe. In the higher primates, where the limbs have become grasping organs, the pads have disappeared, although the skin of palm and sole remains thick and tough. We have in their places friction ridges which help keep hand and foot from slipping. These consist of numerous parallel ridges usually arranged more or less at right angles to the direction in which the hand or foot is most likely to slip, and contain numerous sweat glands which moisten these areas for a better grasp and a reduction in heat of friction. The ridges are, particularly in the position of the old pads on the finger tips and between the fingers, arranged in complicated patterns – arches, loops, folded loops, and circular whorls. These patterns vary from person to person and finger to finger, and the fingerprints of two individuals are never identical. This is of great aid to the police. Many modern hospitals record the equally variable footprints of new-born babies to prevent the possibility of the Cohens having to bring up the Kelley baby and vice versa.

DEEPER LAYERS OF THE SKIN. Beneath the epidermis lies a much thicker portion of the skin – the dermis (or corium). This consists basically of connective tissue, a type of material which is found throughout the body, filling in the interstices between the other structures. Here it is essentially a tough, feltlike material made up largely of a multitude of interlacing fibres. This constitutes the greater amount of the thickness of the skin; prepared animal hide, such as the leather of our shoes, is entirely connective tissue.

In the connective tissue are other structures. Tiny blood vessels pass up to little elevations beneath the epidermis. These are highly important in temperature regulation; when filled with blood (our skin flushed), they give off considerable heat through the skin to the air; when we are cold, these capillaries are automatically shut off and our heat conserved. Here, too, in the dermis, are various types of nerve and organs which register sensations of touch, pressure, pain, heat and cold.

FAT. In the dermis, particularly the deeper portions, are generally depositions of fat. In many marine mammals, such as whales, this fatty layer, the blubber, is quite thick and forms an effective insulation against the cold of the sea water. Even in man, fat in the skin may make up as much as one-fifth the body weight. This skin layer tends to be better developed in women than in men, not only giving more rounded contours to the body, but also giving better insulation.

THE NERVOUS SYSTEM

The nervous system is a skin derivative; in its development it first appears on the surface of the body and only later sinks beneath the surface and is separated from the skin. From this point of view it may not be improper to treat next of this important portion of our body.

BEGINNINGS OF THE NERVOUS SYSTEM. In the simplest animals every cell is sensitive to stimulation from the outside and capable of action in response to such stimuli. But with complexity of bodily build comes specialization. Certain cells, forebears of the sense organs and nervous system, early took upon themselves the tasks of reception of stimuli and the transmission of impulses to the appropriate muscles or glands which should respond. Originally at the surface, the delicate nervous mechanism tended to sink beneath the skin and become protected by more superficial layers of the body. Most animals have evolved some type of central switchboard, or brain, for the sorting-out of various incoming impulses and their routing to appropriate destinations. In active bilateral animals this structure has naturally developed near the front end of the body where the main sense organs have congregated. Bilateral animals have tended to develop a main nerve trunk line back from the brain down the body. In most of the higher invertebrates this nerve cord passes down the belly side of the animal; in vertebrates it has chanced to be a dorsal structure.

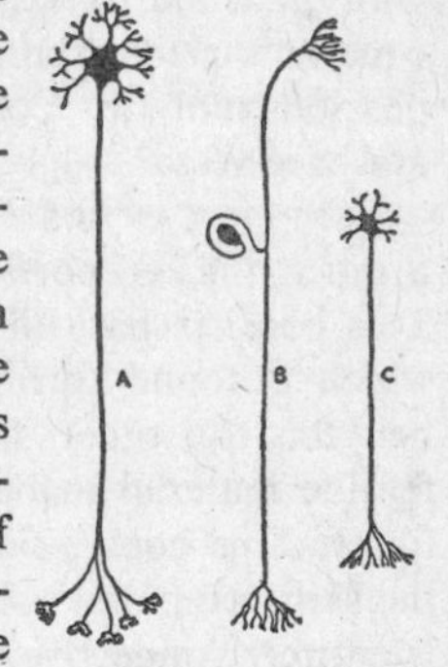

Three of the many types of nerve cells. *A*, a motor cell. Typically such a cell is situated in the cord and sends a long process out in the ventral root of a spinal nerve to muscle fibres. *B*, a sensory cell which has its cell body in the ganglion on the dorsal root of a spinal nerve. *C*. an adjustor cell from the spinal cord.

This basic ground-plan of the nervous system was already well established in the chordate ancestors of the vertebrates. The main changes which have occurred in its later history have been concerned with an elaboration of the nerve connexions, particularly evidenced by complications in the structure of the brain.

NERVE CELLS. Before beginning this story of the large structures of the nervous system, we may briefly consider the units of which these structures are composed. Every organ consists of cells, usually tiny microscopic bits of matter more or less rounded in shape. In the case of nerve cells, the problem of cellular organization is a very peculiar one. The cells must carry nervous impulses between far-distant portions of the body; their function is similar to that of a telegraph wire; length is essential. The main body of a nerve cell, or neuron, is not dissimilar in size or appearance to other types of cells; but out from it grow long processes over which impulses are transmitted. Some of these fibres, thinner than the finest of spider webs, are exceedingly long; for example, the nerve fibres supplying the muscles of our toes run from the spinal cord down the entire length of the leg, a yard or so. Some neurons which carry sensory impulses back from this region may have a second long process reaching up the spinal cord to the brain, the total length of the cell processes here reaching about five feet; and, as can be imagined, even greater lengths are reached in some animals, the whales or elephants for example.

The impulses which travel over these nerve fibres offer a field of study of great interest to the physiologist. The nerve impulses travel with considerable rapidity and can follow one another by only a small fraction of a second. Further, all impulses are the same – either a fibre is stimulated enough to transmit an impulse, or none occurs; there are no halfway measures. Again, a fibre is capable of carrying an impulse equally well in either direction, although the 'wiring' of the nervous system is such that this does not normally occur. Still more interesting is it to realize that the fibre does not, so to speak, 'know' what sort of an impulse it is carrying, for all impulses are exactly alike, and the result of the stimulus depends upon the part of the system that it reaches. A man whose leg has been amputated, for example, may still 'feel' sensations from his missing toes if nerve impulses from elsewhere still reach that part of the brain in which these sensations were once registered.

The exact nature of the nerve impulse is still imperfectly understood. One naturally compares the situation to a telegraph and tends to think of it as an electrical phenomenon. But the speed of the impulse is much slower than that of an electric current. In man it is of the order of but 400 feet per second, or somewhat under 300 miles per hour, and in lower types, as the frog, the rate is only about half as great, hardly comparable with electricity. More probably the basic situation is a chemical one – a burning, or oxidation, of materials which travels along the fibre after the fashion of an ignited powder train. The speed with which a second impulse may occur suggests that there is some mechanism by which the substances 'burnt' are rapidly replaced, and this appears to be the case, although the chemistry of the situation is complex and will not be gone into here.

THE SPINAL CORD AND PERIPHERAL NERVES. The main stem of the nervous system is the spinal cord, reaching the length of the trunk from the brain to the hip region and extending, of course, in more primitive vertebrates out into the tail. It is surrounded and protected by bony arches (neural arches) lying above the main portion of the vertebrae. The cord is a long hollow tube with a small central cavity filled with liquid – the cerebrospinal fluid. This central cavity extends upward into the brain, where it expands into a complicated system of liquid-filled sacs (ventricles).

The spinal cord has a complicated structure. Part of its central area contains the cell bodies of nerve cells arranged in four prominent ridges which in sections give an H-shaped structure, with four prongs or 'horns'. The horns towards the front of the body (anterior, or ventral) contain the cells which send fibres out to the muscles of the limbs and trunk; the back (posterior, or dorsal) horns have cells whose fibres transmit sensations, while intermediate cells are connected with the autonomic nervous system described below. This cell area is grey in colour; the greater part of the cord, however, is white in appearance and consists of exceedingly numerous nerve fibres which transmit impulses up and down the cord and to and from the brain.

To the cord, at every segment, are attached spinal nerves

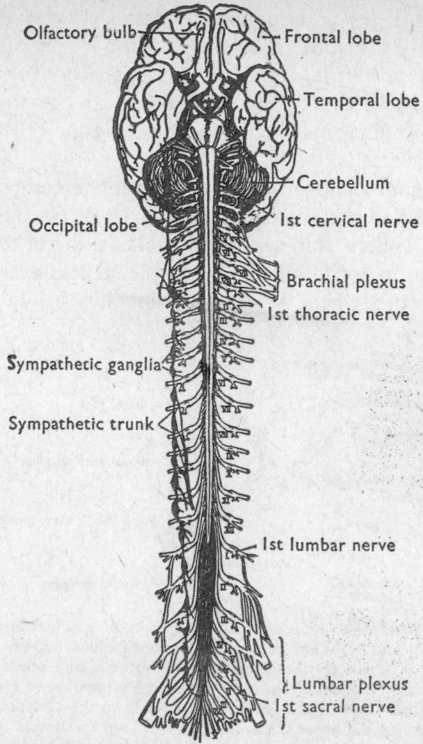

The spinal cord, brain, and connected nerves as seen from the front. At the left side of the figure are shown in black portions of the autonomic system connecting with the spinal cord (sympathetic ganglia and sympathetic trunk). The spinal nerves are numbered in accordance with their position in the neck (cervical), chest region (thoracic), small of the back (lumbar), and hip (sacral) region. Note the two regions of especial nerve concentration for the arms and legs. At the upper end the spinal cord continues without noticeable change into the hindbrain; behind it breaks up in the small of the back into a 'mare's tail' of nerves to the lower end of the body and the legs. (From Harvey, after Morris, *Human Anatomy*, 9th ed.; P. Blakiston's Son & Co., Inc.)

which carry impulses inward from sensory structures in the skin and muscles, and outward from the cord to the muscles of the trunk and limbs (in addition a small branch plunges ventrally to connect with the autonomic system, discussed below). Close to the cord each nerve divides into two roots, or rami. The ventral (or anterior) ramus passes directly inward to the lower part of the cord; it contains motor (or efferent) fibres. The dorsal (or posterior) ramus, carrying sensory (or afferent) fibres, curves upward to enter the cord near the top. Along this root is a swelling, or ganglion, containing the cell bodies of the sensory nerve cells.

In order to gain an idea of the more intimate composition of the spinal cord and the associated nerves, let us trace the events which happen when a skin sensation evokes a direct reaction in which the brain is not involved – a simple 'reflex' action of the sort which occurs when a pin-prick invokes an involuntary jerk of the body.

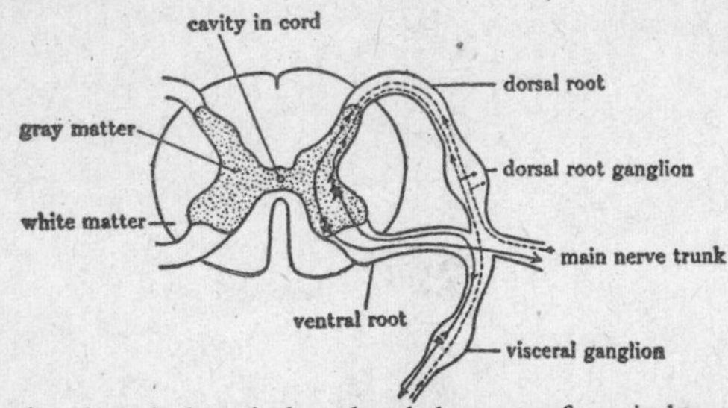

A section through the spinal cord and the roots of a spinal nerve. A few nerve cells and fibres are indicated. The cord includes an inner area of grey matter which consists mainly of nerve cells and outer white matter which is composed of nerve fibres passing up and down the cord and to and from the brain. A sensory impulse from the surface of the body will pass up the nerve trunk (broken line), up the dorsal root of the spinal nerve, past the ganglion where its cell body lies, and into the cord. Here the fibre may branch and make various connexions. In a reflex action connexions may be made with a second neuron, termed an adjustor cell, which has its cell body in the upper 'horn' of the grey matter. Such a cell may transmit the impulse up and down the cord to the brain or to motor neurons on the same or opposite side of the cord. Motor neurons have their cell bodies in the ventral 'horns' of the grey matter. Their fibres (full line) emerge through the ventral roots of the spinal nerves.

Sensations passing from and to the viscera follow essentially similar paths, except that motor impulses are 'relayed' via a second neuron at a ganglion encountered on the way.

The pricking sensation is picked up by a pain receptor in the skin. This stimulates the end of a sensory fibre which carries the impulse up the nerve and, where the roots split, up the dorsal ramus. The cell body of the nerve cell lies in the ganglion here, but the impulse travels on into the cord. There the fibre usually splits up into a number of terminal branches which may pass far up and down the cord. Eventually, however, they enter the grey matter and transmit the impulse to members of a second class of nerve cells, which may be termed adjustors.

The bodies of these adjustor cells are situated in the dorsal horns of the spinal cord; their function is to act as intermediaries between sensory and motor neurons. The adjustor usually has, again, numerous branches which may pass far up or down the body and may pass over to the opposite side of the cord. Eventually, however, every branch descends to the grey matter of the ventral horn and connects there with a motor neuron, the cell body of which is situated in that region. The fibres of these motor cells pass out through the ventral roots and, reaching the muscles, stimulate them to action.

A simple reflex, then, involves three successive types of neuron: sensory, adjustor, and motor. We must not, however, think (as a diagram suggests) that a reflex ordinarily involves but three cells. We have noted that both sensory and adjustor fibres branch, so that a single sensation may reach a very large number of motor cells. And, conversely, a motor cell may be reached and stimulated, through the adjustors, by a large variety of sensory neurons. Still further complications occur, of course, when stimuli pass upward to the brain to enter into more elaborate reflexes or enter the level of consciousness.

This general architecture of the spinal cord and nerves was early laid down in vertebrates and has varied but little throughout the history of the group. We have noted that vertebrates are partially segmented animals; the trunk muscles are arranged in symmetrically paired series, and the bones of the trunk associated with them also assume this symmetrical form. The nervous system shows little trace of any primitive symmetry; probably the serial arrangement of the nerves is consequent upon this type of arrangement of the muscles, for it is to them that a large part of the fibres go.

THE BRAIN. But while there has been little change in the nervous system of the trunk in vertebrates, that of the head region, the brain, has undergone a tremendous amount of evolution in vertebrate history. In lower chordates, such as *Amphioxus*, there is little that can be called a brain, even by courtesy. In man this structure, to which we mainly owe our position in the world, is much larger than the rest of the nervous system put together and is of an exceedingly complex nature. The study of the brain (neurology) is a highly specialized and difficult subject, and we cannot here enter into the details of its structure but shall content ourselves with an examination of some of its more obvious and superficial features. So complicated is this human organ that we are justified in first treating of the brain in some of the lower vertebrate types, where its structure is simpler, and then tracing through a few of the major transformations which the human brain has undergone in rising from this primitive level of organization.

It is only natural that the brain should develop at the front end of the body in any bilaterally symmetrical animal, for it is here that there arise the main sense organs from which are received impulses upon which action is based. In *Amphioxus* the front end of the nerve cord is little different from the remainder of that structure. But even in the lowest of vertebrates a true brain has been evolved; the front end of the nerve cord has expanded and subdivided into a number of portions with highly specialized functions.

The primary divisions of the brain are three in number – forebrain, midbrain, and hindbrain. These divisions are readily apparent in a superficial view of the brain of any type from a fish to a reptile.

HINDBRAIN. Taking them in reverse order, let us consider the hindbrain first. The main portion of this structure is termed the medulla oblongata and in appearance resembles merely a rather swollen section of the ordinary spinal cord. Into or through the medulla pass, of course, all fibres carrying sensations from the body and motor fibres to the muscles of the body. Some of the fibres connecting with the cord pass through the medulla without stopping, but a great part of them have termini in this part of the brain. With this part of the brain, too, connect the cranial nerves bringing sensory impulses from the skin of the head and carrying impulses to the muscles of the head and throat. And, further, there are direct connexions with the lungs and other internal organs by means of which their activity is brought partially under the control of the hindbrain. Except for smell and vision, all sensations which reach the brain come into the hindbrain; except for a small nerve or two to eye muscles,

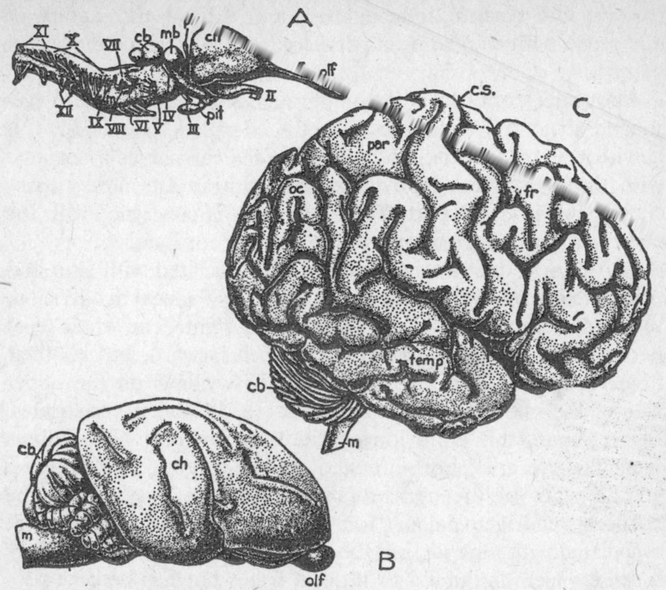

The brain in *A*, a reptile (alligator); *B*, a lemur; *C*, a human (newborn child). In all the brain stem is drawn at about the same actual length; the enormous increase in the relative size of the cerebral hemispheres (*ch*) may be noted. In the alligator the cranial nerves are numbered. *olf*, olfactory bulb; *pin*, pineal eye; *mb*, midbrain region, with optic lobes above; *pit*, pituitary; *cb*, cerebellum; *m*, medulla oblongata.

In the cerebral hemispheres of man the various lobes – frontal, parietal, occipital, and temporal – are indicated, as well as the central sulcus (*c.s.*) dividing the motor area from the sensory area behind it.

all motor impulses which leave the brain leave it through the hindbrain. This structure is thus an immensely important clearing house.

But in addition to these more 'ordinary' functions, we find that the ear lies alongside the hindbrain and is connected with it. There does not, at first sight, seem any particular reason for the association of this organ with a portion of the brain having to do particularly with the muscles and skin; but upon consideration this association is really a perfectly natural one. The primary sensory function of the ear seems to be that of balance, of position, and of movement in space. This is of great importance in relation to the muscular movements by which balance and posture are regulated, and a loose association of this sense with the main muscle-nerve centre of the brain is but natural.

Above the front part of the hindbrain is a large, rather cabbage-shaped structure, the cerebellum, the so-called 'tree of life'. It is with this part of the hindbrain that the ear nerves associated with the registration of balance and position are closely associated, and it is this part of the brain that is concerned with the control of bodily position and muscular coordination.

MIDBRAIN. Just as the hindbrain is associated with skin and primitive ear sensations, so, apparently, was the next subdivision, the midbrain, primarily associated with sight. The optic (eye) nerves enter the brain somewhat farther forward, but all their fibres primitively passed back to small swellings on the upper side of the midbrain, termed optic lobes. In higher vertebrates, such as man, this is no longer the case, for most of the fibres from the eye are 'short-circuited' to the cerebral hemispheres. In the place of the optic lobes are four small swellings, the corpora quadrigemina, or 'four twins'. The front pair are still associated with the eyes, but the back two are centres for hearing, a sense which amounted to little in fishes but has become progressively perfected as mammalian conditions are approached.

In general the midbrain has been the most conservative of brain regions. It has changed but little in size from primitive vertebrates to man.

FOREBRAIN. The forebrain of lower vertebrates is a structure of rather small size which has to do mainly with the sense of smell. At the front end are olfactory lobes in which the nerve fibres from the nostrils terminate; the main centres for the reception of smell are in the cerebral hemispheres, primitively small swellings on the top of the forebrain. Behind is the thalamus (brain 'bed'), connecting the forebrain with other portions of the body. We have noted that the paired eyes attach to the side of the forebrain; in addition there was in primitive vertebrates a third eye, the pineal (no longer functional in man), arising from the top of this brain region. We also find a peculiar organ, the pituitary, attached to the underside of the forebrain; this is discussed in a later section.

This primitive plan of brain structure, which we find repeated with little variation from sharks to reptiles, is a fairly simple one. We have some elaboration of the front end of the spinal cord to sort out specialized sensory impulses and direct them to their appropriate goal. But such an animal is still, to all intents and purposes, an automaton. In mammals, including man, many sensations are received and directly acted upon – reflexes. The whole brain mechanism of lower vertebrates does little more; the special senses of the head merely demand a somewhat more elaborate switchboard for the reception and transmission of their impulses, but the general functions remain much the same.

THE CEREBRUM. In mammals – and particularly in man – we have a much higher type of organization of the mind. More indirect and intricate channels are laid down between sensations and the motor responses to them, brain areas are developed in which there is established a memory, a record of past sensations and activities which influences action resulting from new sensations similar to the old; regions in which consciousness, imagination, and will are evolved.

These higher mental faculties have their seat in the cerebral hemispheres and in areas connected intimately with these hemispheres. The elaboration of the nervous mechanisms of the cerebrum and the great growth of these hemispheres are the central motifs in the development of the brain of man and other mammals from the lower vertebrate types. The remaining portions of the brain have remained as the 'brain stem', practically unchanged; the hemispheres, on the other hand, have grown enormously.

Why have these originally small structures been appropriated for these higher functions rather than some other region of the brain? The answer lies perhaps in the fact that they were originally associated with the sense of smell, and smell in most of our ancestors, although not in ourselves, was the most important of the senses, the greatest portal of knowledge of the outside world. It is readily understandable that the higher mental structures should arise in close connexion with this main source of stimulation of the nervous system.

The cerebral swellings are entirely associated with smell in all fishes and amphibians. In reptiles, however, the surface of the hemisphere shows the beginning of a new area devoted to a higher type of mental activity. This new part of the superficial grey matter has been termed the neopallium, or 'new covering' of the hemispheres. It is this portion, alone, of the hemispheres upon which growth has been concentrated. The cerebrum expands upward, backward, forward, and sideways, while the olfactory 'old covering' becomes confined to a small area at the base. Even in an ordinary mammal the hemispheres are very large and have grown back over the mid-part of the brain. The expansion has continued in the mentally alert higher primates until in man we come to think of the brain at first thought as consisting merely of these hemispheres and forget the old brain, still highly important functionally, which lies beneath them.

The new covering of the hemispheres, the seat of these higher mental faculties of ours, consists of a surface area of grey matter, the bodies of the cells, and beneath this a layer of white matter, the exceedingly complex connecting fibres of these cells. This new covering does not form a solid mass but lies only on the surface of the hemispheres, which are much folded. A deep fold at the side has resulted in the development of a temporal lobe laterally in addition to the frontal, parietal, and occipital regions constituting the main fore-and-aft sections of the hemispheres. Further, in almost every mammal there occur minor foldings and furrowings, convolutions which greatly increase the surface areas of each region. Slightly developed in many of our smaller or more stupid mammalian cousins, they are increasingly complex as we approach the pattern reached in the great apes, and further complicated in man.

CEREBRAL LOCALIZATION. There is a considerable body of evidence, gained from a study of patients whose brains have been injured by disease or wounds, to show that many human mental functions are definitely localized. The frontal portions of the hemispheres seem to have definite connexions with conscious motor activities. Running across the top and down the outer side of each hemisphere is a central groove, or sulcus, in front of which is a series of areas definitely associated with the movement of various specific portions of the body, from legs to head. The posterior portions of the hemispheres are intimately connected with the senses. Sense impressions from skin and muscles are lined up behind the central sulcus just across from the specific motor areas of the frontal lobe; a large area devoted to vision lies at the hind end of the hemispheres; speech reception is localized in the temporal region, not far across the way from the frontal area having to do with speech production; taste and smell are tucked away inconspicuously on the under and inner surface of the hemispheres.

These areas, however, cover only part of the surface of the hemispheres; there are other areas, both in the posterior part and in the frontal region, to which we are unable to assign any such concrete function. These are often called 'blank areas', but the term is a misleading one. Injuries to these regions do not

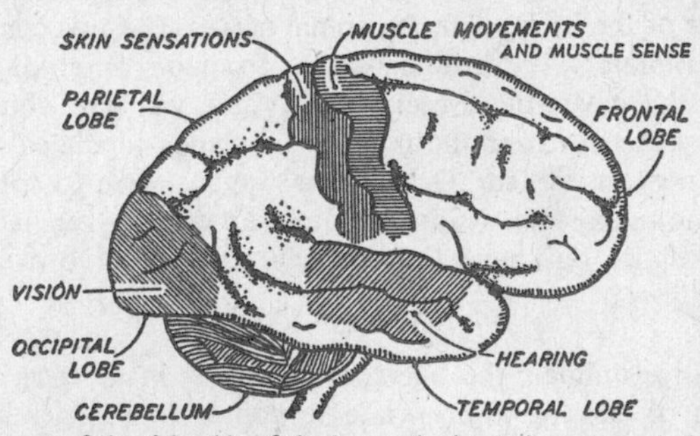

Diagram of the right side of the human brain to show the main lobes and the areas concerned with special functions. The large unshaded regions are association areas concerned with higher mental faculties. (After Carlson and Johnson, *The Machinery of the Body*)

produce a definite flaw in any particular sense of type of movement but do seem to affect deeply, in one way or another, the habits or mentality of the injured person. These blank areas are comparatively undeveloped in apes (particularly the frontal areas), and it seems highly probable that there are here situated the highest of human mental faculties.

Man, as we have said, is not in most respects a particularly outstanding animal. It is only in his brain that he excels; it is the development of his cerebral hemispheres that has enabled him to reach his present position in the world of living things.

AUTONOMIC NERVOUS SYSTEM. So far our discussion of the nervous system has been confined to the central nervous system – the brain, spinal cord, and the nerves directly originating from them, structures whose activities are for the most part within the realm of consciousness and controlled or controllable by the brain.

There is, however, a second type of nervous system within us, the autonomic, or sympathetic, nervous system. This consists of a rather diffuse set of nerves and of nerve cells grouped into ganglia distributed mainly through the interior of the body cavity. It has to do with the movement of the smooth muscles which surround many of the internal organs and the blood vessels and is also in charge of the secretions of glands. The sweat glands and the smooth muscles moving the hairs are the only superficial features of the body with which this system is associated. The autonomic nerve system is connected, in many segments of the body, with the spinal nerves. But this connexion is not intimate; very little sensation from our internal organs reaches the level of consciousness, and we have but little voluntary control over the muscles or glands regulated by this visceral nervous system. Our internal organs seem to constitute an autonomous state within our empire; we may regulate their foreign affairs but have little to say as to their own proper activities.

SENSE ORGANS – GENERAL

In primitive animals the nervous system is, in a sense, merely a means of causing appropriate responses to sensory stimuli. Even in ourselves it is still the stimulation of our sense organs that activates our nervous system, although these sensations are, in great measure, not immediately translated into muscular activity but may be stored in the brain. Sense reception is thus a feature of prime importance in our nervous mechanisms.

SKIN. The skin is, of course, a place of high concentration of sensory end organs. Heat and cold, pain, touch, and pressure are all registered in the skin, each of these sensations being quite distinct in the end organs which receive them. Within the body each muscle has special sensory structures which connect with the brain and give us constant information as to their position and condition, a feature essential in movement and in the maintenance of body posture. The internal organs of the body are not as well supplied with sensory nerve endings. These usually are but poorly connected with the central nervous system and result only in vague sensations localized with difficulty; hunger and thirst, however, which demand conscious tion for their satisfaction, are more vigorous and positive.

is in the head that special and complicated sensory structures are located: taste, smell, sight, hearing, and balance. It is only reasonable that the special sense organs should have this location, for in a primitive water-living vertebrate it is the head end of the body which first comes in contact with new surroundings. Movements or vibrations in the water, materials in solution in it, and light passing through it, all are possible sources of information highly useful to a living creature. Primitive vertebrates had early developed structures to obtain information of this sort.

Before discussing sense organs which we do have, we may briefly mention some of the potential sources of sensation for which we have no receptors at all. Our ears are adjusted to receive only a small portion of the vibratory wave amplitudes of which air is capable; our eyes have a very limited range of sensation in the way of 'ether' waves. We know that in regard to sound and light waves other living animals have quite different ranges of hearing and sight than we have. It is not impossible that in other worlds living things might develop, or have developed, with sense organs quite different from our own. Many types of knowledge of the world about us are brought to us by translation into terms of our own limited sight and hearing. A photograph plate sensitive to ultra-violet light or a radio receiver are examples of the devices by which man has supplemented his inadequate organs of sensory reception.

TASTE. Chemicals given off into the water by neighbouring objects are a great possible source of information as to the nearness of other living or non-living things – friends, foes, and food. Such sensations are of the sort which we know as taste. In ourselves this sense is confined to the interior of the mouth, in taste buds located particularly on the back of the tongue; we live in a medium of air, and animals can experience taste only through the solution of materials in water; the skin is dry, the mouth remains moist. In lower vertebrates which are water dwellers, however, taste may well occur at any place, and many fishes taste the presence of food (or enemies) on the outer surface of the head and body. The 'whiskers' of the catfish are tasting organs, and the long snout of the sturgeon, or paddlefish, has organs on its undersurface which enable the fish to taste food present on the stream bottom along which it moves and thus to give the mouth behind ample warning to take it or reject it.

THE NOSE

A more specialized sense of rather similar nature is that of smell; one difference lies, however, in the fact that the nervous receptors of the nostrils are a specialized part of the brain itself, not scattered skin structures. In *Amphioxus* there is a tiny pit leading into the front of the brain which may have some function of this sort, and in lampreys the single nostril has a similar position. In most vertebrates, as in ourselves, the nostrils are paired and usually are distinctly separated from the main body of the brain. In primitive vertebrates they are usually situated close to the front end of the body; they were originally the most important of the sense organs and thus situated are the advance guards of the body, a skirmish line of scouts to give early warning or encouragement. The nostrils of most fishes are merely paired pockets filled with water and opening only to the outside of the body. On the inside of these pockets are delicate membranes containing sensory cells connected with the brain; these pockets, for increase of sensory area, often have a much-folded surface.

In some of the higher fishes, as we have noted, the lower jaw seems to have elongated, and part of the nostril opening comes to lie on the inside of the roof of the mouth. This is of great aid in breathing but incidentally enables the sense of smell to furnish information as to the nature of the food which lies in the mouth. We all know that food tastes flat when our nose is clogged with a cold; much of our sensation regarding food which we would ascribe to taste is really attributable to smell, from odours passing upward from the mouth to the back entrance of the nose.

The nose functions only in water, like the related chemical sense of taste. In a land form the nasal membranes must be kept moist, so that a watery film may exist on their surface. This, plus the function of the nose as an accessory breathing device, has caused complications in the nasal structure, which we shall mention at a later time.

The nose is still of prime importance in most mammals; but arboreal life seems to have been responsible for its reduced importance in man and other higher primates. In a recent piece of blood-curdling fiction the villain of the story was an orangutan pictured as smelling out the trail of his victim along the ground. This is an absurdity, for the orang probably is able to smell no better than a man.

VISION

While in most animals it is the nose that is the principal sense organ, in man vision is by far the most important of the senses. Our noses practically cease to function every time we have a head cold, but this causes us little concern. Loss of hearing is a misfortune; loss of eyesight is a real tragedy.

While noses have been to the fore in vertebrate history, eyes have not been far behind, either in evolutionary development or in anatomical position. Sensitivity to light is a feature of even single-celled creatures, and in such forms and in many of the simpler invertebrates particular areas related to this light reception are marked by pigmented spots for the absorption of light rays. Many invertebrates, including some worms, almost all arthropods, and even many molluscs have highly developed eyes, some approaching our own in their degree of organization, while among vertebrates even the humblest of fishes have already evolved paired eyes essentially similar to those of man.

THE PARTS OF THE EYE. The construction of a vertebrate eye is essentially similar to that of a camera. There must be a lens; a mechanism for regulating the amount of light reaching it; a focusing device; a dark chamber for the sorting-out of the light transmitted through the lens; and, at the back, a sensitive surface to receive the light. The human eye is protected on the outside by the cornea, a hard layer of skin which is, however, transparent, so that light readily enters the eye. Irregularities in its surface and consequent irregularities in the light refracted through it are a frequent cause of defects of vision, but this usually is easily corrected by eyeglasses. The cornea is but the front part of a spherical layer of tough tissue, the sclera, or outer coat of the eye, which forms a stiff wall about the whole eyeball. The main chamber of the eye, corresponding to the dark inside of the camera box, is filled with a jelly-like transparent material, a 'glassy liquid', as its scientific name (vitrous humour) means. At the opening towards the surface lies the lens, whose function is essentially like that of its namesake in the camera. There is one major difference, however, between the

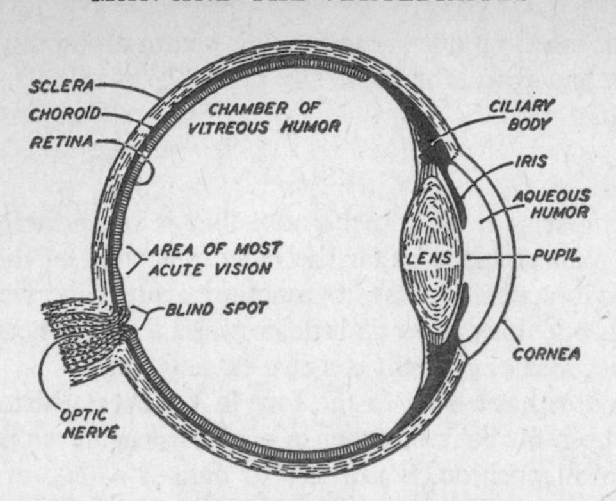

A horizontal section through the human eyeball. The outer layers are the fibrous sclera, continuous with the transparent cornea on the outer surface, and the choroid, a vascular and pigmented area which in front continues into the ciliary body (with the lens muscle and the iris). Inside the choroid layer is the retina, the sensory portion of the eye. The large posterior chamber of the eye is filled with a 'glassy liquid' (vitreous humour), and the anterior chamber in front of the lens has a 'watery humour'. (From Carlson and Johnson, *The Machinery of the Body*)

lenses in the two cases. The camera lens is made of a very hard material, and its focal distance (i.e., the ratio of the distance of object to lens and lens to the back of the internal chamber) is fixed; to change the focus of a camera lens, we must move it back and forth. The same is true in lower vertebrates; the lens is moved in and out within the eyeball for proper focus. In man (and many vertebrates), however, the lens is somewhat elastic. All around its margins are attached the tiny ciliary muscles; their changing tensions cause variations in the curvature of the lens. When tightened the lens is quite curved for near vision; when relaxed the lens is flattened for distant objects. In older people the lens tends to lose its elasticity and to remain in a flattened condition; 'far-sightedness' results.

As anyone who has handled a camera knows, the tinier the hole through which light enters a lens the sharper the image formed; but if the light is dim, a large opening, a 'wide aperture', is necessary. In a camera the light is regulated by a metal diaphragm; in the eye the adjustment is accomplished by the iris, a pigmented circular structure surrounding the pupil, which is continually changing in size of aperture by reflex action.

Beneath the cornea are liquid-filled chambers which form a protection for lens and iris.

THE RETINA. The essential recording mechanism of the camera is the sensitive photographic plate; the recording mechanism of the eye is the retina. Lining the inside of the back and sides of the eyeball is a layer of light-absorbing pigment, the choroid coat; inside of it is the delicate retina, a nervous mechanism which (as shown by its development) is in reality an extension of the brain itself. In the retina are many thousands of sensory cells, termed 'rod' and 'cone' cells because of the shape of their terminal processes. Of these two types the cones react to colour (i.e., to different wave lengths of light) and give perception of detail; the rods are sensitive to dim light not 'visible' to the cones. Cones are absent, or few in number, in fish groups and in amphibians; the presumption is that colour perception is a late acquirement in vertebrates. With these sensory cells are connected others which in turn send long fibres through the optic nerve to the brain. This nerve leaves the back of the eyeball a bit to one side of the centre line; where it plunges through the retina there are no sensory cells present, and there is thus a tiny 'blind spot' in the eye. That the nerve leaves the eye a bit to one side is an important point functionally, since it leaves the very centre available for use. In this central area, where cone cells are thickly clustered in a slight depression in the surface of the retina (fovea centralis), the retinal structure is such that vision is especially acute; we all look directly at an object if we wish to see it clearly, so that its image will fall on this central area. This specialized region was not present in our early vertebrate ancestors; in them vision in general was probably of the rather fuzzy type which is still true of

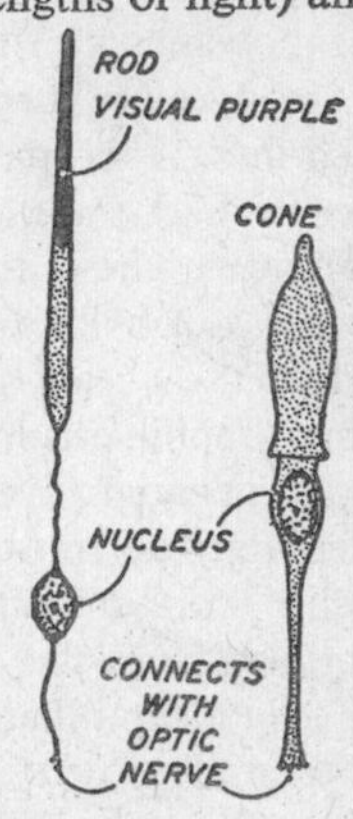

Rod and cone cells, the light receptors of the retina. Rods, containing visual purple at their tips, are sensitive to light but not to colour, the cones alone are colour receptors. Note that because of the peculiar construction of the vertebrate eye the sensitive tips of these cells actually face away from the light (coming, in our diagram, from the bottom of the page). (After Carlson and Johnson, *The Machinery of the Body*)

the margins of our own field of vision. In *Tarsius* this area is only slightly indicated; it is perfectly developed in all monkeys, however.

EYE ACCESSORIES. The eyeball as a whole lies fairly free in the cavity of the eye socket and can be turned through a wide angle in any direction for more direct perception. These movements are accomplished through a series of six small straplike eye muscles running from the margins of the eyeball to the bones about the socket. In primitive vertebrates, where the two eyes are at the sides of the head and directed towards different objects, the eyes in great measure move independently. In man, however, the two fields of vision are practically identical, and the movements of the two eyes are normally perfectly adjusted.

Our eyes are furnished with movable lids tipped with sensitive eyelashes. Lacrimal (or tear) glands bathe the surface of our eyes in fluid, the excess of which is carried into the nose by the tear duct. These accessories are absent in fishes, and the main reason is obvious. Our eye needs protection against drying; but in the ocean the eye is constantly bathed in salt solution. Once amphibians had gained the land, the tear glands and ducts soon appeared. Eyelids, partly for preservation of moisture, but partly also for protection, were slower in development. A 'third eyelid', present in reptiles, bird, and some mammals, and working from the inner corner, is represented in our own eye by only a small half-moon-shaped fold of skin.

STEREOSCOPIC VISION. A curious feature of the vertebrate nervous system is the way in which all its connexions cross over from one side of the body to the opposite side of the brain, so that, for example, the sensations from the right side of our body are received on the left side of the brain. The same is true of the eyes. The two optic nerves in a primitive vertebrate cross one another and go to the opposite sides of the brain. They form a structure known as the 'chiasma', so called from its resemblance to the Greek letter chi, or X. Primitively, it would seem, the stimulation of a definite pattern of nervous units of the retina of either eye resulted in the stimulation of a definite pattern of nervous elements in the brain hemispheres of the opposite side, giving rise to the mental perception of form. This, it will be noted, would result in two distinct pictures; one arising from each eye, the two entirely separated in the brain. This is apparently the case in a majority of living vertebrates. Although they cannot tell us about it, the anatomical evidence leads us to believe that even where, as in many birds, the two eyes see much the same thing, they see it twice, and each picture is flat, like a photograph.

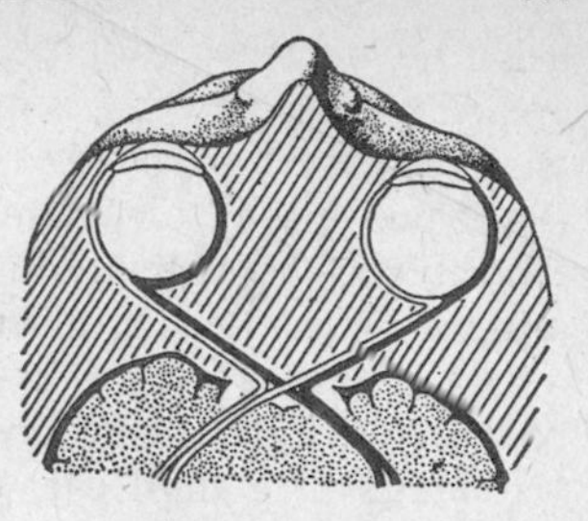

The optic chiasma in man; a diagrammatic horizontal section through the eye region. Fibres from the left halves of both retinas (*white*) pass to the left side of the brain; those from the right halves (*black*) to the right side of the brain.

We can many of us remember the stereoscope which used to adorn the parlour of our grandparents. On flat cards were mounted two almost identical photographs, each as flat as any photograph. But once fitted in the proper slot and the lenses placed before our eyes, lo! there was the Taj Mahal or Niagara Falls seen in a single picture, not two, a picture with depth, three dimensions – a stereoscopic view. This device made use of a peculiar feature of the visual apparatus present in man, monkeys, and various other mammals, whereby the two images on the retina are combined in the brain to a single picture. Our brain took in two quite separate sets of visual sensations, one from either eye, and fused the two into a single picture. How is this done?

We have noted that in most vertebrates the two nerves from the eyes cross each other in the chiasma. In ordinary vertebrates all the fibres plunge straight through this crossroads. Not so in man; half the fibres from each eye turn a right-angle corner and go to their own side of the brain; the other half continue their old path. In this way the fibres from the right halves of both eyes pass to the right side of the brain, those from the left halves of both eyes pass to the left side of the brain. Thus two images of the same thing are 'piled up' in the same brain area, and by little-understood nervous mechanisms the two halves of the picture are fused together. It is this superposition of the pictures from the two eyes, almost but not quite identical, since they are taken from slightly different angles, that helps give us our stereoscopic vision, our depth effects.

This is of great importance to us in our use of eyes. We can, it is true, do much to judge distances and shapes with but one eye. We know how big a man or a chair should be and even with one eye can thus make a fair guess as to its distance from us. But if put in sight of unfamiliar types of objects, our ability to estimate distances breaks down. Even the simple task of lighting a friend's cigarette is a difficult one with but one eye open.

THE PINEAL BODY. We have, so far, spoken only of the paired eyes. But we have previously noted the presence in early vertebrates of a third eye, the pineal, which faced upward in the middle of the skull roof. This seems to have been an important sense organ in early vertebrates. To a primitive bottom dweller his food might lie beneath him, but his enemies would approach from the top.

With the development of a more active life, however, the need for this third eye became less, and by the Age of Reptiles most vertebrates had functionally lost this eye structure; even in fishes it is almost never present today. Some lizards still have a pineal eye complete with lens and retina, but it is a tiny structure which is buried beneath the skin and can seemingly only tell the difference between light and darkness. In ourselves this old eye is present as a small stalked red body lying buried between the hemispheres of the brain. Descartes, in the early days of scientific speculation, suggested that this was the seat of the soul. Today we are much interested in glands of internal secretion, and the pineal body is often referred to as a structure of this sort. But we do not know of any definite function of the pineal body, and this guess has little more foundation than that of Descartes.

THE EAR

THE EXTERNAL EAR. The ear runs the eye a close race for complexity of structure and importance of function. We normally think of an ear as an external flap of skin containing a flexible type of cartilage, a structure of somewhat dubious ornamental value. This is but the beginning of the story. From the centre of this projecting structure there leads inwards a tube, at the bottom of which there is a thin membrane, the eardrum.

THE MIDDLE EAR. Within the eardrum is an air-filled space surrounded by a protective shell of bone; this is the middle-ear cavity. This space connects with the throat by a small tube (the eustachian tube) by means of which air pressure inside may be kept in equilibrium with external pressure so that the delicate eardrum may not burst. This ear cavity contains a very important set of mechanisms – the three auditory ossicles, or 'bonelets'. These are termed the 'hammer', 'anvil', and 'stirrup' (malleus, incus, and stapes), from their fancied resemblance to these implements. The ossicles are arranged in an articulated series. The hammer is attached to the eardrum; the anvil is attached to the inner end of the hammer and, on the other side, to the stirrup; the bottom of the stirrup is fastened into an opening in the side of the braincase, through which it comes into connexion with the internal mechanism of the ear discussed below. These little bones pick up the sound waves caught by the eardrum, amplify them, and transmit them to the internal ear; their function, together with that of the drum, is rather comparable to that of the sound arm of a phonograph.

The middle-ear cavity is an important region for hearing; but it has its drawbacks. Once bacteria have reached this cavity by way of the tube from the throat, they have found a beautifully isolated haven for growth. Inflammations of the middle ear are common, particularly in children. Moreover, behind this cavity are connected air spaces in the mastoid region of the skull; and inflammations spreading inside this bone are not only painful but difficult and dangerous to deal with.

THE INTERNAL EAR. But all the structures so far considered are only accessories for sound reception; the real sense organ, the fundamental ear structure, lies deeper still. Buried inside the framework of the braincase, below and at the side of the back of the brain, lie the cavities of the internal ear. Here there is situated a double series of liquid-filled sacs and canals, surrounded by bone. In the centre of this set of structures is a rounded sac. Above, this connects with a second sac from which spring several semi-circular canals mentioned later. Below, it connects with a long structure which coils up like a snail shell with two and a half turns – the cochlea (spiral). We have noted that the bottom of the stirrup lies in a small opening in the braincase. This opening leads directly to the liquid-filled spaces of the internal ear, and so vibrations transmitted by the ossicles from the eardrum may set up vibrations in these liquids. As these watery vibrations travel up the coil of the cochlea, they are recorded by tiny, delicate, hairlike endings of sensory cells

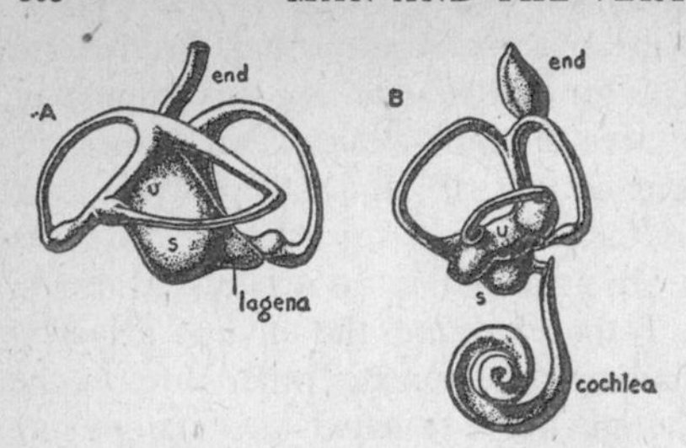

The liquid-filled canals and sacs of the inner ear of *A*, a shark; *B*, man. In both are present three canals sensitive to movement and two cavities, utriculus (*u*) and sacculus (*s*), which record the position of the head relative to gravity. In the shark, however, the only area sensitive to sound lies near the base of the small pocket termed the lagena. In man this has expanded into the coiled cochlea. In the shark a duct from the ear (*end*) still connects with the surface; in man the connexion is lost, and the duct ends blindly. The structures shown are filled with a liquid termed endolymph; between them and the bone of the inner ear are other spaces filled with a second fluid, the perilymph, which is of importance in sound conduction in the ear.

and hearing results. Here, as in the case of taste and smell, air-carried sensations are transformed into water-borne ones before they can be received – still another evidence of our ancestors' water-dwelling existence from which our bodies have never fundamentally departed.

But hearing is not, by any means, the sole function of the ear. Physicians find that diseases which attack the deep part of the organ of hearing also affect the sense of balance; this sense, too, is located in the internal ear. This contains two sac-like structures – a larger one (sacculus) near the cochlea, a smaller one (utriculus) more dorsally situated. The sacs contain areas of sensory cells terminating in hairs on which are suspended flat discs of calcareous material, the 'ear stones' (otoliths). As the head turns, these stones press down the hairs beneath them in a varying fashion; the sensations registered give us our sense of balance, of equilibrium. Connected with the upper sac are three liquid-filled semi-circular canals arranged in planes at right angles to each other, corresponding to those of our three-dimensional space. The movements of our body result in differential movements of the liquids in these canals; these movements, registered by sensory structures in the swollen ends of these tubes, give us our sensation of movement in space.

THE FISH EAR. In fishes the ear mechanism is very different and much simpler. There is no external ear, no eardrum, no middle-ear chamber, no set of ossicles; in fact, none of the accessories of hearing. There is only the internal ear, buried deeply within the braincase and giving little or no superficial evidence of its existence. As in man, we find a series of liquid-filled sacs and canals. But even here there is one striking difference for the cochlea, the particular organ for hearing, is absent. Fish can hear but hear comparatively poorly, it would seem. Water vibrations can reach the ear only if strong enough to set up vibrations within the skull of the animal and, in turn, in the ear liquids. But, on the other hand, the mechanisms for the recording of movements and equilibrium are highly developed in fishes. 'He that hath ears let him hear' is appropriate for a man; 'He that hath ears let him balance' would be a more appropriate admonition for a fish. In almost every fish the sacs and semi-circular canals are as well developed as in a man. This is, a priori, not unreasonable. We have noted that activity is a primary characteristic of backboned animals, and, for effective movement, delicate registration of motion and balance is a prime necessity. Smell, taste, and sight will tell a fish of outside objects; his 'ears' must tell him of his own position in the world.

In passing we may notice that some of the oldest of known vertebrates, such as *Cephalaspis*, pictured in the first chapter (p. 21), have but two canals, as have their most direct descendants, the living lampreys. These ancient sluggish forms seem to have kept generally to the bottom of the streams and ponds; they needed to know fore and aft, left and right, but not up and down; and canals were needed but for two or three directions. We have three canals and live, obviously, in a three-dimensional world. It would be interesting to know what one of these old forms would have had in the way of geometric ideas – if these animals could have thought at all! Perhaps they lived in a two-dimensional world of a single plane; to an intelligent *Cephalaspis*, it may be that the idea of a third dimension would have been as impossible of conception as a fourth dimension is to us.

WATER-PRESSURE ORGANS IN FISHES. Still talking of our piscine relatives, we may mention a sixth sense which they possessed but of which we have no trace left at all. Down each side of a fish's body (and often well concealed by the scales) lies a small canal, the lateral-line canal, open to the surface of the body and lined with sensory cells directly connected with the brain. Running forward, these canals spread out in an elaborate pattern over the fish's head. They are obviously important sense organs, but what they do we can only tell by observation and experiment. Not improbably they record the pressure and flow of water over the fish's body. This would obviously be an extremely valuable source of information to a fish swimming in water currents. If a man swims in a current on the surface, he can tell how it is flowing by means of his eyes; but under water objects can be seen only a short distance, and an extra aid of this sort would be extremely useful to a fish. Some amphibians which remain much in the water still retain this sense; but reptiles and all higher types have lost it.

An interesting point to be noted, however, is that we have here a sense of water pressure; and we have noted that the whole ear mechanism is a device for registering the flow and pressure of liquids. Can these two types of sensory structures be related? Very probably. In man the internal ear is deeply buried inside the head, but there is a small tube (with the long name of endolymphatic duct) which runs a short way up towards the surface. In the shark this tube actually reaches the surface and suggests that the internal ear is, fundamentally, only a part of the lateral-line system of liquid-pressure organs which has sunk deeply beneath the surface and become highly specialized. That this is the case is also suggested by the history of the internal ear in the human embryo, for in ourselves this structure is formed in the skin and only later sinks within the head.

HEARING IN PRIMITIVE LAND ANIMALS. The ear, then, is primarily a balancing and steering device and as such was already highly developed in fishes. These functions of the ear and the parts related to them have been altered but little in the later evolution of vertebrates, but the hearing apparatus has undergone a considerable series of changes, some of which have been briefly touched upon in earlier chapters.

Once vertebrates came ashore, hearing was a new problem. Air vibrations are mostly of a slight and tenuous type and (barring a dynamite explosion) set up but little vibration of the skull which might enable a land animal to hear in fishlike fashion. The higher vertebrates have borrowed heavily from other organ systems to construct an amplifying device which can receive and transmit air waves from the surface of the head to the internal ear. With the disuse of the gills, the first one

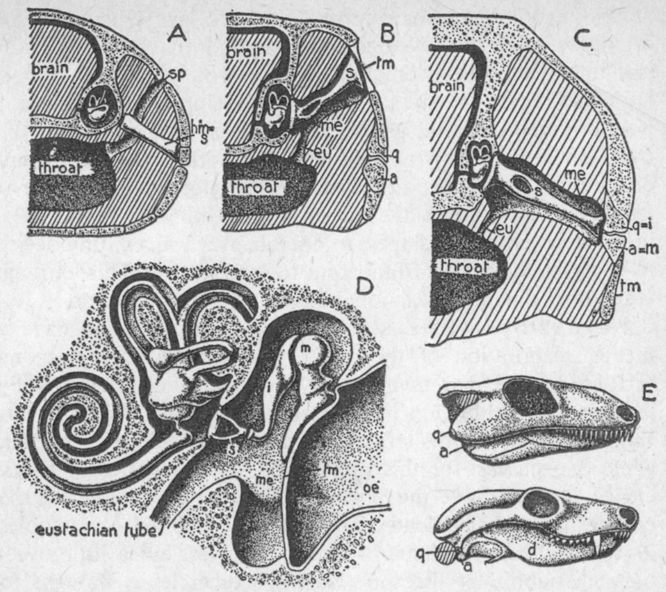

A–D, a series of stages in the evolution of the ear apparatus. *A*, cross-section of half of a fish skull in the ear region. The ear consists of the internal ear, with its sacs and semicircular canals only. *B*, an amphibian. The hyomandibular bone (*hm*) of the fish is pressed into service as a sound transmitter, the stapes (*s*); the first gill slit, the spiracle, (*sp*), becomes the eustachian tube (*eu*) and the middle-ear cavity (*me*), while the outer end of the spiracle is closed by the tympanic membrane (*tm*). *C*, a mammal-like reptile. The stapes passes close to two skull bones (*q a*) which form the jaw joint. *D*, man (the ear region only, on a larger scale). The two jaw-joint bones have been pressed into service as accessory ossicles, the malleus (*m*) and incus (*i*). *E*, a primitive land animal and a mammal-like reptile to show the relation of the eardrum to the jaw joint. At first in a notch high on the side of the skull (the otic notch) occupying the place of the fish spiracle, it shifts in mammal-like reptiles to the jaw region. In mammals the jaw becomes formed of one bone only (*d*, the dentary), and the bones of the jaw-joint region are freed to act as accessory hearing organs. (*oe*), tube of outer ear.

(the spiracle), lying at the back of the head, has been taken over as the tube of the outer and middle ear but is left closed with the drum stretched across its channel. This diaphragm picks up the sounds excellently. Next, how to transmit them to the inner ear in the braincase?

In our first chapter we called attention to a gill-bar element the hyomandibular, which props the shark jaw joint on to the braincase. With the development of a solid attachment of skull and upper jaw, the hyomandibular was 'out of a job'. But it lay close beside the spiracle and the developing eardrum, and its inner end was attached to the braincase just outside of the inner-ear region. Only a slight shift in position, the attachment of the outer end to the drum, and the development of a hole at its base to let it touch the ear cavity beneath, and it was able, in the new guise of a stapes, to operate as a transmitting device to carry sound waves from drum to internal ear. This earbone is the only one present in amphibians, reptiles, and birds.

THE EAR OF MAMMALS. In our own ancestors we have a further elaboration of the auditory accessories. A projecting earfold is a peculiar mammalian development which generally serves a useful function in gathering sound waves into the ear. In most mammals this structure is freely movable, but in man, while the muscles for this motion are still present, only a few envied mortals have the power of flapping their ears for the edification of their friends. The originally pointed ear assumes its rounded human shape in higher primates, but a little overhanging nubbin at the top (Darwin's tubercle) is thought to represent the original tip.

In the mammal-like reptiles there was developing a new type of jaw joint, and the bones (quadrate and articular) which formed the old articulation between skull and jaws became tiny and then useless. But the ear-drum in these forms lay close to the jaw joint, and the stapes ran out to it and touched the bones which made up the joint. In mammals these old jaw bones have been taken over to complete the chain of three ear ossicles.

We have, in these accessory hearing organs, one of the most interesting examples of change of function to be found in any animal. The cavities of the outer and middle ear were originally (as the spiracle) part of the fish-breathing apparatus. The malleus and incus were, in reptiles and lower forms, part of the jaw apparatus; the old jaw joint of our ancestors lies between two of the ossicles of our middle ear. The stapes was, in fishes, a prop for these old jaws. But both jaws and stapes were before this (among the jawless fishes) part of the primitive gill-bar structures. Breathing organs have become eating organs and then hearing organs. The function of these structures has changed radically; but their identity is unmistakable throughout. Nature seldom makes new organs; but she is seldom wasteful and is adept at reshaping useless structures to fill new needs.

CHAPTER 18

The Human Body – *continued*

Internal Organs: Digestive, Respiratory, Excretory, Reproductive, Circulatory, Endocrine

WHEN the first many-celled animals appeared in the world, one of the earliest processes of differentiation which they underwent was, we believe, a division of labour by the production of two layers to the body – an inner and outer layer. This type of structure may be seen today in the coelenterates, such as jellyfishes, sea anemones, and coral polyps, and is a stage which is passed through in the individual development of every higher animal. In a coelenterate the outer of the two cell layers is concerned with the animal's relation to the outside world – protection and information. These functions, served today by the skin and nervous system, were discussed in the last chapter. The inner layer of cells is concerned with the animal's own affairs, the nourishment of the cells of the body, the taking of food, the disposal of waste matters, and the reproduction of its kind. It is with organs which serve these and related functions in the much more high organized human body that we propose to deal in the present chapter.

DIGESTIVE SYSTEM

Eating is the most obvious function undertaken by the internal cell layer of a simple animal. In a coral polyp the inside of the body is essentially a simple sac with but one opening. Food enters the sac by this orifice, is digested by the cells lining this pouch, and waste material is cast out through the same opening. In most bilateral animals, however, a second opening appears, and the sac becomes a tube with a mouth at the front end and an anus at the other. Such forms have laid down the basic pattern for the digestive system of any higher animal.

The human digestive tract leads a hard life. It is in almost continual use, and we subject it to rough treatment. It must take any type of food that we please to offer it, from beer to bananas, from popcorn to spinach, and at least attempt to turn it into a fluid which can be absorbed into the circulation for the nourishment of our bodies. In its work its various parts must receive the food, treat it mechanically and chemically, store it, render the usable portions fluid and absorb them, and get rid of the waste material. For these tasks we have a varied and complicated system of mechanisms.

FOOD MATERIALS. Since much of the work of the gut consists of chemical treatment of food materials, we may briefly consider the nature of these materials at this point.

Water is, of course, a major need of the body but such an obvious one that we tend to overlook its vital importance as a 'food' in the broad sense of that term. Simple salts, too, are needed to maintain the composition of the blood and are necessary, as in the case of calcium, phosphorus, iodine, and iron compounds, for the use of the tissues. However, the amounts needed are very small in bulk, and most such salts are readily absorbed.

Also vitally important but needed only in tiny quantities are the vitamins. These substances are worthy of a volume by themselves if studied in detail. We shall merely list the more important ones, some of their sources, and a few obvious conditions associated with their presence or absence: Vitamin A: necessary for proper growth and development; abundant in cream and its derivatives, egg yolk, and carrots. Vitamin B, including a number of related substances: their absence may cause disorders of the digestive and nervous systems, the characteristic diseases beriberi and pellagra, or even death; this complex of substances may be represented in a variety of foods, including many fresh vegetables, meat, liver, and eggs. Vitamin C: a deficiency may cause scurvy or faulty conditions of the skeleton; green vegetables, citrus juices, and the prosaic tomato are good sources. Vitamin D: lack of it may cause rickets in the young and result in adults in related fragile and soft conditions of the bones and teeth; in foods it is most abundant in fish oils, such as that of the cod's liver, and exposure to sunlight causes production of this vitamin in the skin. Vitamin E: necessary for proper sexual conditions; lettuce and whole wheat are good sources.

All these materials, however, are either readily absorbed or minute in quantity; the main chemical problems of digestion have to do with three types of organic materials, which constitute the vast bulk of the solid foods – carbohydrates, fats, and proteins.

The carbohydrates are relatively simple combinations of the elements carbon, hydrogen, and oxygen; the common forms in which they are found are as sugars and starches. Little chemical work upon them appears to be necessary before they are broken down into simple sugars, when they are readily absorbed into the blood stream and become an important source of energy for the body.

The fats are also, typically, combinations of the same three elements. Their chemical structure, however, is more complex than that of the carbohydrates, and it is apparently a rather more difficult process to break them down into chemical units simple enough to be absorbed. Fats are frequently stored in the body as reserve fuel supplies; they also enter into the composition of the body cells to a greater extent than carbohydrates.

Most complex of food materials are the proteins, particularly abundant in meat and other animal foods. Proteins contain nitrogen in addition to the three ubiquitous organic elements and frequently small amounts of other elements as well. They are of immense importance to the body, since proteins form a great proportion of the materials in the cells themselves and must be frequently renewed. Proteins, however, are generally highly complicated molecules which may contain thousands of atoms. They must be broken down in small fractions before they can be taken into the body, and the problem of protein digestion is the most difficult one encountered in the intestinal tract.

Of importance in the breaking-down of organic compounds in the gut are enzymes, or digestive ferments, which are produced by the cells in various parts of the digestive system. They are complex organic compounds which, although secreted in small amounts, have a powerful action in initiating or speeding up the chemical reactions involved in digestion and are thus in the category of substances known to the chemist as catalysts.

THE MOUTH AND JAWS. Man may use his hands or hand-made machinery for the procurement of food and the first stages in its mechanical treatment, but in most animals this function is performed almost entirely by the mouth and associated structures. The teeth and jaws were, in our ancestors, the sole means of getting hold of food, and, although the human type of food procurement has been associated with a reduction in the power of these structures, they are still of great importance. The upper jaw of man is fixed to the skull; the lower jaw moves freely upon it by paired joints at the back, and by its movement the teeth are brought into play.

The jaws are, of course, part of our skeletal system and are discussed elsewhere. They were absent in our early vertebrate ancestors; in those forms the intake of large or hard objects of food was an impossibility. Food could only be pumped in by passing water through the gills or by the setting-up of inward currents of water by the action of cilia – tiny hairlike movable processes of the cells lining the mouth and throat of our early ancestors. The evolution of biting jaws marked a major stage in vertebrate evolution.

TEETH – THEIR ORIGIN. Jaws would be, in general, nearly useless without the development of teeth. These are really skin structures, but they are so intimately related to digestive functions that they may be considered here. The main bulk of a tooth is formed of dentine, a fairly hard, white substance. The exposed part is covered by a thin layer of shiny enamel. Within the tooth is a pulp cavity which contains small blood vessels, and (as we realize in the dentist's chair) sensitive nerves. Roots at the bottom anchor the teeth in the jaws, the union being aided by an outer coating of a bonelike material called cement.

Teeth were, of course, absent in the oldest jawless vertebrates. They take their origin from small pointed structures found all over the skin of a shark and found frequently on the surface of bony plates and scales in primitive fishes. These superficial denticles ('toothlets') are in structure very similar to teeth, having a root and hollow pulp cavity, a main portion of dentine, and usually a shiny enamel-like surface covering. Presumably teeth arose from denticles which lay over the developing jaws at the margin of the mouth.

HUMAN TEETH. In man there are thirty-two teeth, eight in each jaw half. The front two are rather chisel-like structures, the incisors. Next comes the canine or 'dog-tooth'. This is a

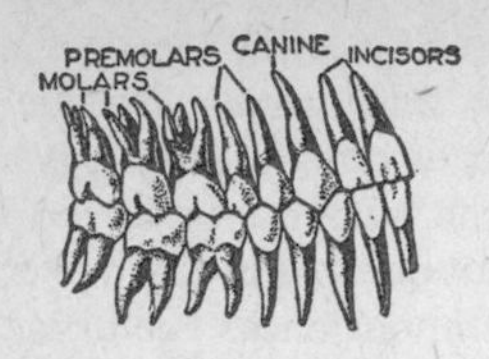

The permanent teeth of man; set of the right side of the mouth.

stout, rather rounded tooth of simple pattern which in our ancestors was sharp and pointed for biting purposes and projected beyond the general level of the other teeth. Behind the canine are two premolars (the 'bicuspids' of the dentist), with some chewing power, and behind these again, the three large grinders, the molar teeth.

These are the teeth which we have as an adult. In the baby, however, the front part of this set had predecessors, the 'milk', or deciduous teeth, consisting of incisors, a canine, and 'milk molars' in the place of the adult premolars. But at about the age of six the first true molars appear behind the milk molars, and in the next few years the first set gradually drops out and is replaced by our second set of teeth – our last, except for such imperfect substitutes as our dental friends can provide for us.

PRIMITIVE DENTITION. A long and complicated history lies behind these teeth of ours. In a shark or any generalized fish the teeth were all sharp and pointed; only in a few types below the mammal stage did any chewing power develop. The teeth were merely for seizing the food and biting it off; it was then swallowed, and the animal's internal organs had to do the rest. Not only in birds but in many reptiles there developed as a substitute for the chewing power of the teeth a 'gizzard' filled with stones or gravel in which food could be ground up.

Teeth were exceedingly numerous to start with. Instead of a paltry eight teeth in each jaw half, there may be several dozen (or even several hundred) in place at once in a fish or reptile. Further, most lower vertebrates have no need of dentists, no worry as to the destruction of a tooth. For in them tooth replacement can go on indefinitely. Beneath each tooth on the edge of a shark jaw lie numerous others developing to replace it continually.

MAMMAL TEETH. This general situation – the presence of almost limitless simple teeth and their replacement – seems to have continued in our own case until the stage of the mammal-like reptiles. In them and the primitive mammals there occurred a great change in dental apparatus – the differentiation of structure and functions in teeth and the reduction in the number of replacements. By the stage of the oldest insect-eating primitive placental animals there had been reached a type with but forty-four teeth, divided into the four kinds present in our own mouth. There were then, however, three incisor teeth rather than two; the canines were long and powerful piercing structures; there were four premolar teeth, not two; and the molars were rather sharp-cusped teeth with little grinding power. In these forms, too, the original free succession of teeth had been abandoned; in almost every case other mammals, like ourselves, have only two sets of teeth, 'milk' and permanent dentitions.

Beyond this stage the evolution of the teeth went on along different lines in various mammal groups. For example, the herbivores tended to elaborate their cheek teeth into a powerful grinding battery for the chewing of vegetable food, and front teeth are often reduced; the pure flesh-eaters, such as cats, have emphasized biting and slicing powers and have reduced their grinders almost to the vanishing-point.

TEETH IN PRIMATES. Man and his primate relatives, with a mixed diet, have compromised between these two types of adaptations. We have retained our front teeth, except that we have lost one incisor in each jaw half; the canine has come down to the proportions of the other teeth but has retained a stout root; two of the four premolar teeth have been lost, with the effect of shortening the tooth row; the molars are still present and moderately well developed, with four rounded cusps, and have a fair degree of usefulness in chewing. The reduction in the tooth row apparently began well back among our arboreal ancestors, for even in the Old World monkeys the tooth count had been reduced to our thirty-two instead of the original forty-four. This reduction in the number of teeth is very probably associated with the early development of the use of the hands as accessory feeding organs in primates.

Perhaps the reduction in tooth replacement may have been a useful adaptation in our early mammalian ancestors. But today, on our visits to the dentist, where we try with anguish to salvage a badly battered tooth for a bit more service before it goes for ever, we may wish that we were happy and carefree fishes or reptiles which could shed teeth with impunity, knowing that in a few days new and shining successors would arise to replace those lost.

The reduction process is still going on, it would seem. In modern races of man the last molars, the wisdom teeth, usually appear only in adult life, are crowded into the tooth row with difficulty, and usually function but little. Perhaps in a hundred thousand years or so they will disappear altogether.

Has evolution ceased? Evolutionary processes have gone on for many hundreds of millions of years. A few creatures seem to have survived for long periods of time without undergoing much modification, but in most types the fossil record shows that there has been a gradual but continuous process of change. We have no reason to think that such processes have ceased to operate or that man is an exception to the general rule. Man may well continue to evolve and change not only in dental characters but also in other respects, and at some time in the far-distant future there may come to be some type of creature far above us that will look back upon his curious human forebears as we look down upon our simian cousins.

THE TONGUE. This structure, lying within the mouth, is much larger than we usually imagine, for it is merely the tip of it which we ordinarily see (next time you meet a whole ox tongue at the table note the contrast between the small skin-coated tip and the much larger underlying part of this structure). Its functions are varied. Its rough tip is a useful licking organ (the cat has a much better rasp); the taste buds are mainly located on its back surface; it moves the food about during chewing; and (especially important for the infant) it is an effective sucking organ. There is no movable tongue in a typical fish; we have developed it from some of the remains of the old gill-breathing apparatus, and some of the old gill-bar skeletal elements are embedded in its base.

In the mouth, too, are the numerous salivary glands, whose secretions are of use not only in softening the food but in starting its chemical treatment. They contain an enzyme which commences the digestion of starchy food.

The food, passing back through the pharynx, the cavity of the throat, enters the oesophagus, a long, tough tube, which, by waves of contraction in its walls, passes the food on down to the stomach.

THE STOMACH. The upper part of the digestive tract is mainly concerned with the intake of food; the main digestive processes

A CHEVROTAIN or 'mouse deer'; tiny Old World tropical animals which are ruminants, but of a primitive sort, close to the ancestry of more advanced cud-chewers. The form shown here (*Tragulus*) is from the Malay region; a second genus is present in Africa. (This is a stuffed specimen.)

THE LLAMA of the Andes (*below*) is a humpless member of the camel group, descended from North American ancestors. (Photograph courtesy American Museum of Natural History, New York.)

CAMELS, although once natives of North America, are now inhabitants of the Old World. *Top*, the two-humped bactrian camel; *lower*, the dromedary of Arabia. (Photographs courtesy New York Zoological Society.)

THE GIRAFFE is a ruminant related to both the deer and cattle groups but representing a family of its own. Like other members of the ruminants, it possesses 'horns'. These, however, are easily overlooked, for they are present only as a pair of short hair-covered processes. This specimen, photographed in its native Africa, stood 17 feet high. (Photograph courtesy American Museum of Natural History, New York.)

THE OKAPI, a short-necked relative of the giraffe. Ancestral giraffids with short necks have been known as fossils, but it was not until a few decades ago that this living form was discovered in the depths of the forests of the Belgian Congo. Except for the neck and the different skin colour, the animal is very similar to the giraffe. (The photograph is from a mounted group in the American Museum of Natural History, New York.)

THE PRONG-BUCK or American 'antelope'. This western-plains animal is the only survivor of an American ruminant family common in fossil form. It is characterized by its peculiar 'horns', which include a simple bony core which is not shed and a forked horny sheath which is shed annually. (Photograph courtesy New York Zoological Society.)

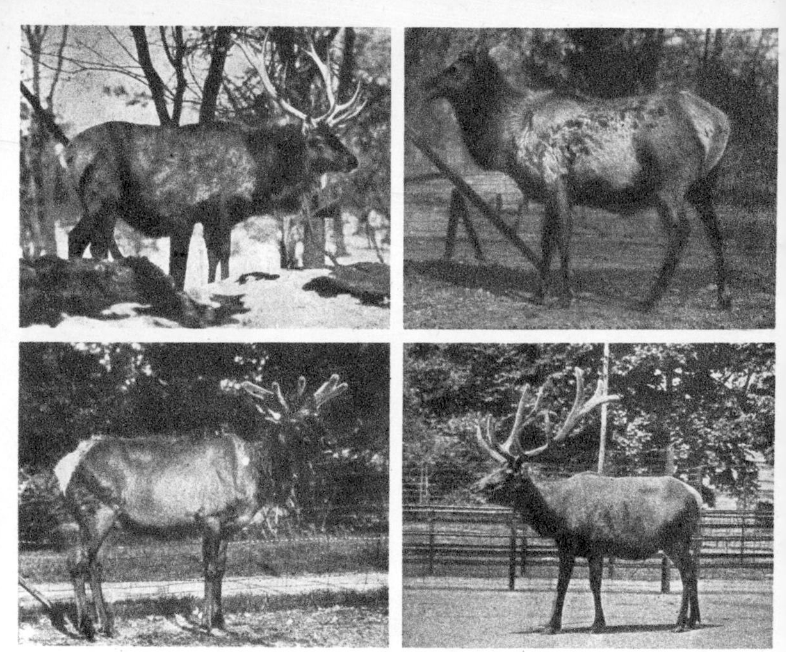

THE ANNUAL REPLACEMENT OF THE ANTLERS OF DEER. A series of photographs of an American elk or wapiti (*Cervus canadensis*) at various seasons of the year. *Upper left*, winter: The antlers developed the previous year are still present. *Upper right*, early spring: The antlers have been lost by resorption of bone at the base (the winter coat is also being shed). *Lower left*, late spring: The new antlers are growing rapidly. *Lower right*, summer: The antlers are fully grown but still covered with skin (velvet), which will presently dry up and be rubbed off. (Photographs courtesy New York Zoological Society.)

THE 'IRISH ELK'. This extinct European deer had the most ponderous antlers of any known deer; it would seem as if they would have been a handicap rather than a help to the animal. However, it was abundant in Europe in the Ice Age. The name is derived from the fact that the best remains are from Irish bog deposits. (From a mural by Charles R. Knight; photograph courtesy Field Museum of Natural History, Chicago.)

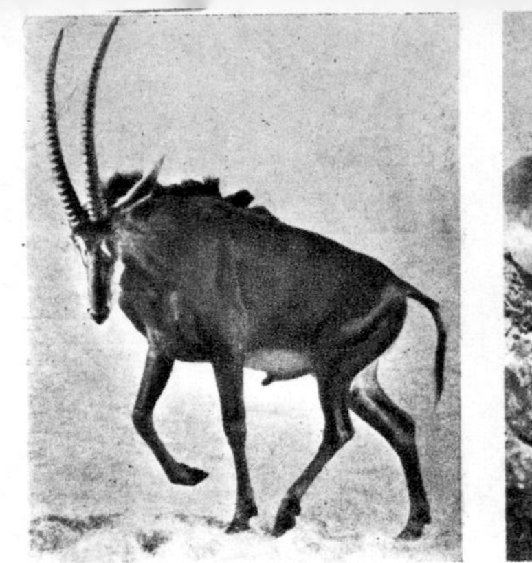

BOVIDS. The family *Bovidae* includes ruminants which possess true horns – that is, simple (although usually curved) bony projections covered by a horny sheath and never shed. The family is a group mainly inhabiting the Old World where, in addition to wild sheep, goats, and cattle, there is a great host of varied forms lumped together in popular usage as antelopes (the sable antelope of Africa is shown above at the left). Only three bovid types, illustrated here, reached America. *Above centre*, the sure-footed mountain goat (photographed in his native haunts in the northern Rockies by John M. Phillips). This form is not a true goat but belongs to a separate genus (*Oreamnos*). *Top right*, the mountain sheep. To represent the bison we have shown not the familiar American species but the European one, now close to extinction. (Left two photographs courtesy American Museum of Natural History, New York; right photographs courtesy New York Zoological Society.)

THE BANKS OF A KANSAS RIVER IN THE EARLY PLIOCENE. Proboscidians, although not native to North America, had at that date arrived in that continent and are represented by a primitive mastodon (*Trilophodon*). In these forms both upper and lower jaws were long, so that there was probably but a short length of free trunk. The tusks, too, were short and were present in lower as well as upper jaws.

Left, representatives of a short-legged rhinoceros (*Teleoceros*) which appears to have had amphibious habits and rather resembled the hippopotamus in general proportions. Only a tiny horn appears to have been present. (From a mural by Charles R. Knight; by permission of the Field Museum of Natural History, Chicago.)

AN ASIATIC ELEPHANT, from a group in the American Museum of Natural History, New York, mounted by Louis Paul Jonas; a fine example of the art of the modern taxidermist. *Below*, a restoration of the American mastodon of the Pleistocene, a form in which the lower jaw and lower tusks have been reduced, very much as in the true elephants. This form persisted in America after the final retreat of the ice. (From a mural by Charles R. Knight; photograph courtesy Field Museum of Natural History, Chicago.)

EUROPE IN THE ICE AGE. A scene in France during the latter part of the Ice Age or Pleistocene, perhaps 25,000 years or so ago. A common inhabitant of all northern regions of both Eurasia and North America at that time was the woolly mammoth. This large elephant with shaggy hair and a domelike head is known not only from its bones but from paintings and engravings by cave men and from frozen corpses found in the Siberian tundra.

Right, the woolly rhinoceros of the colder regions of Eurasia at the time, a form well protected from the cold by its covering of thick hair, which contrasts strongly with the nearly naked skin of typical rhinoceroses. (From a mural by Charles R. Knight; photograph courtesy Field Museum of Natural History, Chicago.)

A SEA COW swimming. This figure shows some of the specializations of these ungainly sirenians – the paddle-like front limbs, the absence of the hind legs, the horizontal tail, rather comparable to that of a whale. The form shown is the American manatee. (Photograph courtesy New York Zoological Society.)

CONIES – mother and young. The conies (*Hyrax*) are animals of Africa and Syria which in habits (and also in their relatively small size) invite comparison with the rodents. In their structure, however, they are clearly quite another sort of creature and represent an archaic African stock of hoofed mammals from which both proboscidians and sirenians have arisen. (Photograph courtesy New York Zoological Society.)

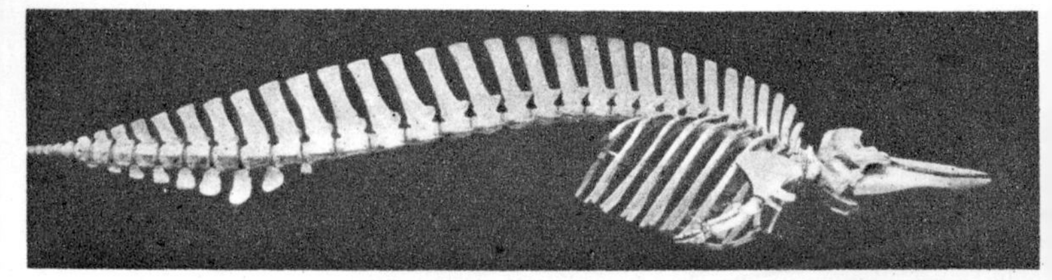

THE SKELETON OF A WHALE (*Ziphius*), to show the extreme specializations of the cetaceans. The hind legs have been lost, the front legs shortened into steering paddles. The seven neck vertebrae are extremely shortened, and the head is also much modified. (Photograph courtesy American Museum of Natural History, New York.)

RODENTS, or gnawing animals. Characteristic of this order are the two pairs of continuously growing, chisel-like gnawing teeth well seen in the 'portrait' below. A few representative forms are illustrated on this page. *Right*, a Brazilian tree porcupine, peculiar in the development of a prehensile tail. *Below* this, the familiar beaver. *Bottom left*, a colony of prairie dogs, related to the squirrels and woodchucks. *Bottom right*, the giant of all rodents, the capybara of South America, a relative of the guinea pigs, which grows to the size of a hog. (Photographs courtesy New York Zoological Society.)

ARCHAIC WHALES. In the Eocene are found the oldest and most primitive whales, usually known as zeuglodonts. Although already aquatic, they show many features suggesting descent from archaic land carnivores. (From a mural by Charles R. Knight; photograph courtesy Field Museum of Natural History, Chicago.)

BLACKFISH stranded on Cape Cod. This is a small whale (maximum length 28 feet; genus *Globicephala*) related to the dolphins and porpoises. Whales are helpless when beached; the blackfish travels in schools which not infrequently run ashore. (Photograph courtesy American Museum of Natural History, New York.)

UNBORN YOUNG OF A SPERM WHALE. This fetus, close to the stage of birth, was removed from the body of the mother, a pygmy sperm whale (*Kogia*) stranded on Staten Island, New York. It is perfectly formed except for the umbilical cord still attached to the navel. The two-foot rule gives the size. The sperm whales are toothed forms in which the expanded snout carries a 'case' full of oil and waxy spermaceti. (Photograph courtesy American Museum of Natural History, New York.)

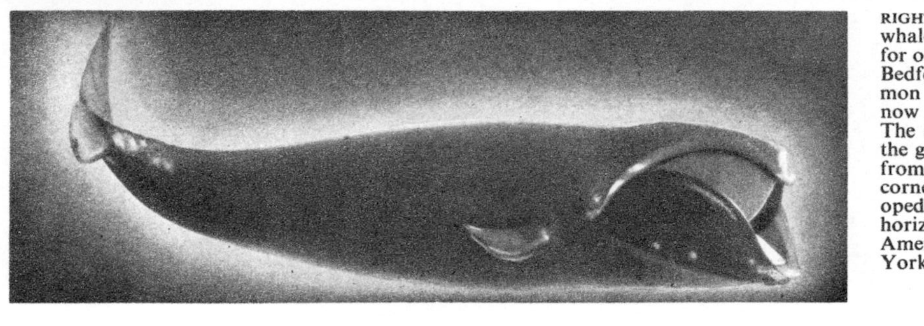

RIGHT WHALE (*Balaena*). These whalebone whales were considered the 'right' whales for oil as well as whalebone by the old New Bedford and Nantucket whalers. Once common in both Atlantic and Pacific, they are now relatively rare. Length about 60 feet. The model photographed here shows well the great strainers of whalebone suspended from the upper jaw, the tiny eye at the corner of the mouth, the front limbs developed as flippers, and the tail developed into horizontal flukes. (Photograph courtesy American Museum of Natural History, New York.)

A FINBACK, hauled ashore on the Norwegian coast. The finback (*Balaenoptera physalus*) is a very large whalebone whale reaching a maximum of 80 feet in length; the closely related blue whale reaches 100 feet and is the largest of all known animals. These and other closely related whales, known collectively as rorquals, are the major prey of the modern whalers. (Photograph courtesy American Museum of Natural History, New York.)

A BAT ON THE WING. This small insect-eating bat is seen in an instantaneous photograph made with the stroboscopic camera by Professor H. E. Edgerton of Massachusetts Institute of Technology. The structure of the outspread wings is well displayed. Note the extra membrane area in front of the elbow and the membrane between the hind legs. The first finger has a free claw for clutching purposes.

EDENTATES. The major group of edentates, so-called toothless mammals, is of South American origin. Its ranks include five main types: anteaters, armadillo, tree sloths, and the extinct ground sloths and glyptodonts. The fossil forms are illustrated on plate 79; *above*, representatives of the three living types. Most prominent feature of the large anteater, *Myrmecophagus*, is the long tubular snout, from which may emerge a very slender, sticky, and still longer tongue as an ant-catching device. Among the varied armadillos, the two illustrated are a giant South American form (*Priodon*) and the familiar nine-banded form (*Dasypus*).

EDENTATES. The tree sloths suspend themselves from boughs by their sharply curved claws. The specimen shown is a two-toed form (*Choloepus*): a three-clawed form also exists.

The aard-vark, 'earth pig', of South Africa (*right*), is generally classed as an edentate despite the presence of teeth (rather poorly constructed). However, he is not at all closely related to the South American forms, although his adaptations for ant-eating are similar to the anteaters of the latter continent. (All photographs courtesy New York Zoological Society.)

GIANT SOUTH AMERICAN EDENTATES OF THE PLEISTOCENE. Giant mammals were present at the time of the Ice Age in all continents. Characteristic contributions of South America were the ground sloths and glyptodonts illustrated here. The ground sloths were related to the living tree sloths and probably were also leaf-eaters. They had abandoned the trees for the ground, however, and grew to large size; *Megatherium*, shown above, was the size of a modern elephant. The glyptodonts were related to the armadillos but had a solid domed shell of bone rather than the more flexible armour of their surviving cousins. Note the tail, a bone-sheathed club with a spiked end. These edentates were South American natives, but several genera of ground sloths invaded North America in the Pleistocene, and glyptodonts reached the region of the Gulf of Mexico. (From a mural by Charles R. Knight; photograph courtesy Field Museum of Natural History, Chicago.)

LIFE OF A PLEISTOCENE TAR PIT. At La Brea, in the suburbs of Los Angeles, vast quantities of bone have been discovered belonging to animals which were caught there in tar deposits in late Pleistocene days. The forms found probably include all the animals then common in the region, many of them now extinct. There are representatives of various other forms of ungulates and herbivores (such as the native horses seen in the background). Much more common, however, are flesh-eaters attracted to the spot by the easy prey afforded by animals mired in the tar; the carnivores in turn became mired themselves in enormous numbers. The two commonest mammals are the great sabre-toothed 'tiger' (*Smilodon*) and the dire wolf, a species distinct from the modern wolf. Common too was a giant vulture (*Teratornis*), standing 2½ feet high and with a wing-spread of at least 9 feet; it ranks among the largest known birds of flight. (From a mural by Charles R. Knight; photograph courtesy Field Museum of Natural History, Chicago.)

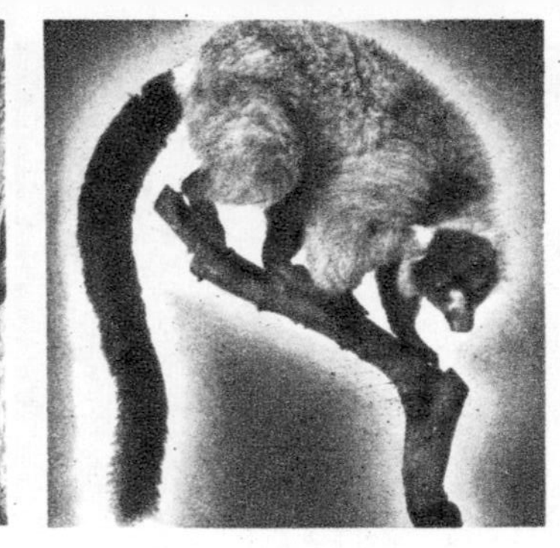

LEMURS. *Upper left*, a restoration of the Eocene fossil lemur *Notharctus*, which may be close to the ancestry of modern forms. *Centre*, a typical lemur of the type common today on the island of Madagascar. *Upper right*, a slender loris, an advanced type of lemur from south eastern Asia; this specimen was captured in Siam. Note the relatively short face and also the peculiar foot structure. *Bottom*, a family of galagos; parents and twin offspring. The galagos, or 'bush babies', are inhabitants of continental Africa. In these advanced lemurs the eyes, as can be seen, are large and turned well forward in the fashion of higher primates, and the nose is much less prominent than in the typical lemurs. (*Notharctus* from a painting by F. L. Jaques under the direction of W. K. Gregory; photograph courtesy American Museum of Natural History, New York: loris, photograph by American Primate Expedition, courtesy Sherwood Washburn; galagos photograph courtesy F. de L. Lowther.)

TARSIUS. A portrait of one of the only pair of these delicate little oriental primates ever successfully 'exported' from their native country. These specimens were brought to America by aeroplane and lived more than a year in the laboratories of Yale University. The photograph shows the large eyes, reduced nose, and the specialized pads on the toes. (Photograph courtesy John F. Fulton, Yale University.)

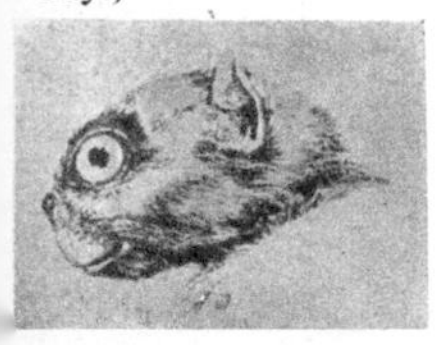

AN EOCENE TARSIOID. A restoration of the head of an early member of this group, also a large-eyed, small-nosed form. (From Scott, *Land Mammals in the Western Hemisphere*, by permission of the Macmillan Co., publishers.)

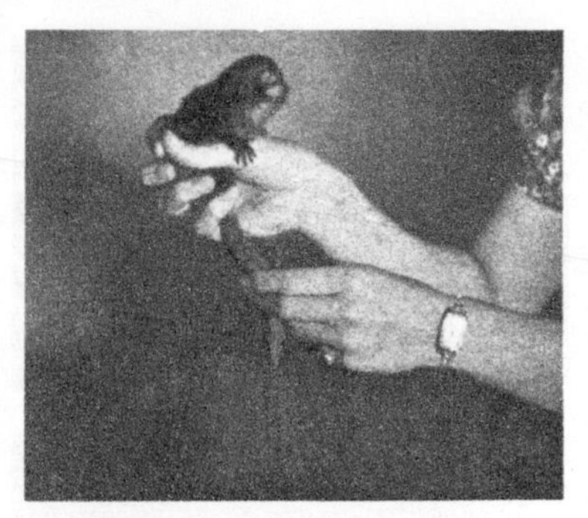

MONKEYS. Monkeys are sharply divisible into South American and Old World groups, the former the more primitive. Two of the South American forms are illustrated above, a pygmy marmoset (*Callithrix*) and the black spider monkey. The marmosets are the smallest of all monkeys and, except for their faces, look as much squirrel-like as monkey-like. A more 'normal' group of South American monkeys includes such forms as the capuchin monkey, favoured by organ grinders, and the spider monkeys (*Ateles*), agile acrobats which in the use of their long arms parallel the gibbons among the great apes.

Here are three examples of the Old World monkey group. *Right*, the Hanuman monkey, the sacred langur of India. *Bottom left*, the black guenon (*Cercopithecus*), typical of the African arboreal monkeys. *Bottom right*, the mandrill, peculiarly pigmented, long-snouted, and short-tailed, an extreme example of the ground-dwelling baboon type. (All photographs courtesy New York Zoological Society.)

BRACHIATION is the term applied to the arm-over-arm type of locomotion highly developed in great apes, in contrast with the pedestrian locomotion of most primates. This type of swinging through the trees is comparable to the use of 'travelling rings' in a gymnasium. In such progression the body is held, of course, erect. Long-continued retention of this type of locomotion may be associated with the development of relatively long arms and reduction of the thumb in great apes. In the four views above a gibbon is seen swinging his way along a limb in the Siamese forests. *Upper left*, the beginning of a swing to a new hold, reached in the third figure; in the fourth, a second swing has begun. (Photographs from American Primate Expedition, courtesy Harold J. Coolidge.)

IN FULL FLIGHT. An enlargement of a telephoto moving-picture 'shot' of a gibbon in the middle of a long leap in the treetops in Siam. (Photograph by American Primate Expedition, courtesy Harold J. Coolidge.)

PORTRAIT OF AN ACROBAT. A gibbon, captured in Siam, of the species seen in action on the opposite page. (Photograph by American Primate Expedition, courtesy Harold J. Coolidge.)

MEDITATION. Meshie, an adolescent female chimpanzee. She was reared for some years with the children of an American family. (Photograph courtesy Harry C. Raven.)

AN ADULT MALE HIGHLAND GORILLA (*left*), shot in the Kivu district of the Belgian Congo. This animal weighed more than the three scientists, shown in the photograph, put together. (Photograph courtesy Harry C. Raven.)

ORANGUTANS, young and old. *Left*, a young specimen, showing the concave profile characteristic of this East Indian ape. Hands and feet are well shown and illustrative of the great ape type, with small thumb and with an opposable big toe on the handlike foot. *Right*, an old male, showing the characteristic development of a ring of calloused skin around the face and a skin-fold below the chin. (Photographs courtesy New York Zoological Society.)

CHIMPANZEE LIFE. Extensive studies on the behaviour and mentality of apes, particularly chimpanzees, are being made at the Yale Laboratories of Primate Biology by Dr R. M. Yerkes and his associates. On this page are shown photographs of characteristic activities.

Upper left, a six-year-old female chimpanzee using a 'chimpomat' (variety of automat) to get food as reward for success in an experiment. (Courtesy of Drs J. B. Wolfe and H. W. Nissen.)

Upper right, half-grown chimpanzees working co-operatively to get food by drawing a box toward them. (Courtesy of Drs M. P. Crawford and H. W. Nissen.)

Left, a chimpanzee family: mother at left with two-weeks old infant clinging to her while she busily grooms the father. (Courtesy of Dr R. M. Yerkes.)

Bottom, a full-grown female chimpanzee using a push-button fountain to get water to wash her hands. She is pressing the button with one foot while catching the water with her cupped hands. (Courtesy of Dr R. M. Yerkes.) (All photographs courtesy of Yale Laboratories of Primate Biology.)

A MOUNTAIN GORILLA
Mbongo, long resident at the San Diego zoo. A male about thirteen years old when the photographs were taken and weighing 602 pounds. The upper picture shows well the quadrupedal pose assumed by gorillas on the ground. The crest atop the head is characteristic of the mountain gorilla of central Africa and is absent in the gorillas of the western part of the continent. (Photographs courtesy Belle J. Benchley, Zoological Society of San Diego.)

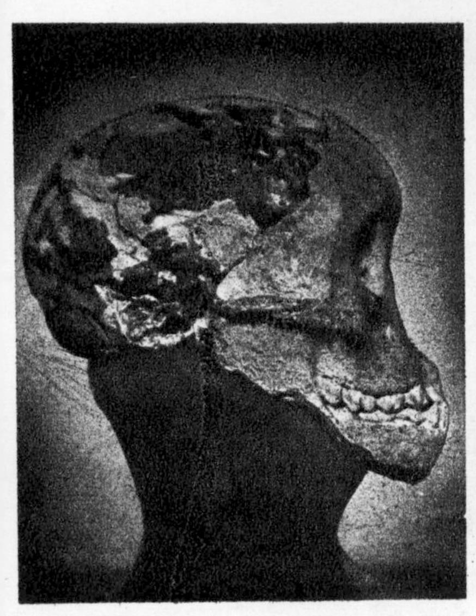

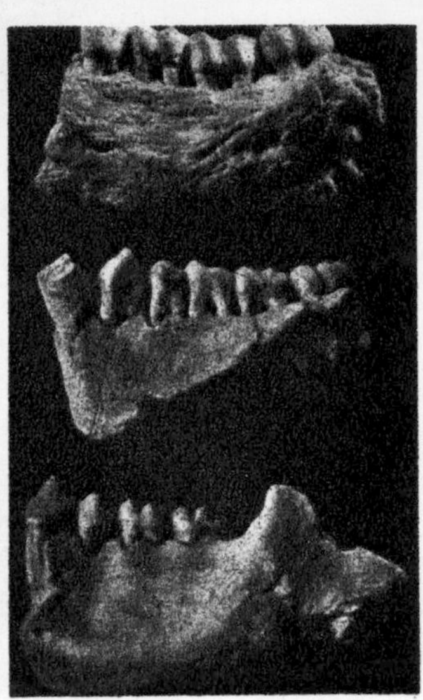

FOSSIL APES. Tertiary man-like apes are known only from fragmentary materials, such as the jaw fragments of *Dryopithecus*, the 'oak ape' of India and Europe, shown directly above. From South Africa come remains of Pleistocene fossil apes much closer structurally to man. *Australopithecus*, the 'southern ape', was founded on the skull of an infant, illustrated at the upper left (and shown restored in the text). *Plesianthropus* is based on remains of adult apes of a similar nature. As will be seen from the restored skull *below*, the adult, of course, looks much more ape-like, with projecting brow ridges and jutting snout, than the young *Australopithecus*. (Photographs courtesy American Museum of Natural History, New York; *Dryopithecus* after Gregory and Hellman; *Australopithecus* after Dart; *Plesianthropus* after Broom.)

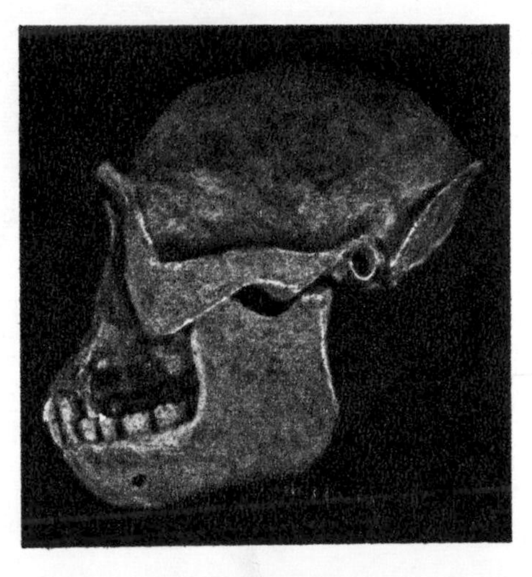

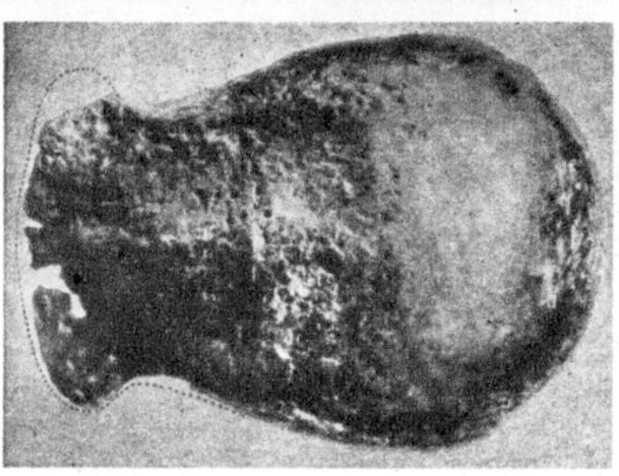

PITHECANTHROPUS, the Java ape man. The original remains were found on the banks of the Solo River, near the village of Trinil. The site is shown at the right. Most of the excavation was made by a later expedition which found, however, no further human bones. Next below (*right*) is a view of the original skull-cap seen from the upper surface. *Lower left*, a restoration by Dr J. H. McGregor of the skull seen in side view. The dark line from brow ridges to the back of the skull marks the lower limit of the part preserved in the original specimen. Below this point at one time, reconstruction was hypothetical. New and better braincase finds, together with considerable portions of upper and lower jaws, now enable us to picture the entire skull with considerable confidence. This skull is closely comparable to *Sinanthropus*, pictured over page. *Lower right* a bust in which the flesh and skin have been carefully restored by McGregor to give an idea of the appearance of *Pithecanthropus* in life. (Site after Selenka and Blanckenhorn; other photographs courtesy J. H. McGregor.)

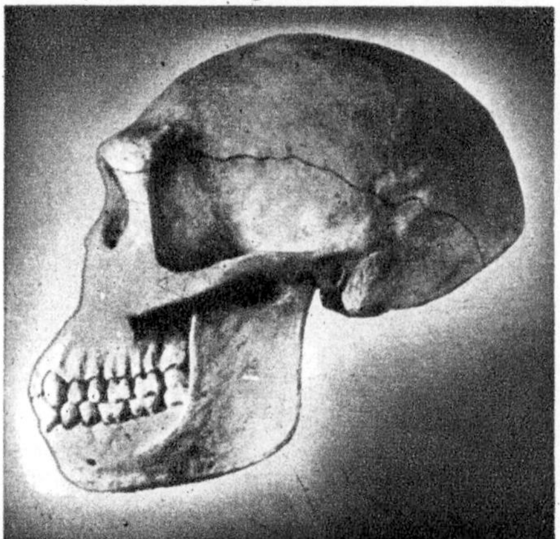

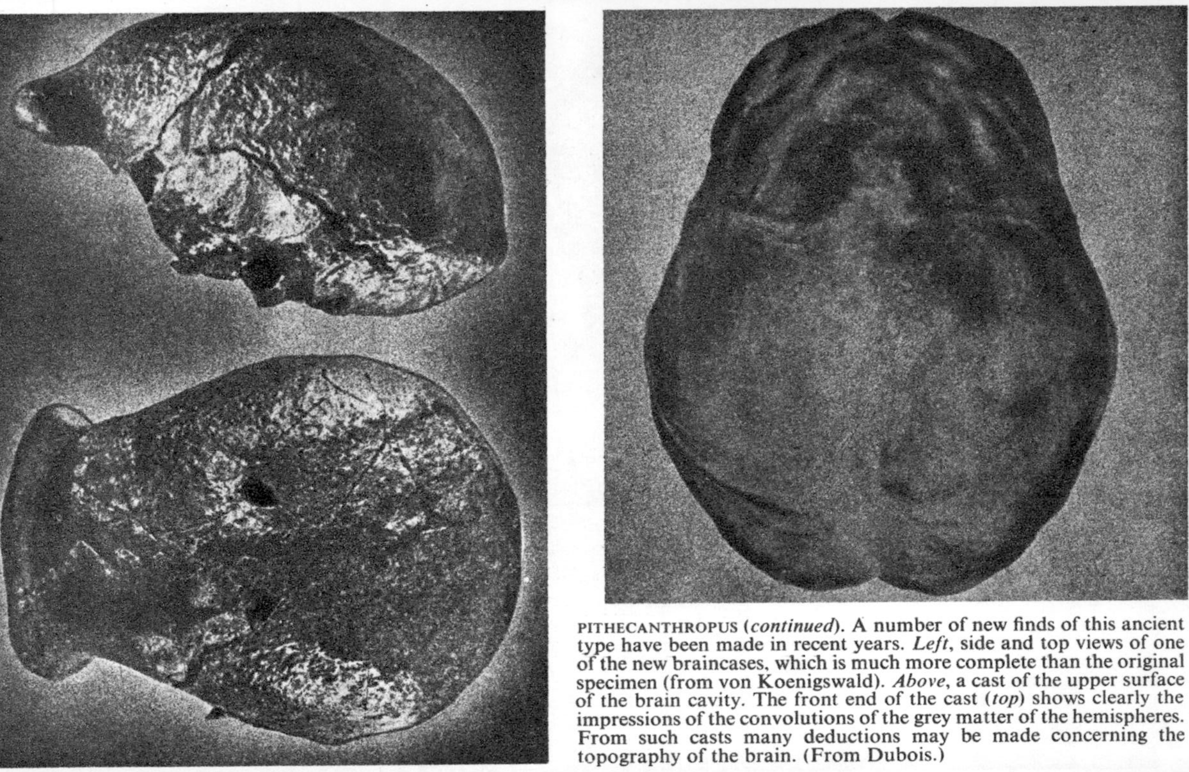

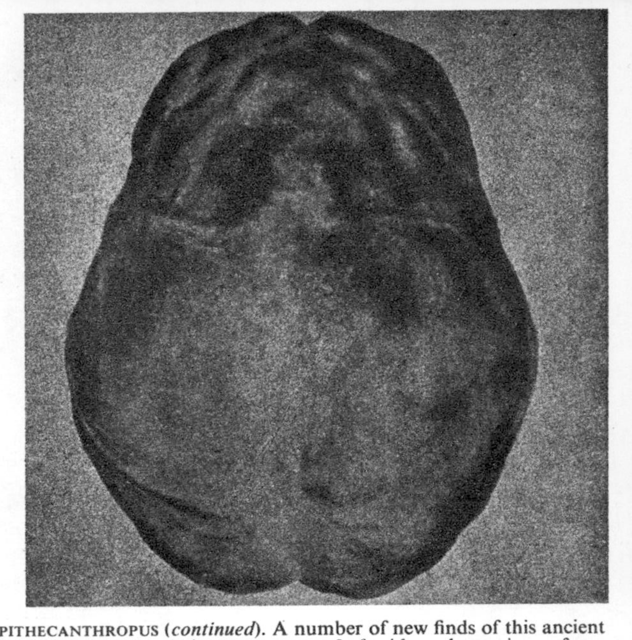

PITHECANTHROPUS (*continued*). A number of new finds of this ancient type have been made in recent years. *Left*, side and top views of one of the new braincases, which is much more complete than the original specimen (from von Koenigswald). *Above*, a cast of the upper surface of the brain cavity. The front end of the cast (*top*) shows clearly the impressions of the convolutions of the grey matter of the hemispheres. From such casts many deductions may be made concerning the topography of the brain. (From Dubois.)

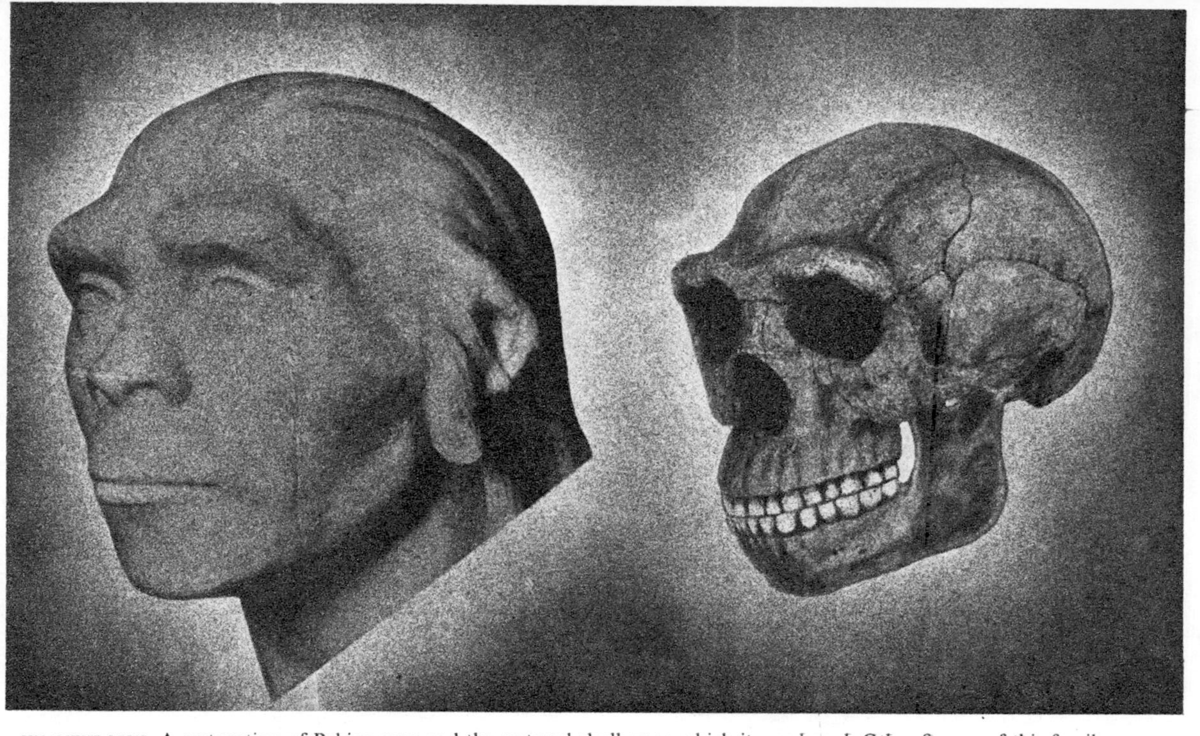

SINANTHROPUS. A restoration of Peking man and the restored skull upon which it was based. Other figures of this fossil man are shown on plate 93.

PEKING MAN. The remains of this early and primitive man have been obtained from Choukou-tien, near Peking, where former caves in a limestone hill have been filled with hard material containing remains of man and many other Pleistocene mammals. *Left,* part of the vast excavations that have been made there in the search for this fossil man. The white lines mark off numbered sections of the quarry so that finds can be accurately located. *Above, right,* is a view of one of the skullcaps seen from above (compare with *Pithecanthropus*). Below this are side and front views of a skull reconstructed from numerous specimens. (All *Sinanthropus* photographs by Dr Franz Weidenreich, Cenozoic Research Laboratory, Peking, courtesy American Museum of Natural History, New York.)

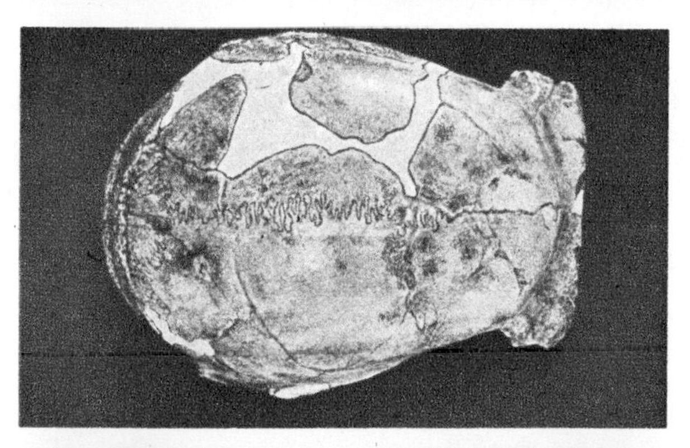

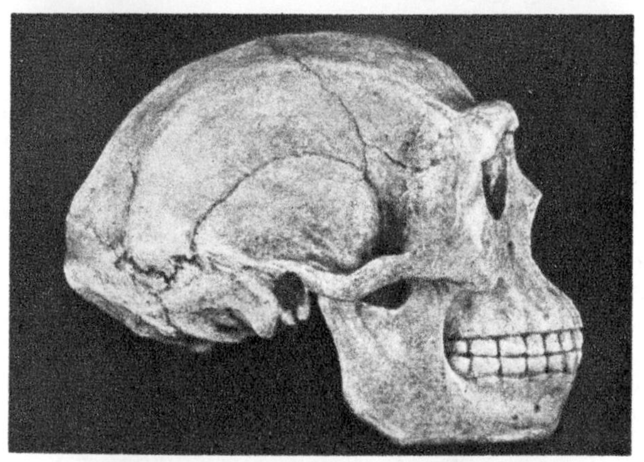

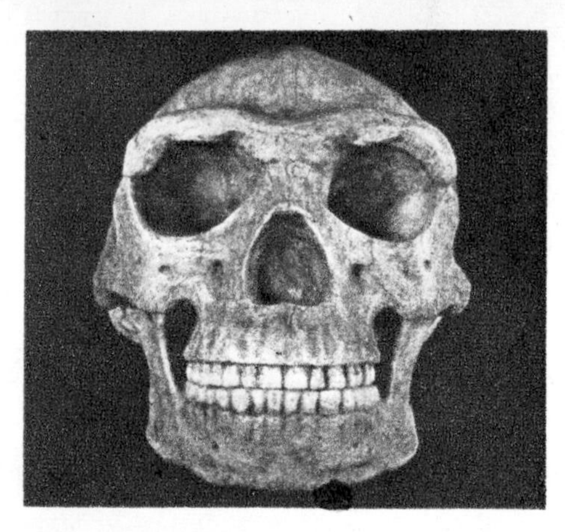

'PILTDOWN MAN'. The material belonging to the cranium came from the excavation shown in the upper figure, and the jaw was 'discovered' there also. Holding the sieve is Dawson, the discoverer, and beside him Sir Arthur Smith Woodward, distinguished paleontologist, who described the material and whose integrity is unquestioned.

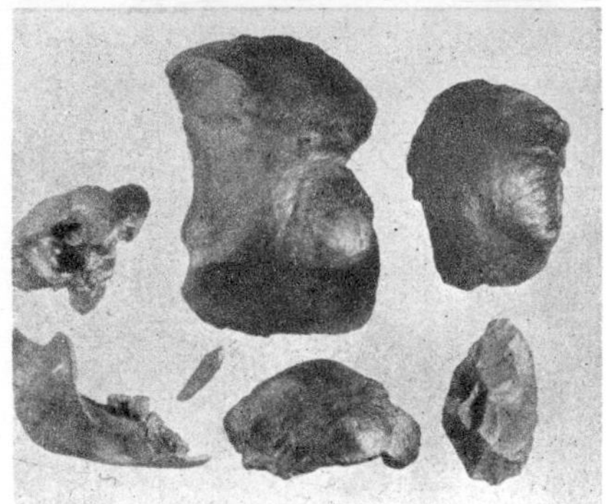

Left, the authentic skull fragments (top row and centre of bottom row). In the bottom row are the ape jaw, a canine tooth, and a flint instrument 'found' at Piltdown – all three apparently 'planted'.

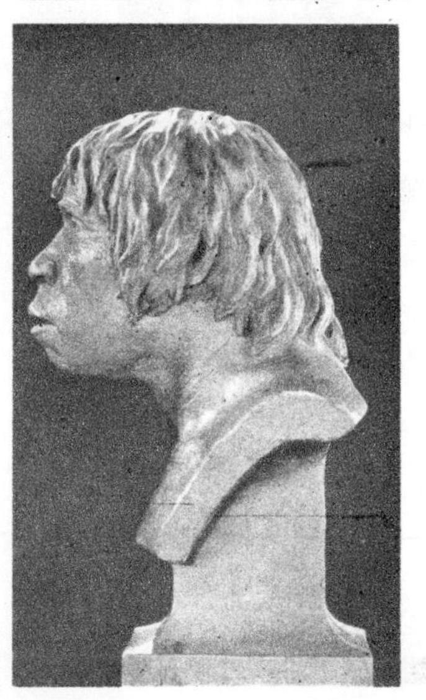

Below, Smith Woodward's reconstruction, one of several attempts to fit together the fragments, and *left* a life reconstruction of Piltdown man, executed by Dr J. H. McGregor; in both reconstructions the spurious jaw is included. (Photographs courtesy American Museum of Natural History, New York.)

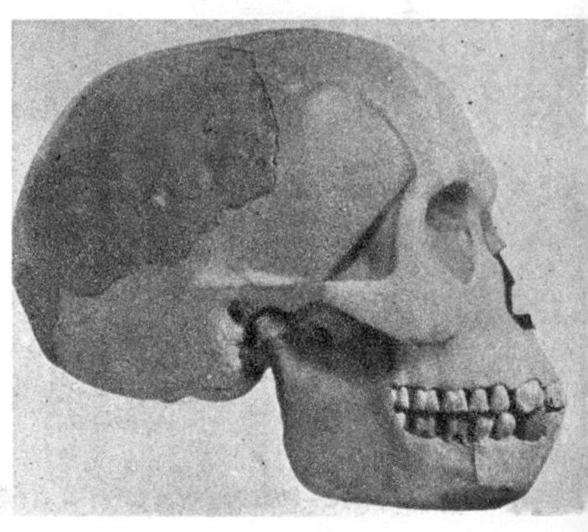

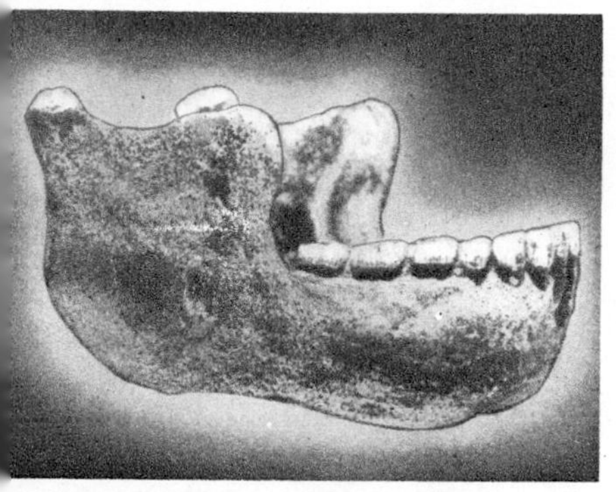

THE HEIDELBERG JAW. A massive specimen showing resemblances both to the early men of eastern Asia and to the later Neanderthal type, was found, at the spot marked, deep in a sand pit at Mauer near Heidelberg. These deposits were certainly formed well back in the Pleistocene and possibly during the first inter-glacial stage. (Illustrations after Schoetensack.)

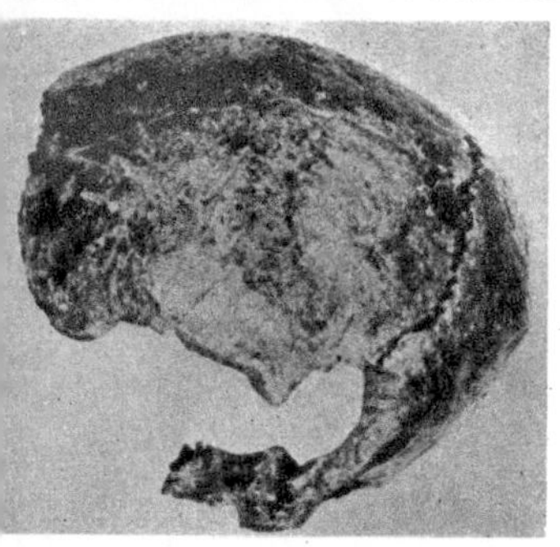

THE SWANSCOMBE SKULL FRAGMENT is the only human fossil definitely associated with the hand axe cultures of the Lower Paleolithic. It includes only the large parietal bone, covering much of the skull roof, and the occipital bone forming the back of the skull. These are shown articulated, from the left side. The rounded skull contours are more similar to those found in our own species than in Neanderthal, etc. *Right*, the undisturbed Acheulean deposits in which the specimen was recovered: white spots above the level of the rod indicate the exact layer. (Photographs from Oakley and Morant.)

THE GALLEY HILL SKELETON, of which the skull is shown (*right*), came from a near-by pit and is obviously a specimen similar to modern man. Although it has been thought to come from these same early deposits doubts exist as to its history. (Photograph courtesy American Museum of Natural History, New York.)

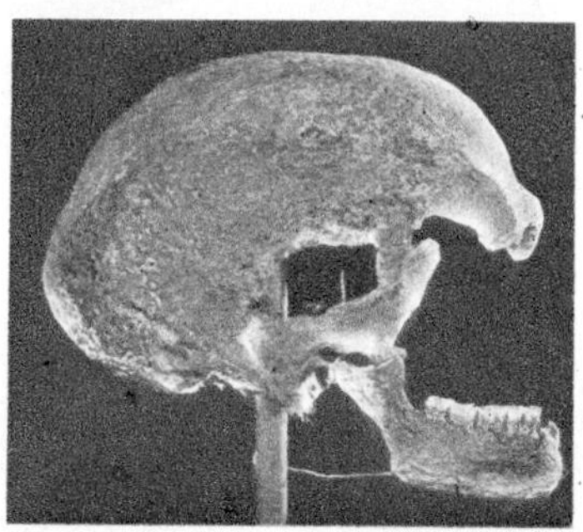

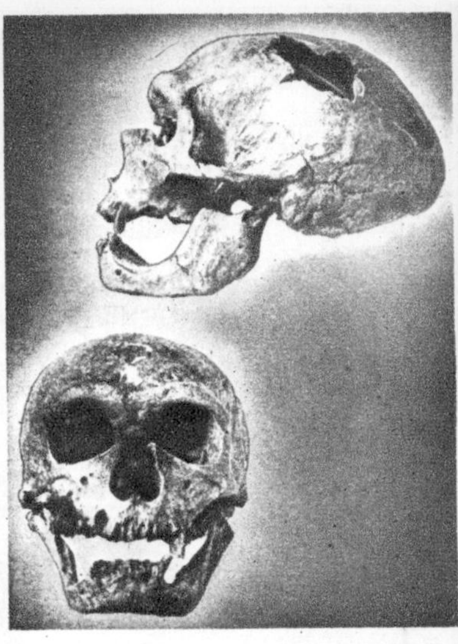

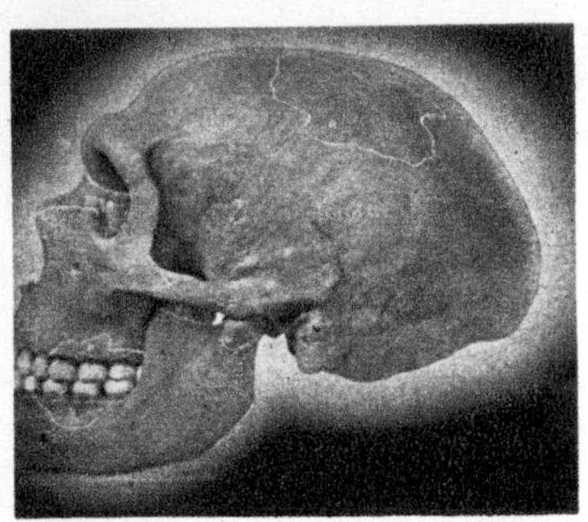

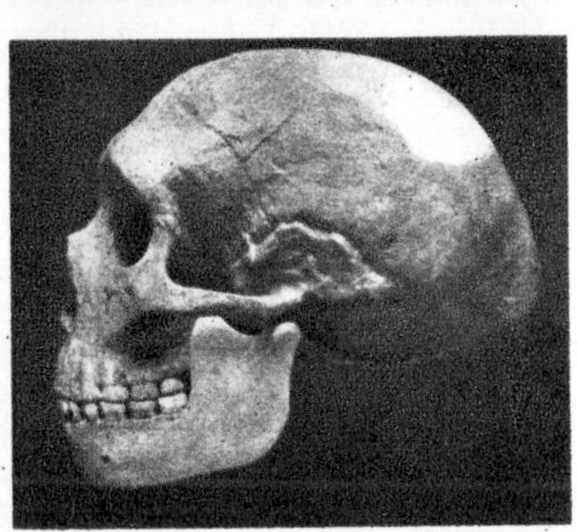

NEANDERTHAL MAN. This inhabitant of Europe in the earlier part of the last glaciation is known from numerous skulls and considerable parts of the skeleton, so that attempts at complete bodily restoration (as in the scene, *upper left*) are warranted. The most adequately known specimen is the skeleton of an old man from the cave of La Chapelle aux Saints, described by Marcellin Boule. The skull is pictured above (*right*). *Centre left*, the same skull with teeth and other missing parts restored by Dr J. H. McGregor. *Bottom left*, the skull of a female from Gibraltar; the contours are more rounded, brow ridges less exaggerated, etc. (Restoration at upper left by F. L. Jaques, under the direction of W. K. Gregory; photograph courtesy American Museum of Natural History, New York; La Chapelle skull unrestored from Boule; lower figures courtesy Dr J. H. McGregor.)

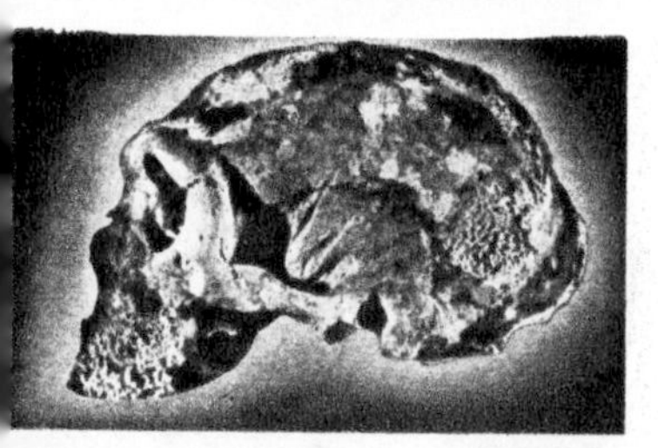

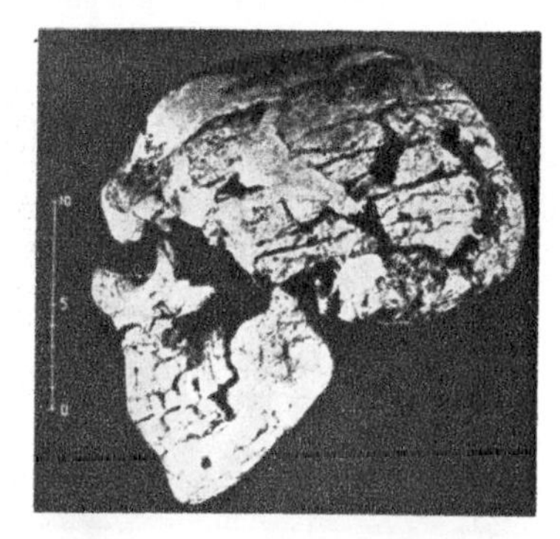

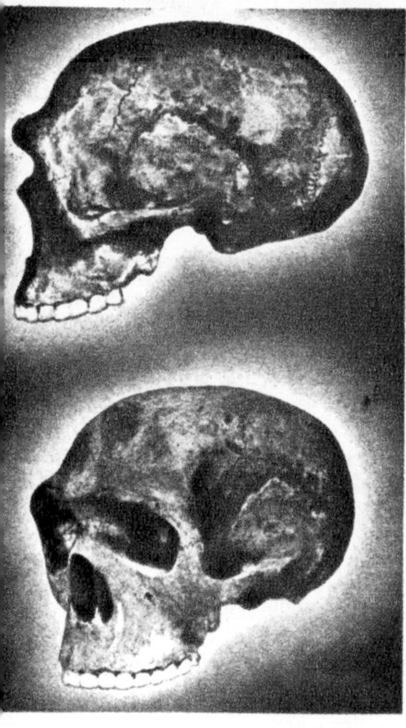

NEANDERTHAL VARIANTS. While typical Neanderthal remains are those of inhabitants of Europe during the Wurm glaciation, other specimens are found which are earlier in time or from western Asia rather than Europe; these may vary considerably from the typical Neanderthal structure. *Upper left*, a skull from Mount Circeo on the Italian coast near the Pontine marshes, which is from an earlier time – the last interglacial stage – but is structurally similar to later finds. Next *below*, two views of another skull from the last interglacial (from *Steinheim* in southern Germany), which is less typically neanderthaloid in its skull contours and rather closer to modern man despite its antiquity. Of great interest are the finds from Mount Carmel in Palestine, which show many structural intergrades between Neanderthal man and our own species. One of the Mount Carmel skulls is shown *top, right*; note the contrast with typical neanderthals in the skull contours, jaw outlines, etc. *Centre, right*, is shown one of the Mount Carmel skeletons in process of excavation. *Bottom, right*, the bluff containing the Mount Carmel caves. In the centre is the cave of Skuhl where most remains were found. Other caves close by contained other Middle and Upper Paleolithic remains. (Mount Circeo skull, after a photograph by Dr A. C. Blanc of Pisa, its discoverer; Steinheim skull from Weinert; Mount Carmel skull from McCown and Keith; Mount Carmel scenes from Bulletin American School of Prehistoric Research, courtesy Dr G. G. MacCurdy.)

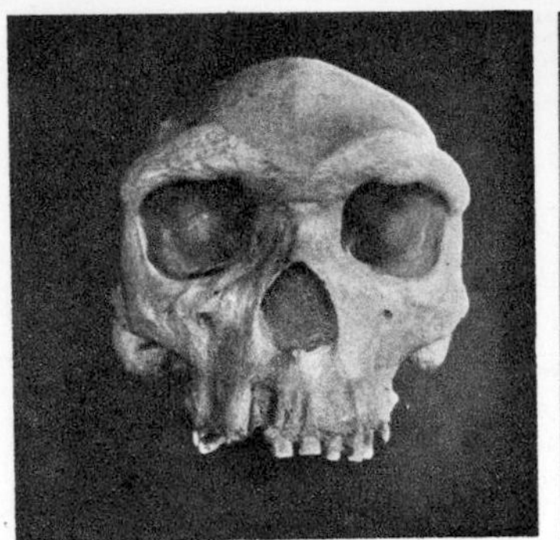
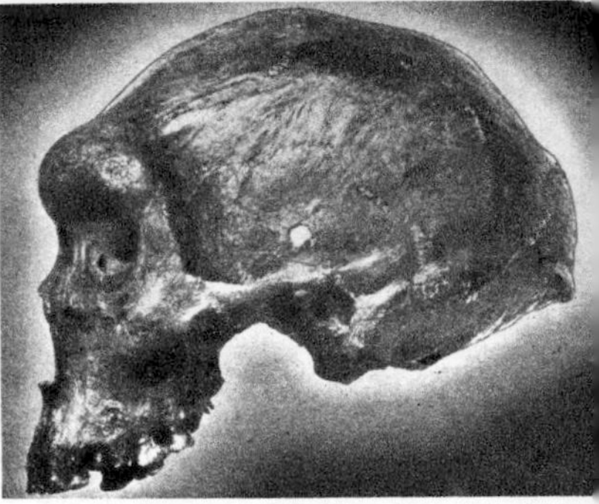

THE RHODESIAN SKULL comes from a cave deposit at Broken Hill, Northern Rhodesia, which is of unknown date, although not improbably late Pleistocene. Front and side views of this massive skull are shown above (from Pycraft). Although the brow ridges suggest comparison with Neanderthal man, other features are rather more 'modern', and close comparison is possible with the braincase of Solo man, seen below at the left.

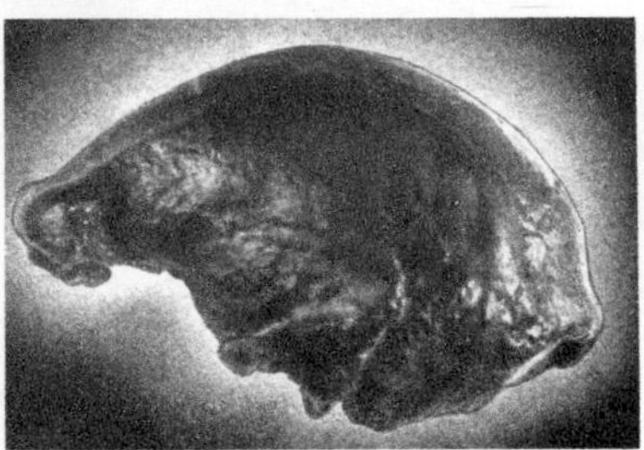
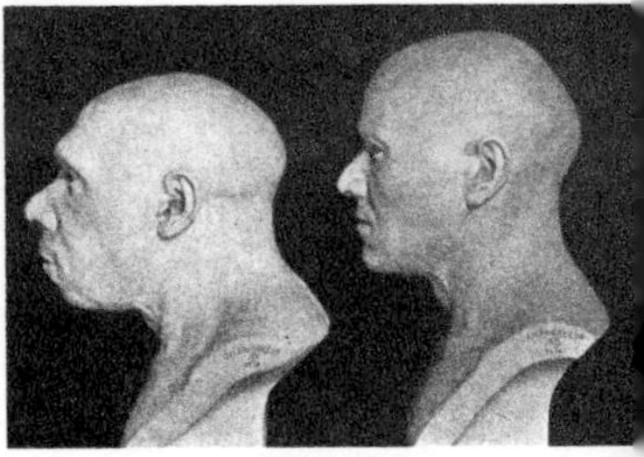

SOLO MAN (*Homo soloensis*) from the late Pleistocene of Java is known from a number of skullcaps, the most complete of which is shown above at left. (From a cast; originals described by Oppenoorth and von Koenigswald.)

RESTORATIONS OF NEANDERTHAL AND CRO-MAGNON TYPES by Dr J. H. McGregor. *Above, right,* the soft anatomy of the head has been carefully restored and gives a close approximation to the actual structure in life. *Below*, the hair has been added (although of course we have no certain knowledge of this) to give a more 'natural' appearance.

CRO-MAGNON MAN. The upper Paleolithic men of western Europe, oldest known representatives of our species in that region, are generally termed the Cro-Magnon race. The name is derived from the French rock shelter of that name (shown over page), whence a typical example of the race was derived. Although variations occur, most of the skeletons from the Upper Paleolithic of Europe vary little from the typical Cro-Magnon type. The men were tall, ruggedly built, and large-brained, with high foreheads and long heads. *Below*, two typical skeletons of tall individuals from the Grimaldi caves of the Riviera. *Below*, two skulls. *Top*, the type of the race, an old man from the Cro-Magnon shelter (teeth restored); *bottom*, a closely comparable skull from Grimaldi. Cro-Magnon man is of interest for his artistic productions (examples of which are shown overpage); *above*, a restoration by Charles R. Knight of a group of Upper Paleolithic artists. (Upper figure, courtesy American Museum of Natural History, New York; old man of Cro-Magnon, restoration by Dr J. H. McGregor; other figures after Verneau.)

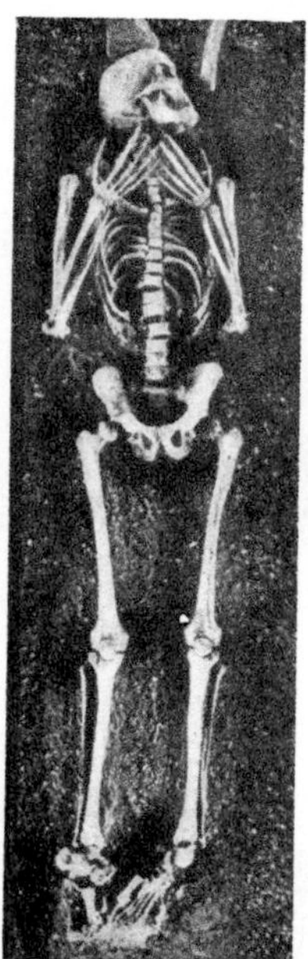

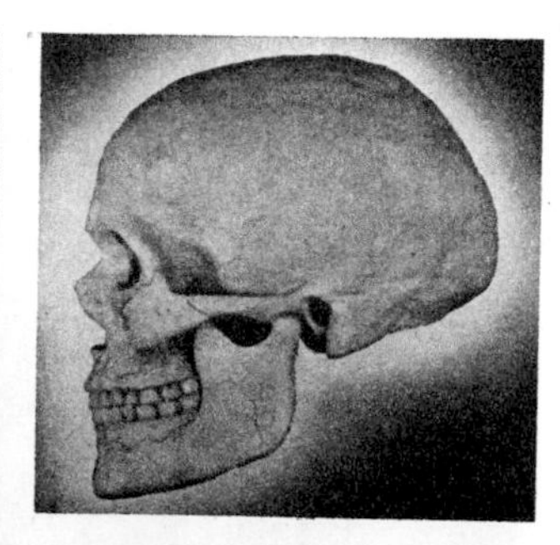

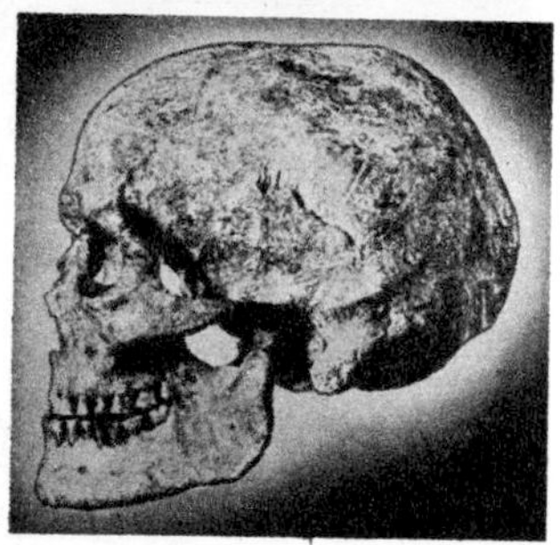

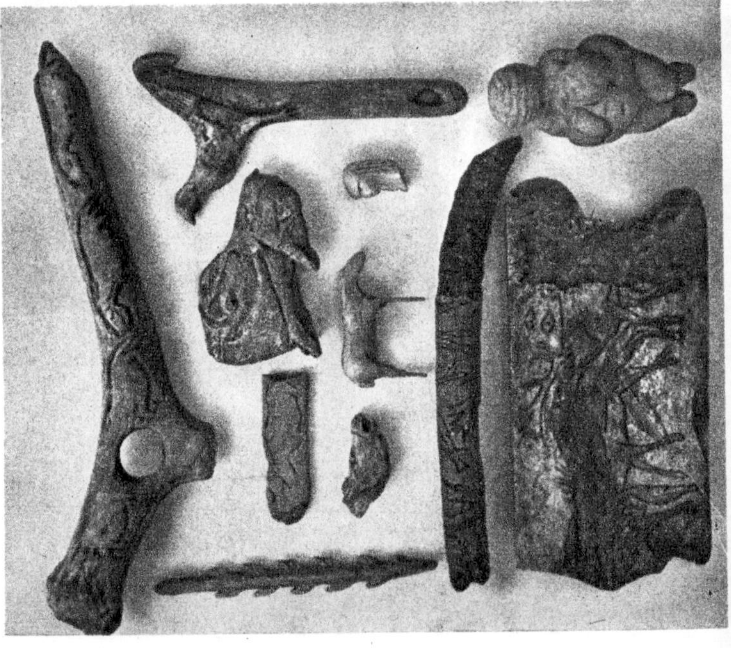

ART OF UPPER PALEOLITHIC MAN. Artistic impulses, unobserved in the cultural remains of earlier human types, were strong in the days of Cro-Magnon man in Europe. Antlers, bone, and soft-stone materials were carved or engraved, as in the examples seen at the upper left. Particularly striking are the finds of engravings and paintings on cavern walls in southern France and northern Spain. *Above, right,* a part of the cavern of Font-de-Gaume in the Dordogne region of France. A series of bisons were painted on the bosses of the rough rocky wall at the left of the photograph. One of these bison is illustrated, as well as a pair of reindeer from another part of the same cavern. (Mobile art objects courtesy American Museum of Natural History, New York; other figures from Capitan, Breuil, and Peyroney.)

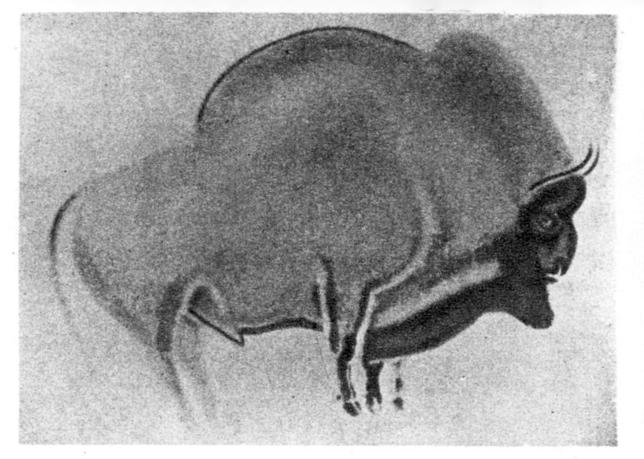

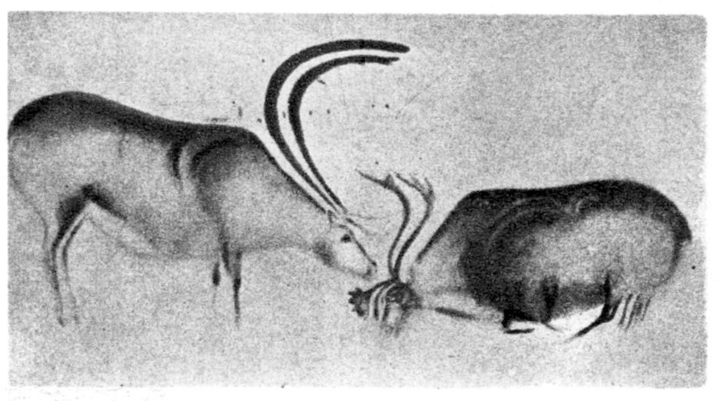

TWO FAMOUS UPPER PALEOLITHIC SITES. *Left,* the village of Les Eyzies in the Dordogne region of southern France. Behind the houses at the base of the cliff was the Cro-Magnon rock shelter containing the skeleton of the type of this race. (Photograph courtesy American Museum of Natural History, New York.) *Right,* the grottos of Grimaldi, on the Riviera. Several of the series of caves with Upper Paleolithic implements, human skeletons, and fossil animals are seen at the left as crevices in the cliff. (After Verneau.)

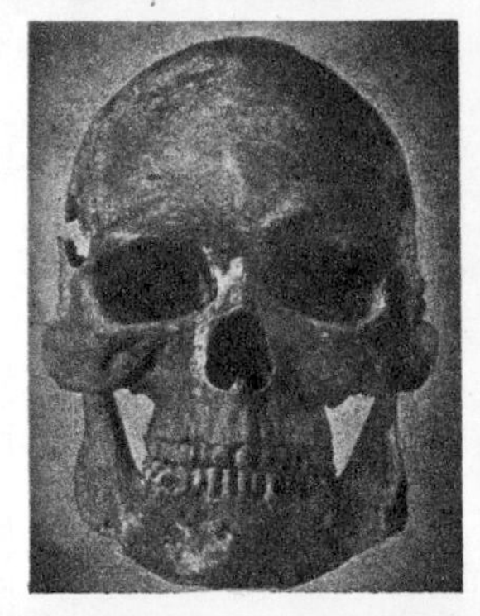

THE CHANCELADE-OBERCASSEL RACE. A variant from the Cro-Magnon type in the European Upper Paleolithic is represented by skulls from Chancelade in France and Obercassel in Germany. Both finds are of Magdalenian age. *Right,* a figure of a male from Obercassel (the teeth restored). Some writers believe these specimens to show Eskimo-like features. (After Bonnet.)

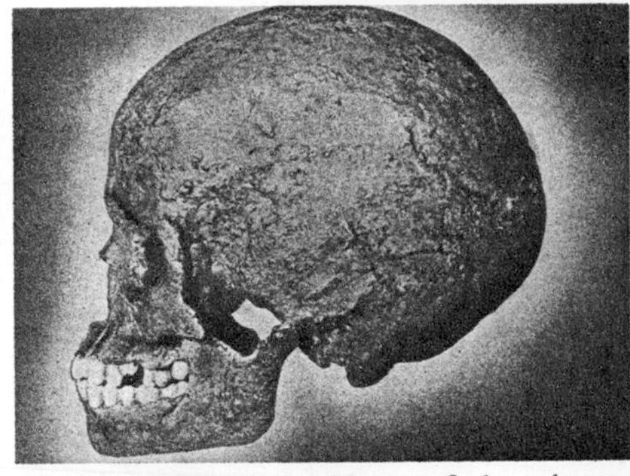

THE GRIMALDI RACE. At Grimaldi, besides typical Cro-Magnon finds, a lower Aurignacian level revealed the skeletons of two individuals of a somewhat different type, with projecting teeth and other features which some believe suggestive of Negroid affinities. These skeletons and one of the skulls are shown above. They represent a middle-aged woman and a youth, possibly mother and son. (After Verneau.)

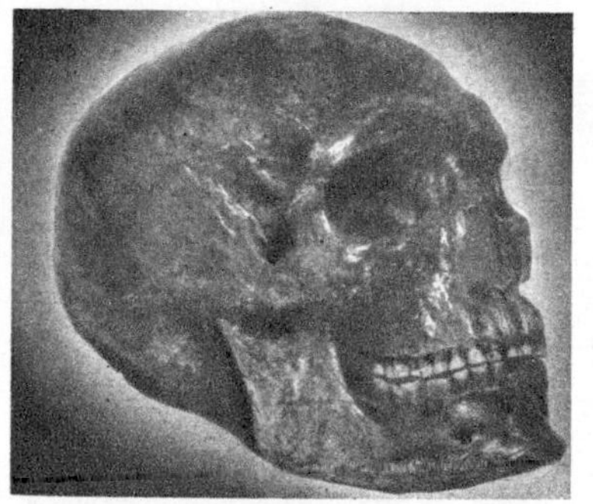

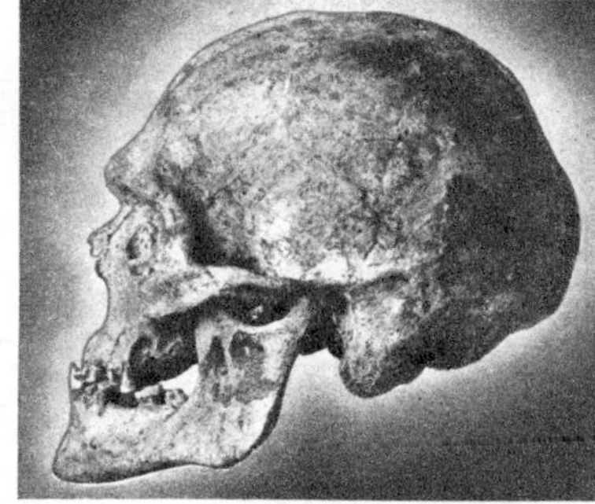

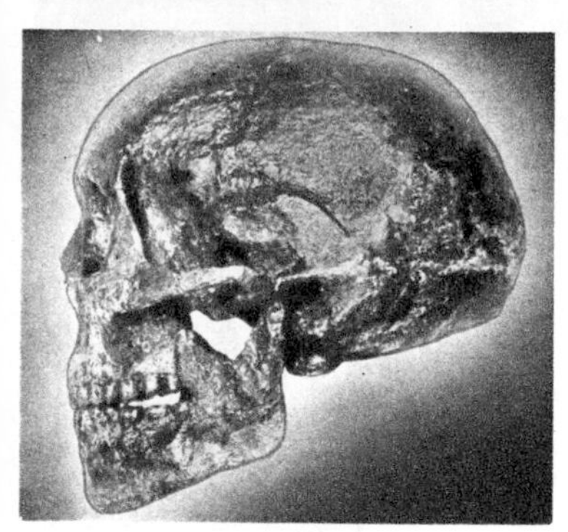

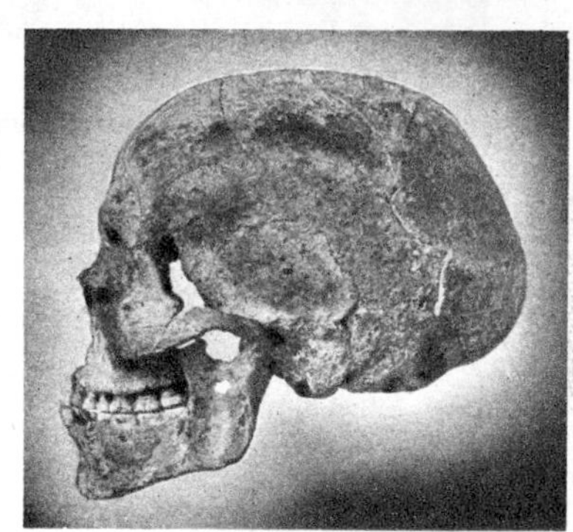

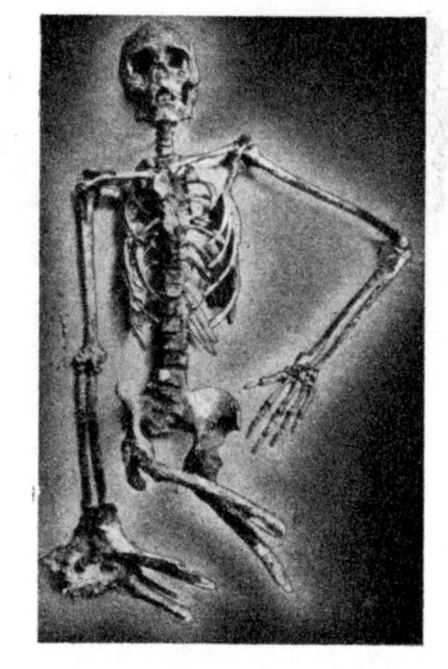

UPPER PALEOLITHIC MEN OF ASIA AND AFRICA. Although most of our knowledge of ancient races of our own species has been obtained from Europe, the last two decades have seen the extension of our knowledge to other Old World areas. The Choukoutien cave in China has yielded from an upper level several skulls of this age (*upper left*). These Chinese men show few if any of the specialized features of the Mongoloid races now inhabiting this area.

North Africa has yielded Upper Paleolithic skulls at a number of sites. *Upper right*, a male from the cave of Beni Segoual in Algeria. The brow ridges are rather heavy, but in general this type of skull is not far from that of Cro-Magnon man. *Lower left*, one of several skulls from Gamble's Cave in Kenya Colony, East Africa, where an Upper Paleolithic culture was present. Although well down into Africa, these men of Kenya show little trace of Negroid affinities. *Lower right*, a skull from Asselar in the southern Sahara; the skeleton is shown at the right. While the date is uncertain, the specimen appears to be of considerable antiquity and does show Negroid features. (Choukoutien from a cast, courtesy Dr Franz Weidenreich, Cenozoic Research Laboratory, Peking; Beni Segoual from Boule, Vallois and Verneau; Gamble Cave from Leakey; Asselar, from Boule and Vallois.)

NEGROIDS. *Above*, two types of African Negro, including: (1) a Zulu and his wife. The once warlike Zulus are typical members of the Bantu group of central and southern Africa, Negroes with an admixture of 'dark white' blood from the north. (2) A Kru from Liberia, a typical Negro of the general sort from which many of the slaves brought to the United States were derived. *Right*, two oceanic Negroes. *Upper right* (3), a Papuan from New Guinea, of a tribe more than suspected of cannibalism. *Opposite at the right* (4), a Melanesian from the Admiralty Islands. Also cannibalistic and 'reported to be unfriendly to strangers'. *Below*, Pygmies. *Left* (5), African Pygmies from the forests of the Belgian Congo, photographed with a European of normal stature. *Right* (6), an Aeta girl from the Philippines. (1, 2, courtesy Peabody Museum of Anthropology, Harvard University; 3, courtesy, J. D. Ripley; 4, 6, courtesy, American Museum of Natural History, New York; 5, courtesy H. C. Raven.)

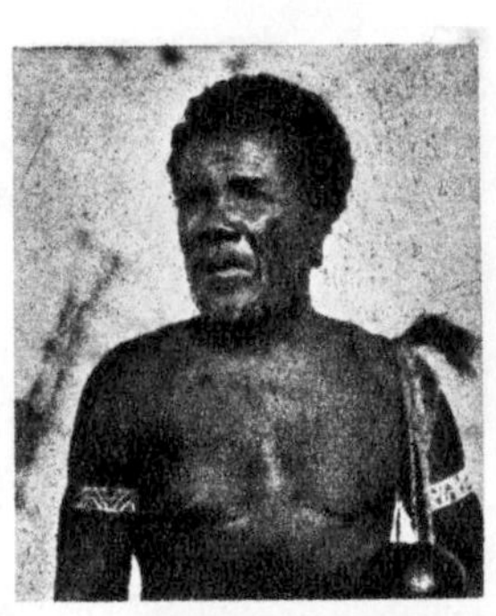

NEGROIDS (*continued*). *Left*, a native Tasmanian lady (by the name of Betsy). (Courtesy Beattie Studios, Hobart, Tasmania). *Right*, a Bushman of South Africa (Photograph by George Leith, courtesy Peabody Museum, Harvard University.)

AUSTRALOIDS. *Left*, a Veddah of Ceylon, member of an archaic group probably related to the Australians. (After the Sarasin brothers.) *Right*, an Australian from Cooper Creek, South Australia. (Photograph courtesy Peabody Museum, Harvard University.)

EASTERN RACES WITH MEDITERRANEAN BLOOD. *Left*, a Polynesian. A 'dark white' stock with Mongoloid and Negroid strains. (Courtesy American Museum of Natural History.) *Right*, an Ainu. Essentially archaic 'white' with some Mongoloid admixture, Ainus usually have excessive hirsute adornments but this young man would pass unremarked on a European street. (From Kubo.)

DARK 'WHITES' OF SOUTHERN ASIA. Although India is a land of varied racial components, the typical Hindu (*left*) is in essence a dark, long-headed, wavy-haired type related to the Mediterraneans of more western areas. East of India strong admixtures of this same Mediterranean strain are to be found in the races of south eastern Asia and the adjacent East Indian islands. The Muruts of Borneo (*right*) appear, for example, to be basically Mediterranean people with an infusion of Mongoloid blood. (Hindu, courtesy Griffith Taylor; Muruts, courtesy Peabody Museum, Harvard University.)

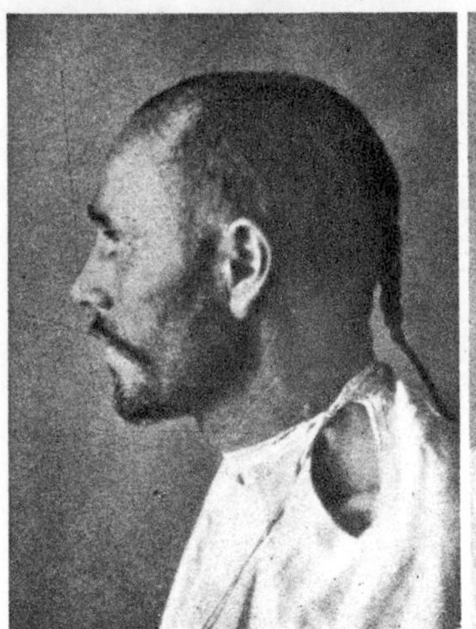

A MEDITERRANEAN FROM NORTH AFRICA. Hammu ben Haddu, from the Rif country of Morocco, seen in profile and full face. Somewhat lighter and with thinner lips but in general much the same type as the Indian native shown above or the Portuguese below. (Photograph courtesy Carleton S. Coon.)

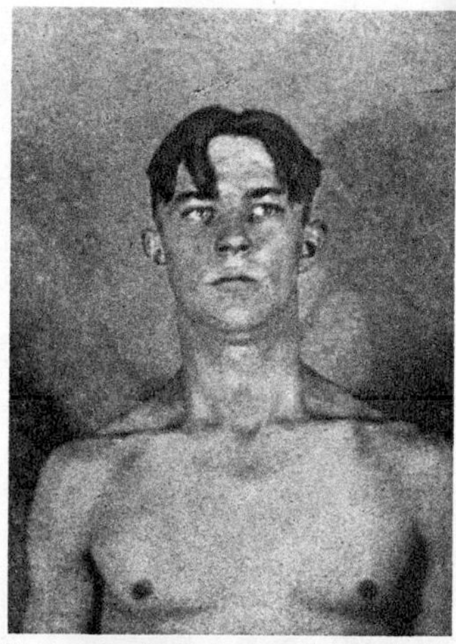

EUROPEAN LONGHEADS. *Left*, a Mediterranean from Portugal, not distant in physical type from the North African native shown above. *Right*, a Nordic, a native of Sweden, with light complexion, blue eyes, and (despite the appearance in the photograph) blond hair. (Photographs courtesy Harry L. Shapiro and American Museum of Natural History, New York.)

UPPER PALEOLITHIC SURVIVORS. It is probable that the blood of Cro-Magnon man still flows in the veins of many people in north western Europe. The Irishman from Leitrim (*left*), with rugged features, red hair, and blue eyes, shows many morphological features suggestive of Cro-Magnon ancestry. (Photograph courtesy Hooton and Du Pertius.) The Swede from Gothenburg (*right*) has the light hair and blue eyes of his Nordic neighbours but is probably in the main a broad-headed descendant of Upper Paleolithic man. (From C. S. Coon, *Races of Europe*, by special permission of the Macmillan Co., publishers.)

EUROPEAN BROADHEADS. *Left*, a typical Alpine (from Bavaria), with brown eyes and hair, nose not particularly prominent, and a stocky bodily build. *Right*, a Dinaric from Albania, with taller stature and prominent nose. (Photographs courtesy Carleton S. Coon.)

EUROPEAN BROADHEADS (*continued*). *Left*, an Armenoid from the Lake Van region of Armenia, with the very prominent nose characteristic of that type. *Right*, an east-European broad-headed type (from the Ukraine), with brown hair and blue eyes. (From C. S. Coon, *Races of Europe*, by special permission of the Macmillan Co., publishers.)

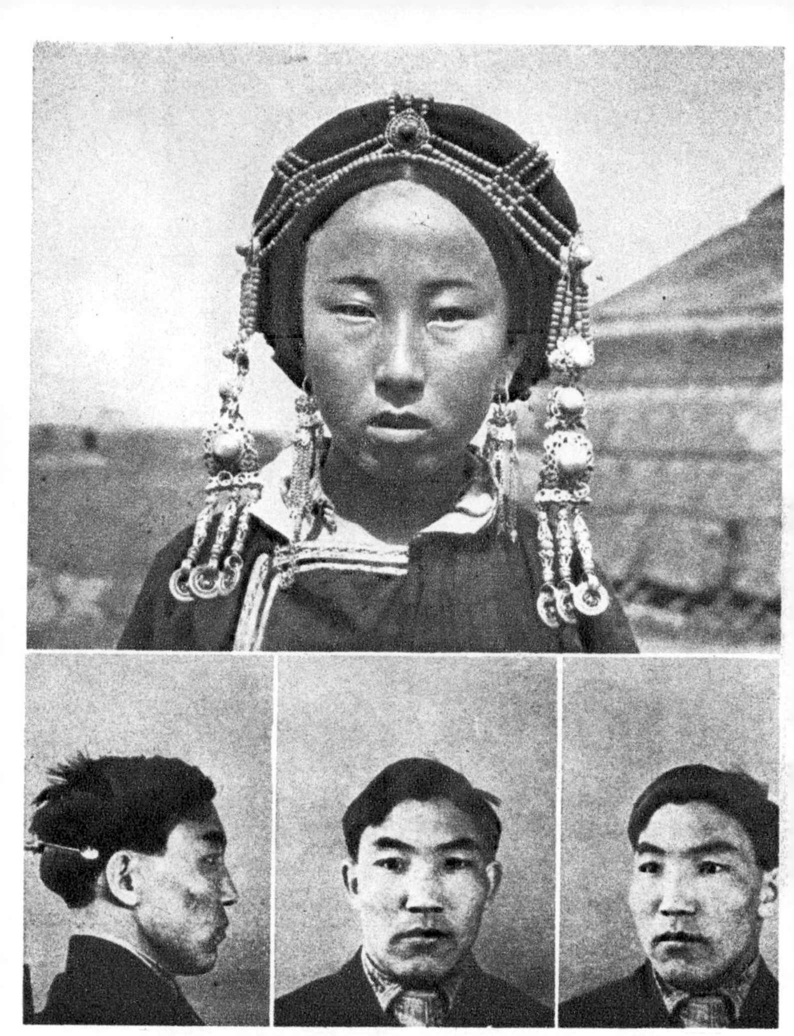

MONGOLOIDS. *Above*, a girl from Inner Mongolia. Note the typical Mongoloid eye fold. *Below*, a Chuckchi from the Kolyma district of north eastern Siberia. This race shows resemblances to certain North American Indian groups.

Above, a Malay. The Malays show only partial Mongoloid characteristics and are to some extent similar to the dark 'white' Mediterraneans. *Below*, a Visayan girl from the Philippines. The Visayans are typical Filipinos, related to the Malays and, on the other hand, showing resemblances to the Japanese, in whom a strong Malayan strain exists. (Mongolian and Visayan, courtesy American Museum of Natural History, New York; Malay and Chuckchi courtesy Peabody Museum, Harvard University.)

AMERICAN MONGOLOIDS. *Left*, Black Heart, a Blackfoot Indian. *Top, right*, a group of Ona Indians from Tierra del Fuego, at the southernmost extremity of South America. This is a tribe in a low stage of culture and now nearly extinct. These men are characterized by unusual height. A windbreak of hides was a usual shelter. They were expert archers; their main food supply was the guanaco (a wild relative of the llama). *Right*, a Mamayauk Eskimo girl from Langton Bay (on the Arctic Ocean east of the Mackenzie River). (Photographs courtesy American Museum of Natural History, New York.)

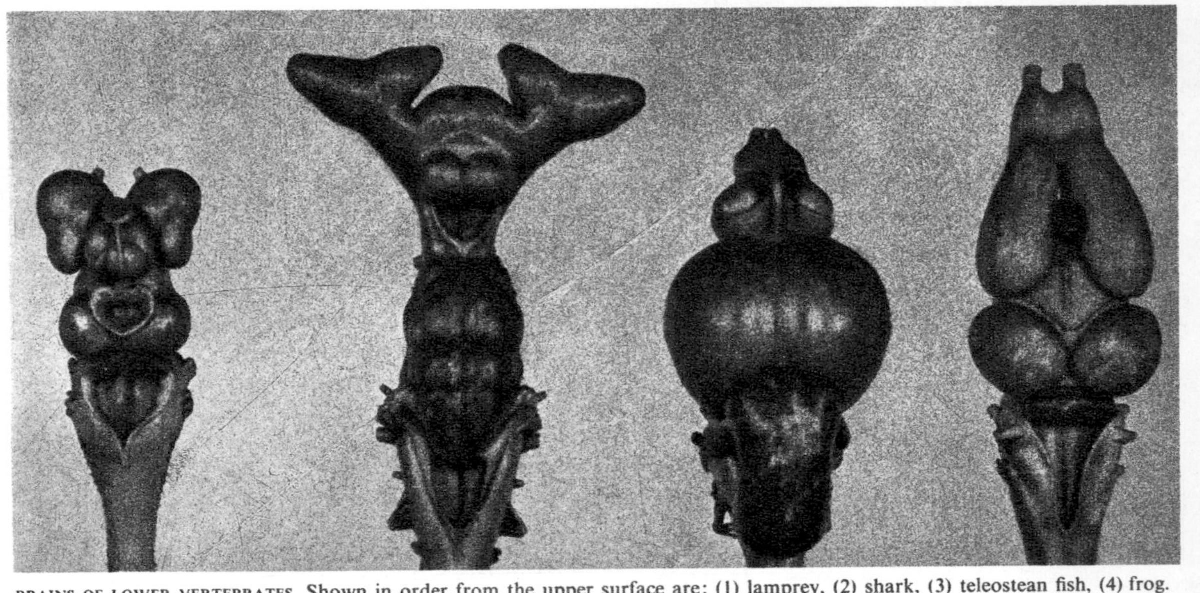

BRAINS OF LOWER VERTEBRATES. Shown in order from the upper surface are: (1) lamprey, (2) shark, (3) teleostean fish, (4) frog. The medulla oblongata, at the bottom, and connecting with the spinal cord, is similar in all forms. The cerebellum, here darkly coloured, is very large in teleost and shark, very small in the frog. The paired optic lobes, in which visual sensations are received in lower vertebrates, are enormous in the teleost, moderate in the frog, small in the others. At the front of each brain are olfactory lobes and cerebral hemispheres, here devoted mainly to smell. These structures are well developed in all except the teleost. The mammal brain differs from lower types mainly in the enormous development of the hemispheres. (Photograph courtesy American Museum of Natural History, New York.)

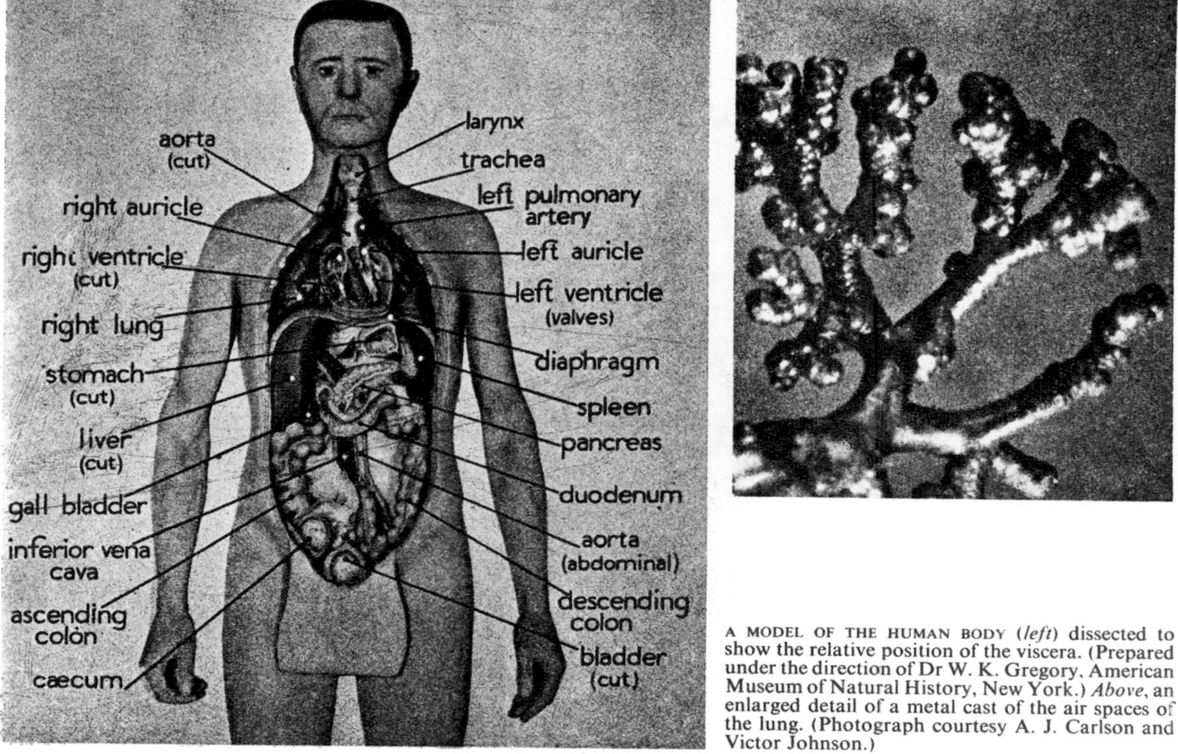

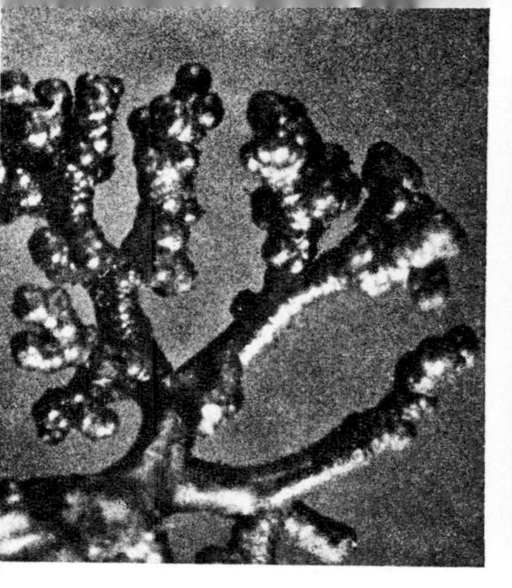

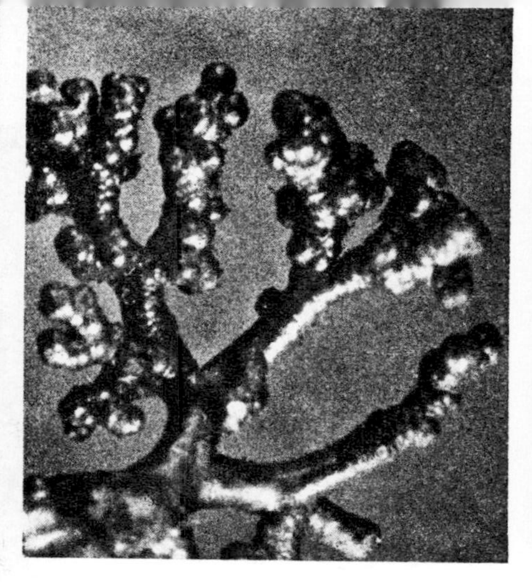

A MODEL OF THE HUMAN BODY (*left*) dissected to show the relative position of the viscera. (Prepared under the direction of Dr W. K. Gregory, American Museum of Natural History, New York.) *Above*, an enlarged detail of a metal cast of the air spaces of the lung. (Photograph courtesy A. J. Carlson and Victor Johnson.)

MAMMAL TISSUES, seen in highly magnified sections. *Below top*, a portion of the ovary of a mammal. The circular structure of varied sizes are eggs, contained in follicles bordered by large masses of small cells. These cells produce important hormones. The ovary pictured, that of a cat, shows an unusual condition in that some of the follicles contain two eggs. *Below, bottom*, part of a mammalian testis. A number of sperm-forming tubules are cut in cross-section and are seen as circular structures. The cells closest to the cavity in the centre of each tubule are maturing sperm.

Right, top, a smear of human blood. Most of the cells are red blood corpuscles; there are, however, present several white blood cells, with darkly staining nuclei.

Right, centre, a section through the lining of the stomach. At the surface are crypts in which a mucous material is secreted; below are slender tubular glands, the cells of which produce pepsin and hydrochloric acid. At the bottom of the section is part of the muscle lining of the stomach.

Right, below, a section through the skin of the palm. The upper portion of the section is through the epidermis, or 'outer skin', with a lightly stained cornified part and a deeper, dark-stained portion. Below this is the dermis, a leathery mass of connective tissue. Finger-like papillae containing sensory structures and capillaries project into the epidermis. The light ovals at the bottom are fat accumulations. (Photographs copyright General Biological Supply House, Chicago.)

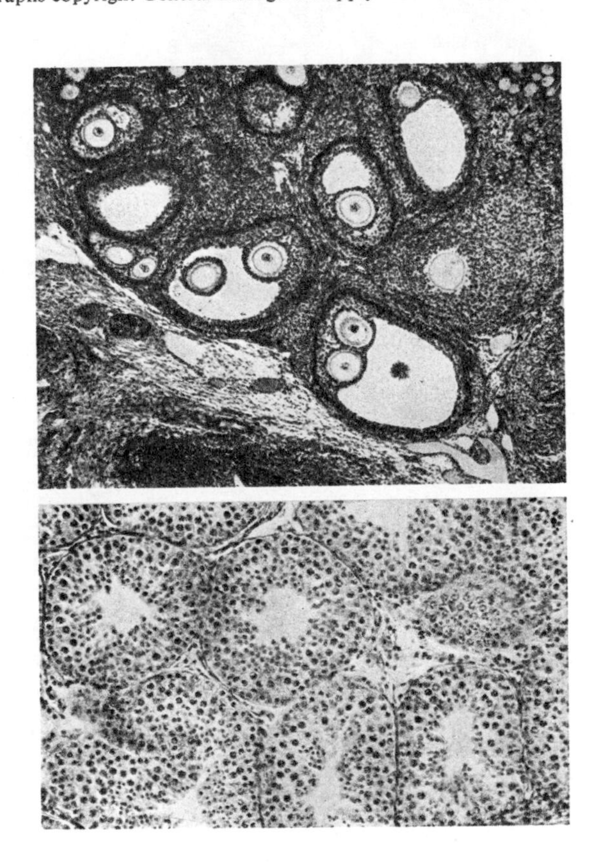

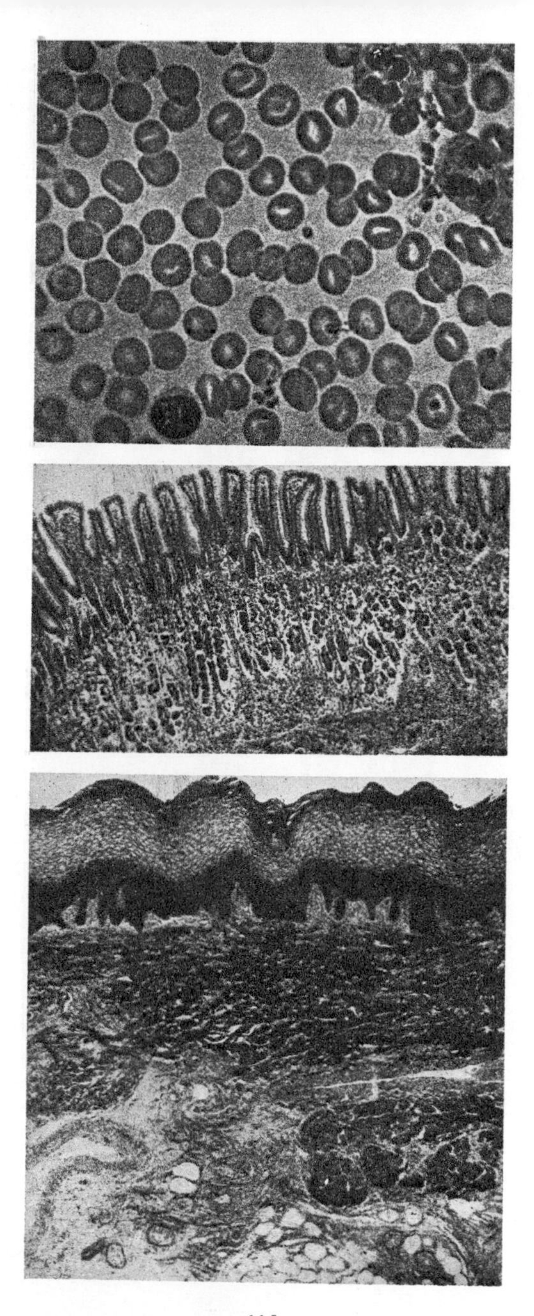

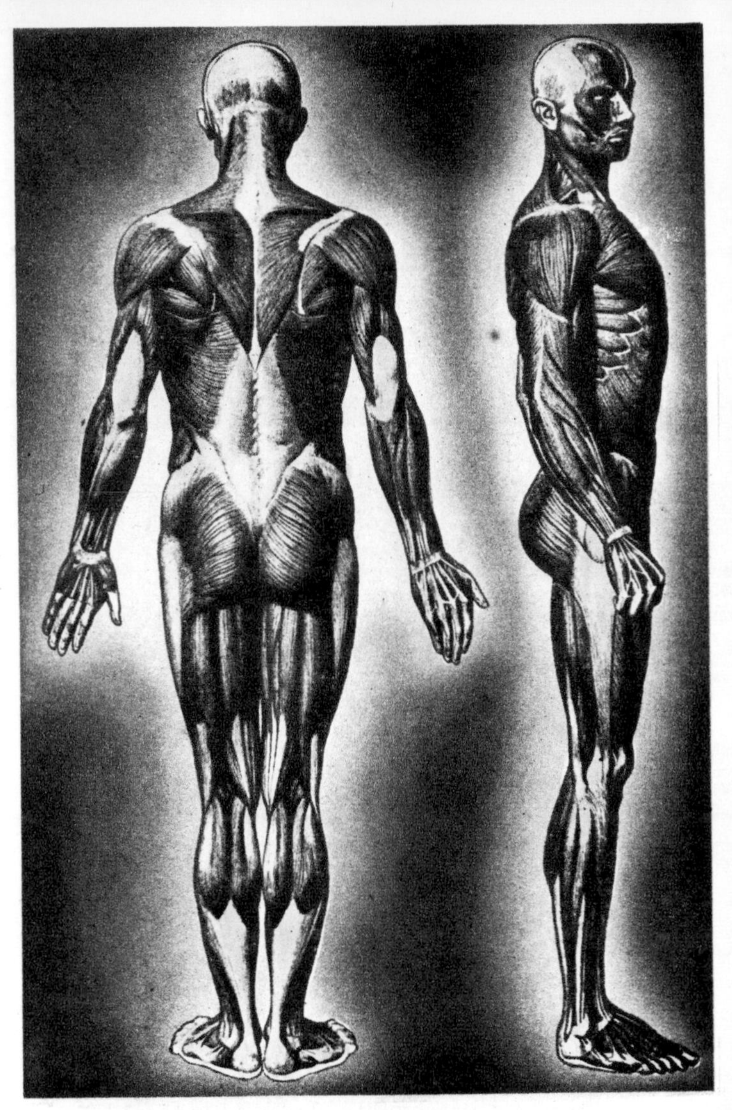

MUSCULATURE OF THE HUMAN BODY viewed from the rear and side. In fishes almost all the musculature pertains to the trunk. In man and other mammals trunk musculature is much reduced in amount. In the rear view of the musculature almost no axial muscles are visible. In side view, however, there can be seen some of the abdominal musculature and several muscle slips attached to the ribs. Apart from muscles connecting limb girdles with the trunk, the muscles of each limb include two main sets, one extending to the elbow or knee, and a second set below these joints. (After Tandler, *Lehrbuch der systematischen Anatomie*.)

STRIATED MUSCLE FIBRES, seen at a magnification of about 575 times natural size. Parts of two fibres are shown; the dark spots are nuclei, a number included in each fibre. (Photograph copyright General Biological Supply House, Chicago.)

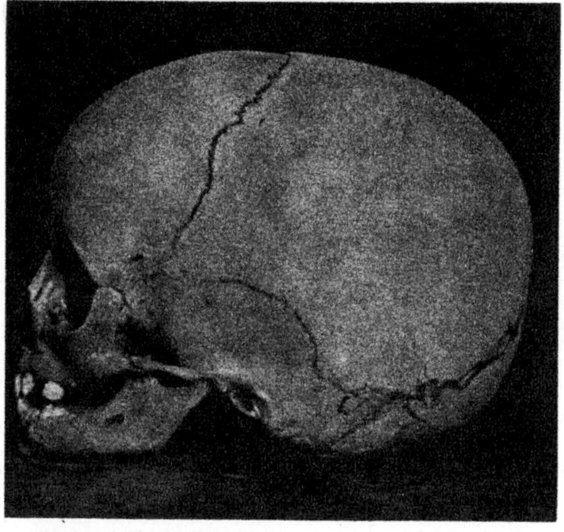

A BABY'S SKULL. In the unborn young the brain grows with great rapidity, so that at birth the braincase is relatively enormous. In later life the open sutures seen here between the bones close, and growth of the braincase ceases; on the other hand, the bones of the face and jaws continue to grow, accommodating the developing tooth row. (Photograph courtesy American Museum of Natural History, New York.)

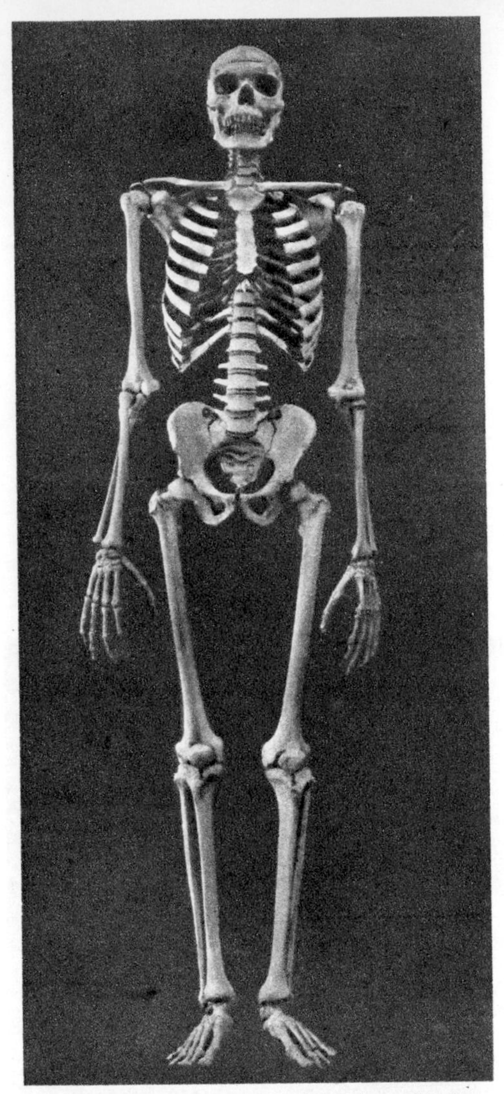

THE HUMAN SKELETON, seen in front view. This figure is unlabelled; if compared with the labelled gorilla skeleton in the sub-section on 'Limbs' in Chapter 19, it will be seen that all elements are readily comparable. (Photograph courtesy American Museum of Natural History, New York.)

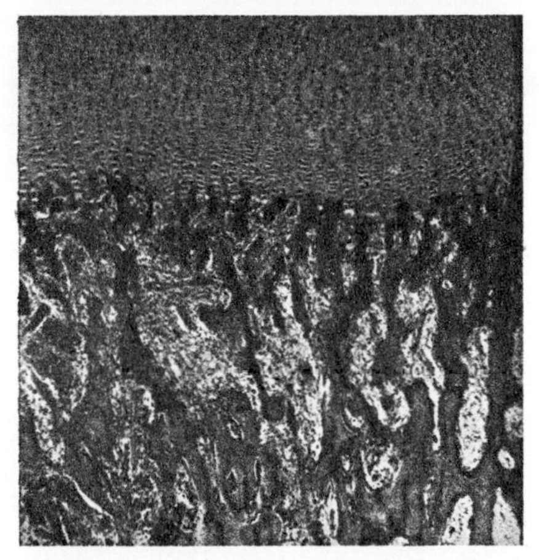

DEVELOPING BONE. A highly magnified section of one of the long bones of a developing skeleton. In the upper part of the figure is cartilege, of which such a bone is completely formed in the early embryo. In the centre, the cartilege is seen breaking down and in the lower part of the section is replaced by darkly stained bone, with spaces occupied by blood vessels between the strands of bone tissue.

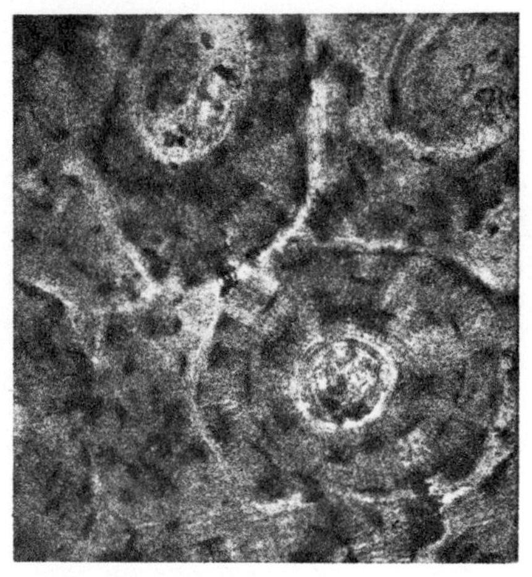

ADULT BONE. A section of a bone magnified to about 180 times natural size. The dark spaces are the areas occupied by irregularly branching bone cells. The bone is arranged in concentric rings around blood vessels (lightly stained). (Photographs copyright General Biological Supply House, Chicago.)

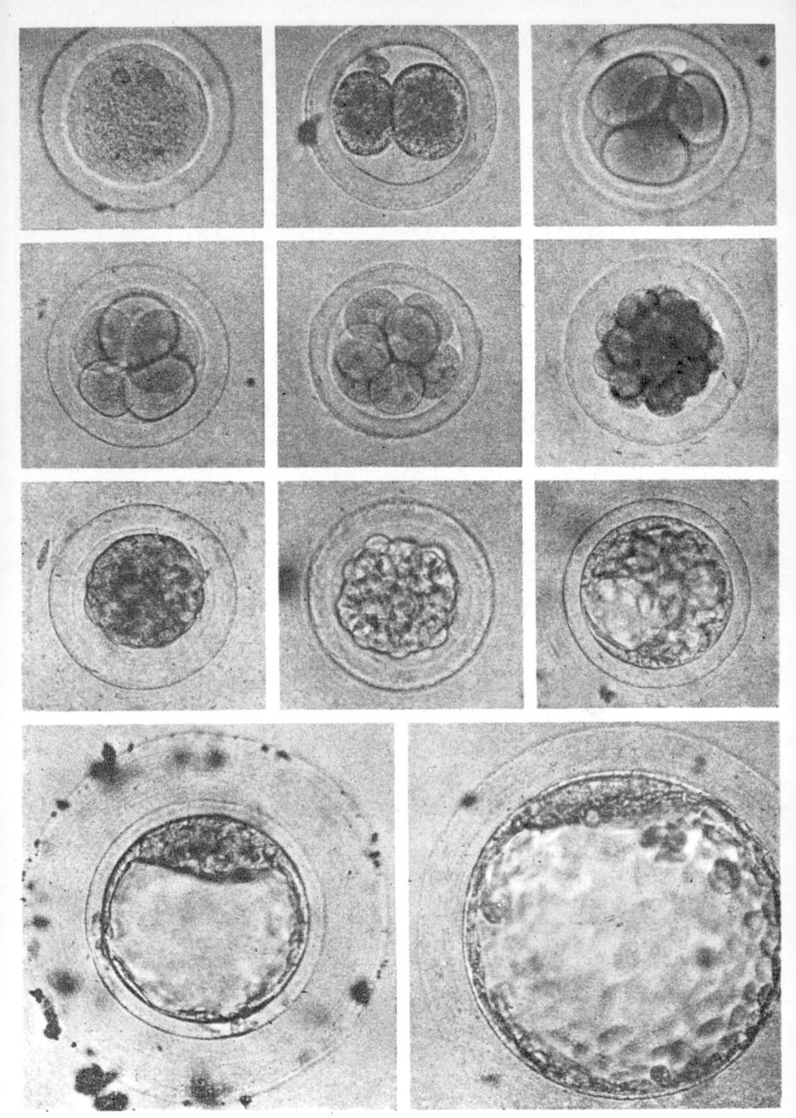

DEVELOPMENT OF THE MAMMAL EGG. A series of photographs (enlarged about 150 times) showing the early development of the rabbit egg; the early stages in man are poorly known but appear to be similar in nature. Cleavage eventually results in the development of (1) an outer sphere of cells (trophoblast) which come into contact with the uterine walls as the primary portion of the chorion, and (2) an inner cell mass from which the embryo develops. (From G. L. Streeter, Carnegie Institution of Washington, Department of Embryology.)

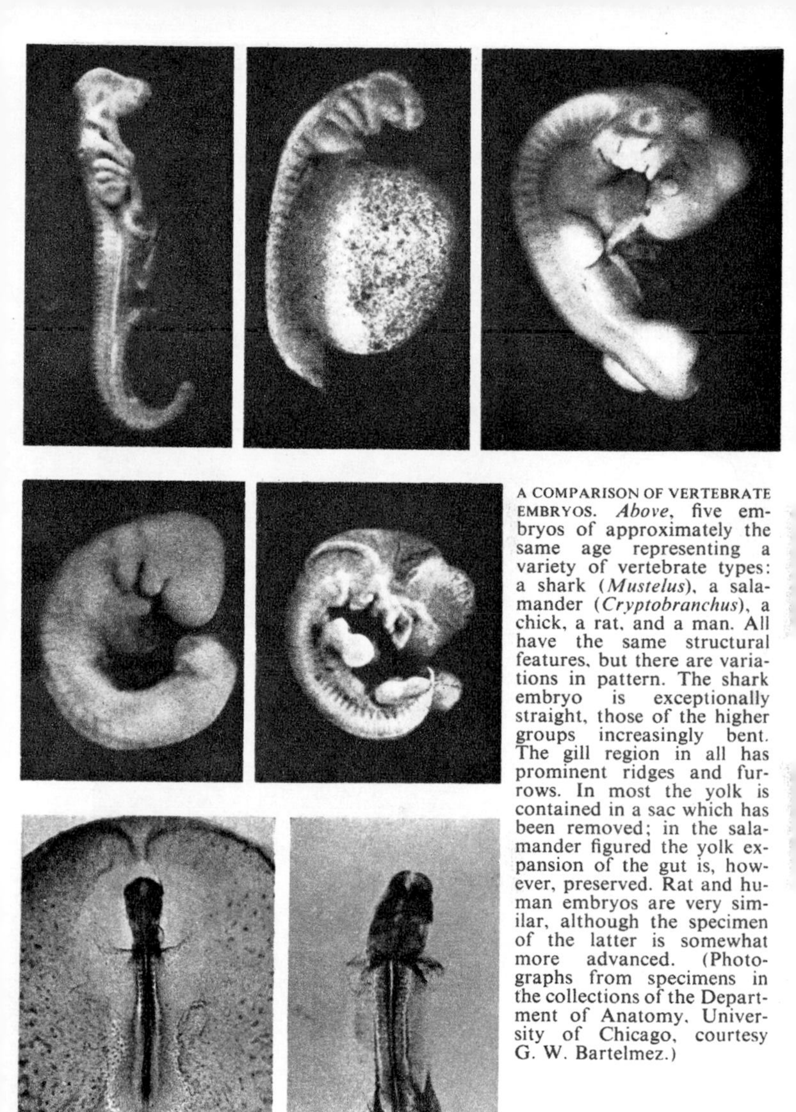

A COMPARISON OF VERTEBRATE EMBRYOS. *Above*, five embryos of approximately the same age representing a variety of vertebrate types: a shark (*Mustelus*), a salamander (*Cryptobranchus*), a chick, a rat, and a man. All have the same structural features, but there are variations in pattern. The shark embryo is exceptionally straight, those of the higher groups increasingly bent. The gill region in all has prominent ridges and furrows. In most the yolk is contained in a sac which has been removed; in the salamander figured the yolk expansion of the gut is, however, preserved. Rat and human embryos are very similar, although the specimen of the latter is somewhat more advanced. (Photographs from specimens in the collections of the Department of Anatomy, University of Chicago, courtesy G. W. Bartelmez.)

Lower left, dorsal views of early embryos of chick and rabbit. The main structural features, spinal cord, brain, and mesodermal somites are similar in the two cases and also similar to the human embryos seen from this view in a text figure. (Photographs copyright General Biological Supply House, Chicago.)

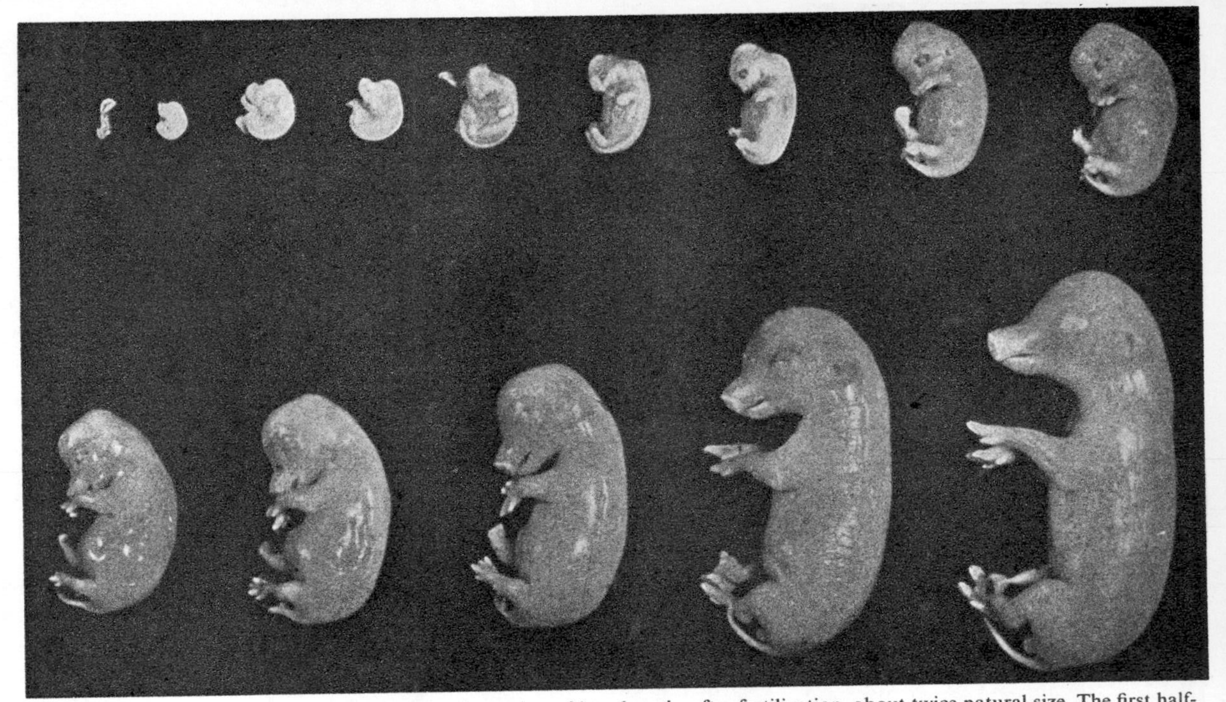

PIG EMBRYOS. A series of 14 specimens ranging from about $2\frac{3}{4}$ to 6 weeks after fertilization, about twice natural size. The first half-dozen little specimens are closely comparable to the earlier members of the human series shown on the pages following (much more enlarged); in the larger specimens, however, pig rather than human features gradually emerge. (Photographs copyright General Biological Supply House, Chicago.)

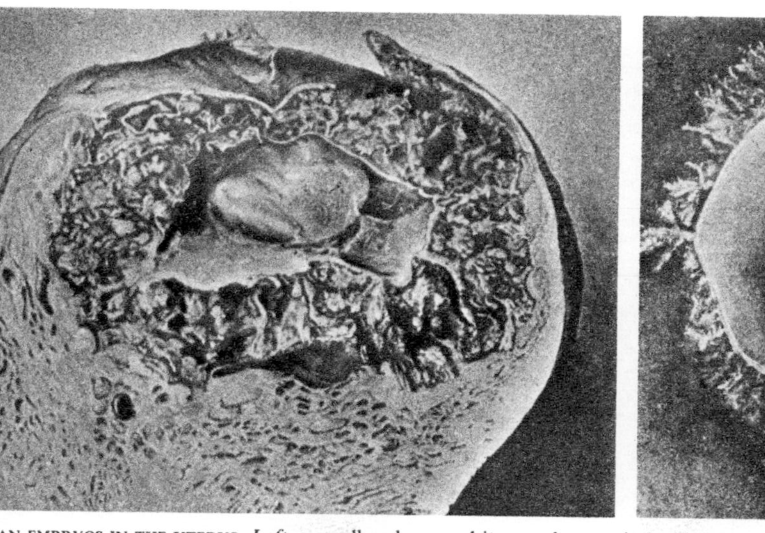

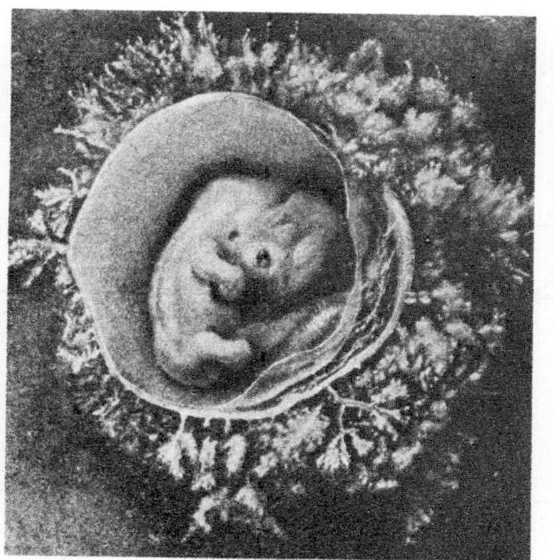

HUMAN EMBRYOS IN THE UTERUS. *Left*, a small embryo and its membranes, imbedded in one wall of the uterus. The spongy tissues at the bottom are maternal tissues of the uterine wall; these extend upward to enclose the embryonic tissues. In the centre is the embryo, enclosed, and nearly concealed in the amnion. More superficially, the rather loose tissues are those of the chorion, coming into contact with those of the uterine wall to form the placenta. *Right*, a later embryo, of about seven weeks. This has been removed from the uterus, so that all the tissues seen are those of the embryo. The greatly expanded amniotic cavity has been cut open to expose the embryo. Extending out from the embryo is the body stalk (in process of relative reduction to an umbilical cord), which connects the embryo and its membranes. At the surface is the tufted chorion. (From *Carnegie Institution Publications in Embryology*.)

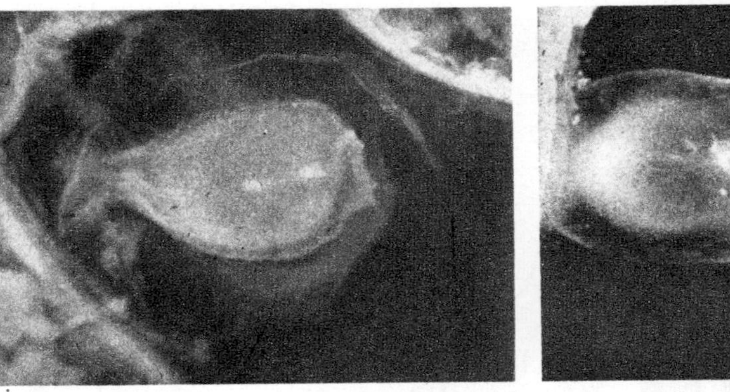

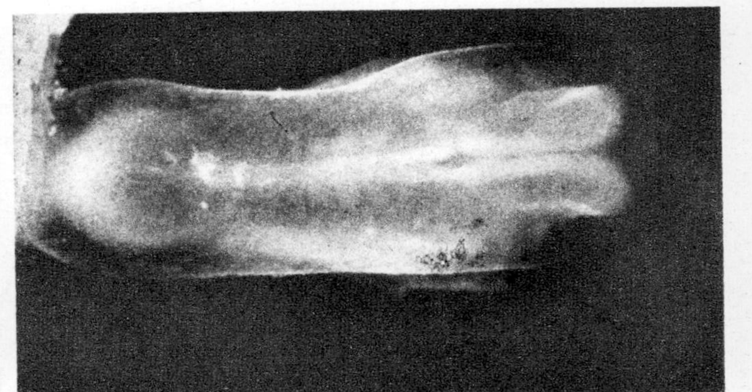

HUMAN EMBRYOS IN THEIR MEMBRANES. *Above*, two early embryos seen from the upper surface; these are comparable with those in an accompanying text figure. *Left*, an embryo of about three weeks, still in a 'pancake'-like stage, with little apparent differentiation of structure. The embryonic disk is seen through the translucent amnion. At the back end (*left*) is the body stalk through which the embryo is attached to the surrounding chorion. *Above, right*, a similar view of a four-weeks embryo. The body has grown out greatly anteriorly, i.e., to the right, where folds of nervous tissue are forming the brain; back of this is already much of the spinal cord, while on either side are a number of somites of mesoderm.

Below, side views of two early embryos. *Left*, an embryo of three and one-half weeks; *right*, the same embryo of four weeks shown above. At the left in both cases is the body stalk. The embryos are surrounded above and at the sides by the amnion. Beneath is the large (but nearly empty) yolk sac. (Embryos from the collections of the Department of Anatomy, University of Chicago; photographs courtesy Dr G. W. Bartelmez.)

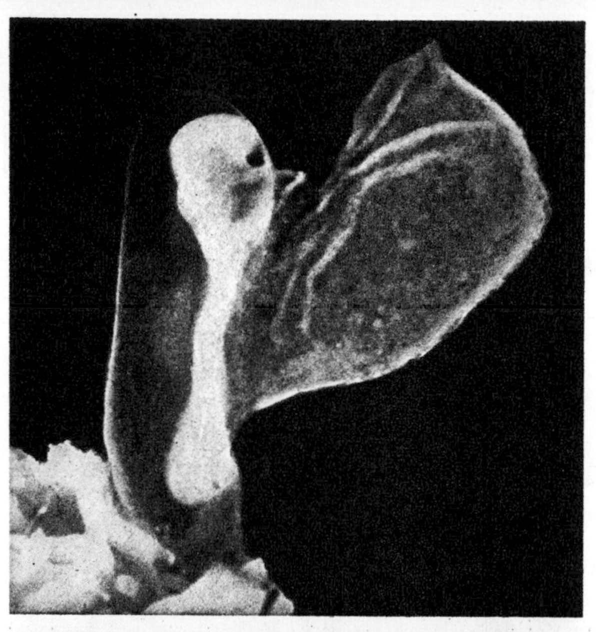

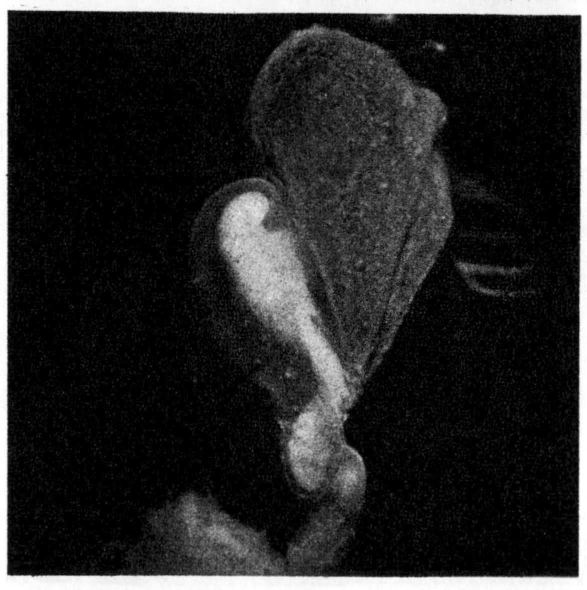

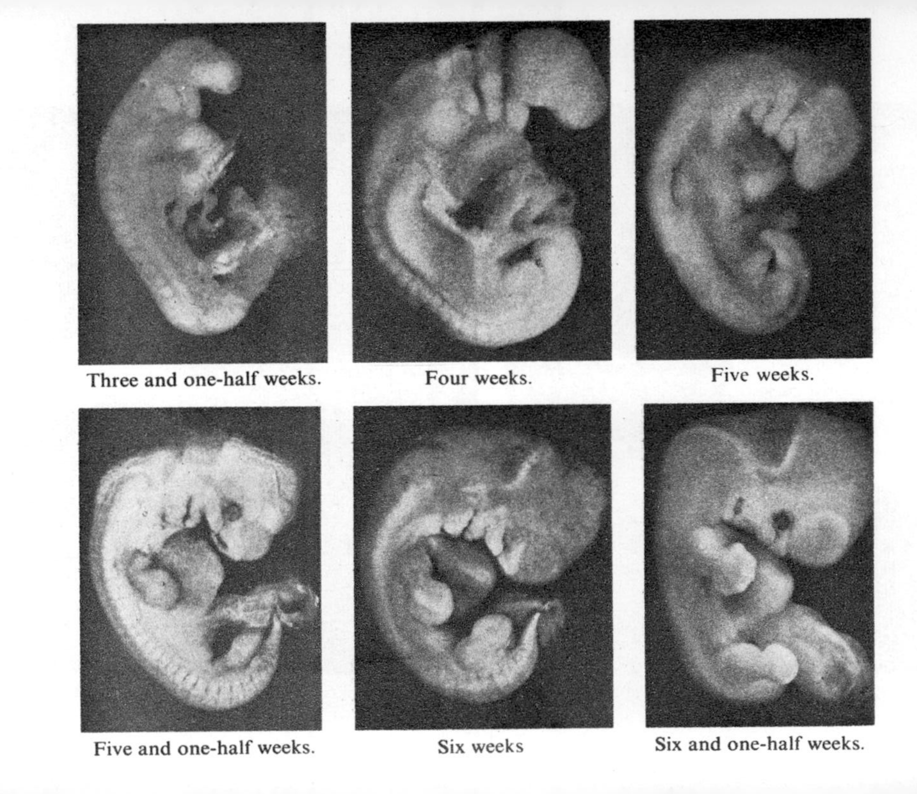

Three and one-half weeks.

Four weeks.

Five weeks.

Five and one-half weeks.

Six weeks

Six and one-half weeks.

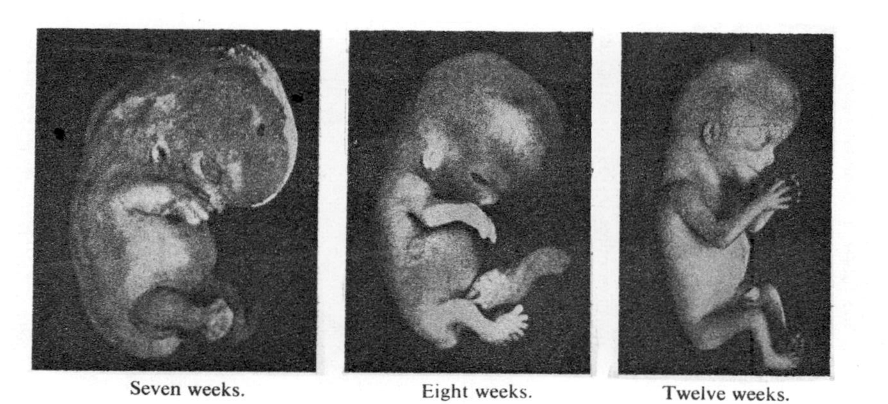

Seven weeks. Eight weeks. Twelve weeks.

AN ALBUM OF HUMAN EMBRYOS. A series from the age of about three and one-half weeks after fertilization of the egg to about three months, to show the development of bodily form. The youngest stages are very similar to those of other mammals; only gradually do distinctive human features appear. Noticeable during the second month is the relatively enormous growth of the brain. The limbs appear relatively late. The earliest stages show a distinct tail. At first the active heart projects prominently from the chest. In all stages may be seen a body stalk at the right connecting with the surrounding membranes and placenta; this gradually narrows to form the umbilical cord. The embryos are shown of the same absolute size to facilitate comparison; there is, however, great growth during this period. The smallest shown is about $\frac{1}{4}$ of an inch in length, the last about $2\frac{1}{4}$ inches long and hence close to the size shown. (Embryos in the collections of the Department of Anatomy, University of Chicago; photographs courtesy Dr G. W. Bartelmez.)

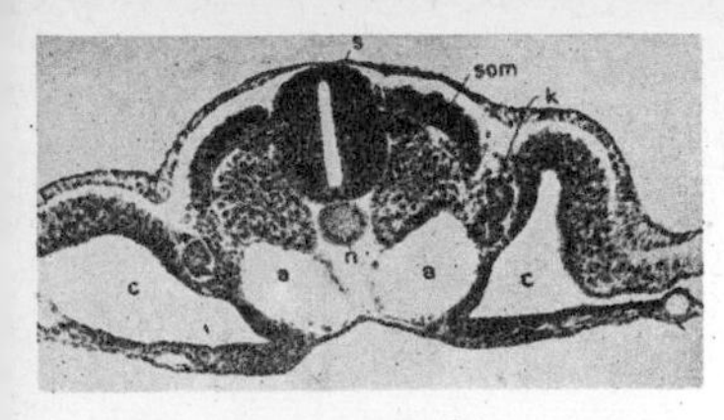

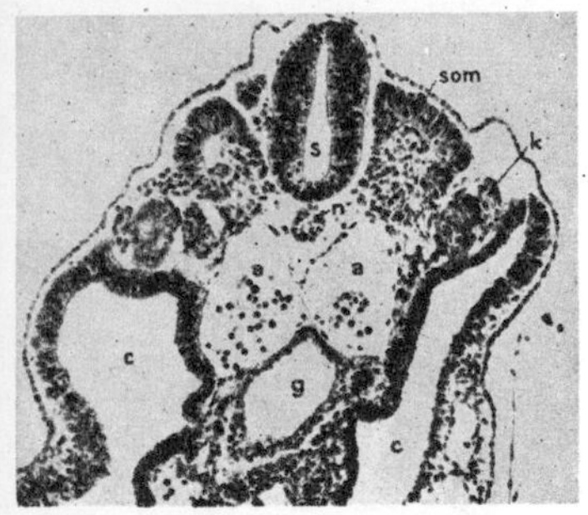

CROSS-SECTIONS THROUGH CHICK AND HUMAN EMBRYOS. *Left, above*, a thin section, highly magnified (about 55 times natural size), through the body of a chick embryo after two days' development, to show the early ground plan of the body. At this stage the embryo is spread out over the top of the egg yolk; the under edge of the specimen is the upper side of the lining of the digestive tract. The cavity at either side (*c*) is the future abdominal cavity. The large circular cavities (*a*) are cross-sections of the dorsal aorta – here a paired structure. Above it is a cross-section of the notochord (*n*); the vertebrae have not yet begun to form. The large oval at the top is a section through the spinal cord (*s*). The large masses of tissue at either side of the nerve cord are the somites (*som*) of the mesoderm (which show prominently as blocks of tissue in surface view). From these arise much of the muscles, connective tissues, and skeleton. Small lumps of tissue lateral to and below the somites are the primitive kidneys (*k*).

Below the chick is seen a comparable section through a human embryo at the age of about four weeks. Here the bottom of the animal has been, so to speak, 'buttoned up' so that the gut (*g*) is closed below and appears as a round opening. Except for this, every human structure is closely comparable to that seen in the chick embryo. (Photographs courtesy G. W. Bartelmez, from embryos in the University of Chicago collections.)

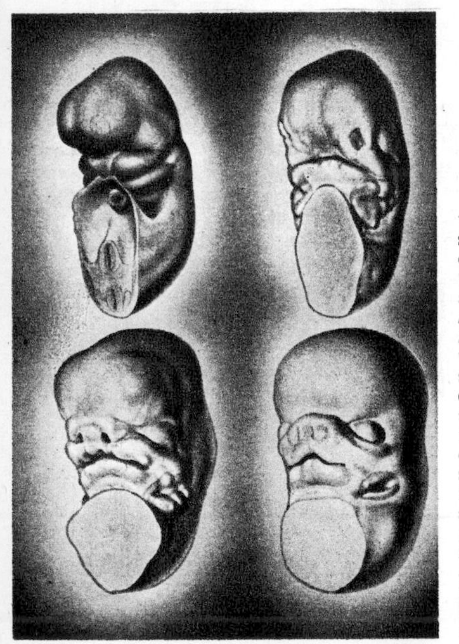

THE DEVELOPMENT OF THE FACE. A series of views of human embryos, in each of which the body is cut off through the chest region. *Upper left*, about five weeks old (× 15); *upper right*, about six weeks old (× 12); *lower left*, about six and one-half weeks old (× 10); *lower right*, about seven weeks old (× 8). The future ear region is rather more deeply shaded. In the first figure the future mouth is merely a pocket beneath the expanded brain; in the neck are several swellings between the gill furrows. In succeeding figures are seen the gradual development of jaw processes, the development of the nostrils, the appearance of the eye, and the reduction of the gill region to the ear pit alone. (From G. L. Streeter, *Carnegie Institution Contributions to Embryology*.)

begin when we reach the cavity of the abdomen and encounter a chain of three great organs which fill a major part of that cavity – stomach, small intestine, large intestine.

The upper part of the digestive tube, where rough material is present, is lined with a thick skinlike coating; the lower parts

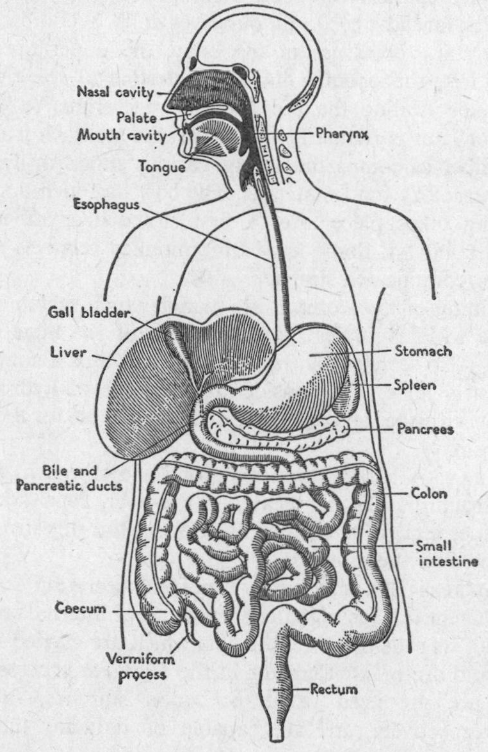

The digestive organs of man. (Redrawn after Morris, *Human Anatomy*)

of the system are lined with a very thin and delicate layer of cells which manufacture digestive fluids or absorb the liquid food-products into the body's circulation. This membrane is exceedingly thin but it heavily reinforced by outer layers. The outer coats are in great measure made up of bands of smooth muscles, by the wavelike movement of which the food materials are carried along through the various parts of the digestive tract. Between the successive organs are valves – circular bands of muscle which can be constricted and thus regulate the flow of material from one region to the next.

The stomach is an ancient piece of digestive apparatus where the physical preparation of food is completed, and its chemical treatment is far advanced. In ourselves it is a comparatively simple sac slung crosswise of the body, the upper opening a bit to the left, the opening into the intestine at the right. In some animals leading the life of pure vegetarians (a life for which we are not particularly well fitted) the stomach is divided into a number of compartments for various stages in the treatment of refractory food materials. The cow has such a system: cud-chewing takes place after a first stomach treatment and before a second try. Some leaf-eating monkey relatives of ours also have a complicated stomach.

In the lining of the stomach are glands which secrete pepsin, an enzyme which initiates the splitting-up of the huge protein molecules. Also secreted by these glands, and thus a component of the gastric juice, is a considerable amount of hydrochloric acid, which furnishes an acid medium indispensable for the action of the pepsin.

PANCREAS. A short distance beyond the stomach two important structures, the pancreas and the liver, send ducts into the intestine, and we shall turn aside from the digestive 'main line' to consider these organs.

The pancreas is a small but important secreting structure. To some extent it is (as noted later) a gland of internal secretion, but most of its cells produce ferments which are carried into the intestine and are major elements in the digestive process. Three ferments are produced which act upon starches, fats, and proteins respectively, and are capable of reducing these substances to a point where they can be absorbed.

LIVER. The liver is an enormous but rather flabby and formless structure which occupies much of the upper part of the abdominal cavity. Originally it may have been merely a gland secreting materials into the intestine. It still preserves this function, for little ducts drain from it into the gall bladder, whence its products, as the dark-coloured bile, pass into the intestine. The bile, however, consists mainly of waste products formed in the liver; its only usefulness appears to be that it contains certain salts which aid the digestion of fats by breaking up fatty materials into tiny droplets of a size which the appropriate enzymes from the pancreas can act on more readily.

The major function of the liver appears after the food has been absorbed into the body. As will be seen, all the blood from the intestine, rich in food, drains through the liver before reaching other parts of the body. In this organ occur many important processes associated with food utilization. Most notable is the fact that large quantities of carbohydrates are stored in the liver in the form of glycogen, or 'animal starch', until this is needed for fuel by the muscles and other body organs.

INTESTINES. Beyond the stomach lies the small intestine, sinuously coiled about in the abdominal cavity and continuing the digestive tube for somewhat over twenty feet of the total distance. Into the small intestine are poured, near its upper end, the secretions of the pancreas and liver, and further enzymes are formed by glands in its walls. Much digestion, therefore, takes place here. And it is here, and here alone, that there takes place the final act in this process – the absorption of the simplified food materials into the walls and their passage into the blood and lymphatic vessels which carry them on into the body.

In many small animals the small intestine is comparatively short and little coiled; in a cow it is about one hundred feet in length. These differences are partly related to the varying types of food and the comparative difficulties in their digestion. But there also comes into the matter our old problem of trying to keep up surfaces, which only square with growth, to the pace of bulk, which increases by cubes. An animal twice the size of another has eight times the bulk, needs nearly eight times the food. But the absorption of food depends on the area of the intestinal lining, which has increased only four times. Putting more length into the tube helps solve the problem. An additional way of increasing surface is by folding the inside of the tube; and the inside of the human small intestine has an extremely wrinkled and folded surface.

The large intestine is a final major section of the digestive tract, lying folded along three sides of the abdominal cavity and leading finally to the rectum and the anus. It functions not only as a place for storage of waste awaiting disposal but also as a place where food is obtained from material which higher parts of the system have failed to treat; bacterial action plays a large part in this. Here, too, large quantities of water are absorbed and, on the other hand, there is a considerable amount of excretion.

The small intestine does not open into the end of the large intestine but a bit to one side; below the opening there is a blind sac, the caecum. In some herbivorous animals the caecum is very long; in carnivores with simpler digestive problems it may be absent altogether. Here, as usual, man occupies a middle ground. At the end of the caecum is the small wormlike vestigial appendix, which is a fashionable seat of disease.

RESPIRATORY SYSTEM

Breathing – the intake of oxygen and the giving-off of carbon dioxide – has been a function closely associated with the digestive tract throughout vertebrate history. In his breathing system, however, man differs radically from his early vertebrate ancestors. Lungs and accessory structures are absolutely undeveloped in the lowest of vertebrates; on the other hand, the elements of the primitive gill apparatus for water-breathing have disappeared or been transformed for other uses long before reaching the human stage of development.

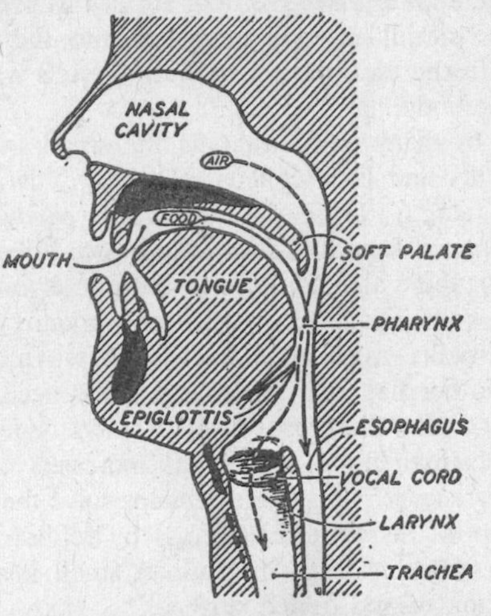

A diagrammatic section through the human head to show the relationships of the passageways for food and air. The two channels cross in the pharynx, or throat region. (From Carlson and Johnson, *The Machinery of the Body*)

THE LARYNX. It is one of the minor defects in our bodily construction that food destined for the stomach and air bound for the lungs must both pass through the cavity of the throat – the pharynx. The entrance to the windpipe leads off this channel at the back of the tongue. Normally open, it may be closed momentarily by a flap at the top for the cross-passage of food supplies; even so, something may start to 'go down the wrong way', with explosive results. The initial part of the air passage is the larynx, familiar to us as the 'Adam's apple'. This box has a skeleton of cartilage (the only part of the old gill-bar system which still retains a function related to breathing). Within are an air chamber and a second protective valve device; as its most interesting contents, the larynx houses the vocal cords, which can be opened and closed, tightened and loosened. Vibrating when air is forced between them, these cords form our own personal musical instrument, the tones of which are modified by movements of our throat and mouth. Vocal expression is almost entirely a possession of the higher vertebrates – the birds and mammals; except for the frogs, reptiles and lower types are almost incapable of vocal sounds, although a violent escape of air may result in a hiss or a grunting sound. The song of birds is produced not by the larynx but by a different type of structure located farther down the windpipe.

LUNGS. Below the larynx is the trachea, or windpipe, stiffened by incomplete hoops of cartilage to prevent collapse when the air is expelled. This divides into two tubes (bronchi) leading to the lungs; within the lung there are finer and finer ramifications of these tubes until the final tiny air sacs are reached. These, arranged along the air tubes like grapes in clusters, are small but very numerous (several hundred million). Each sac has a moist membrane beneath which are numerous tiny blood vessels; here the exchange of oxygen for waste carbon dioxide takes place.

We speak of 'expanding our lungs', but the lungs are not muscular and can do no work themselves. They are, however, highly elastic and can expand or contract to almost any required degree. In primitive animals with lungs the air is actually swallowed by movements of the throat muscles; but in ourselves the trick is accomplished by a vacuum pump. The lungs lie freely within the walls of the chest cavity. Outside this closed space are the ribs; below it a muscular partition, the diaphragm, separates chest and abdomen. By raising the ribs and by lowering the domelike diaphragm, we can increase the size of the lung cavity by a maximum, in deep breathing, of about two hundred cubic inches. The lungs, in 'avoiding a vacuum', expand to fill this space and, in their expansion, may pull into their cavities as much as three quarts of air, at an outside figure.

ORIGIN OF LUNGS. We have noted earlier that such structures as lungs did not exist at all in the more primitive vertebrates; lung development seems to have been at first only a 'happy accident' in the adaptation of some fishes to life in inland regions subject to drought. Any moist, thin area of skin or skinlike material is capable of absorbing oxygen (some small land-dwelling salamanders are quite lungless and breathe through their skin, but this is an exceptional development). Very probably air-breathing started in the moist lining of the floor of the fish's throat; it is from this region that the lungs develop. The lungs are rather simple sacs in such fishes as have them and in amphibians and many reptiles; the amount of actual 'breathing surface' in them is not large. But in mammals, and particularly big mammals, the structure of the lungs is exceedingly complex; the area of the lung surface in man is about seven hundred square feet. We meet here, again, the old problem of necessarily increasing surfaces in big animals; but equally important is the fact that in mammals, in the maintenance of high temperature in the body, fuel consumption is enormous, and oxygen intake to feed the fires must be correspondingly great.

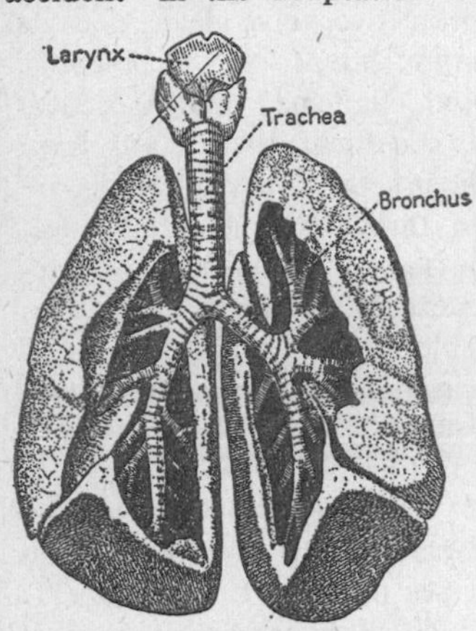

The breathing apparatus of man, seen from the front. Above, the larynx with its surrounding cartilages – the 'Adam's apple' – and below it the trachea, or windpipe, surrounded by hoops of cartilage. The lungs have been partially dissected to show the bronchi – subdivisions of the windpipe – and their branches. (Redrawn from Toldt)

NASAL STRUCTURES – THE PALATE. The nose is (or should be) an important accessory breathing organ. We have previously pointed out that its primitive function was only that of a smelling organ in lungless early fishes. This organ lay on the underside of the head in many fish and had sometimes a double opening. In some such forms the lower jaw seems to have grown forward so far that the back opening of the nose came to lie inside the mouth cavity and the pocket became a tube, a useful means of getting air into the mouth and thence to the lungs without shipping water. In amphibians and many reptiles this

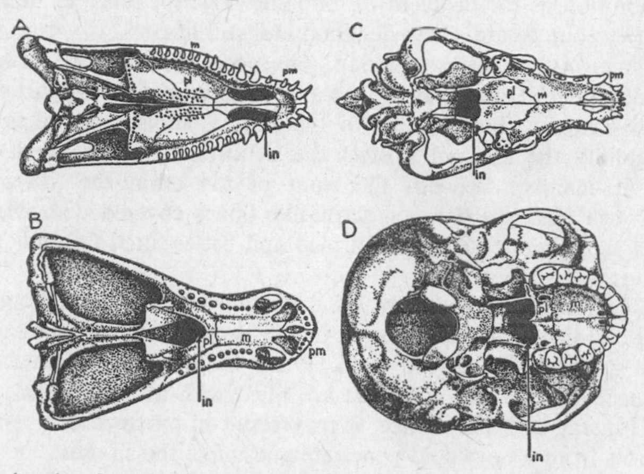

A series of skulls viewed from the underside to show the development of the secondary palate. *A*, *Dimetrodon*, a primitive mammal-like reptile showing primitive conditions, the nostrils opening at the front of the roof of the mouth; *B*, *Cynognathus*, an advanced mammal-like form; *C*, dog, showing a generalized mammalian condition; *D*, man. *in*, internal opening of the nostrils. The secondary palate is formed by an overgrowth of the premaxillae (*pm*), maxillae (*m*), and palatines (*pl*).

primitive condition still holds; the inner opening of the nostrils lies just behind the front teeth in the roof of the mouth.

But in mammal-like reptiles there developed a new structure – a hard bony palate bridging the roof of the mouth below the nostrils and separating the food and air passages for a distance. In mammals this partition has been extended backward by a continuation of this structure, the soft palate, so that the air and food passages meet only at their crossing-place in the cavity of the throat.

The utility of this arrangement is obvious as a further aid to breathing. In a reptile continuous breathing is not necessary.

If the mouth is filled with food, the passage of air may be interrupted for some time without serious harm being done; a rattlesnake may spend hours swallowing a rabbit, and during that time very little air, if any, can reach its lungs.

But in mammals the situation is different. We must breathe continuously; a stoppage of the breath for only a short time means death. This separation of nose and mouth passages offers a solution to the problem of food-chewing; we can, but thanks only to our palate, chew our food and still live.

THE CAVITY OF THE NOSE. The nose, too, acts as an 'air conditioner'. Hairs near the entrance remove many dust particles and bacteria. The interior of the nose is moist and helps to humidify the air and protect the delicate lungs. In the large nasal chamber beneath the front of the brain the air goes through passages between scroll-like bones covered with warm wet skin; here cold air is warmed and better fitted to enter the lungs.

The bones of the front of the skull and cheeks are stout structures which are hollowed out, with the result of lightening the dead weight of the head. These hollows, or sinuses, are connected with the nose and are filled with air. While this is, in general, a useful device, it may result in much discomfort if germs from a nose cold penetrate and infect the sinuses.

Behind these air spaces the air descends behind the soft palate into the pharynx. At the top of this throat passage is a small patch of lymphoid tissue (a material discussed later) – the palatine tonsil – and at the entrance from the mouth at either side are larger areas of this soft tonsillar tissue. It has been thought that the function of these structures is to catch air-borne germs. But, if so, their utility is a dubious one; often they 'back-fire' and become infected, causing serious discomfort. The palatine tonsil, if swollen in this way, results in adenoids which may block the air passages in children.

THE HISTORY OF THE GILLS. But these breathing mechanisms are all new ones. What has beome of the gill-breathing structures of the fishes? These old water dwellers had complicated set of gill slits in the side of the throat, with a stout series of skeletal elements and muscles connected with them. In air-breathers their old functions have gone, but many of the gill structures have been retained in other guises. We have noted elsewhere the use the human ear has made of gill structures; the primitive jaws are derived from the gill-bar skeleton; the tongue has grown from similar beginnings; and most of the muscles of our head were originally gill muscles.

At this time, however, we wish merely to speak of the actual gills themselves. In the fish embryo these structures develop as pockets growing out from the inside of the throat; these meet corresponding depressions from the outside, become connected with them, and in this passage gill membranes develop.

In man five pouches develop in the early embryo, as they have developed in his ancestors for hundreds of millions of years. But they never open, never function for breathing. The first one functions as the ear cavity. The second remains undeveloped. The third, fourth, and fifth sprout out but lose their connexion with the throat and remain in the neck as glands of internal secretion – the thymus gland, highly developed in infants, and the small but essential parathyroid glands. In our breathing apparatus we have become profoundly modified from the primitive vertebrate condition. We have scrapped a whole system of organs. But nature has salvaged it, has saved most of its parts and put them to good use.

EXECRETORY SYSTEM

We have been much concerned in systems so far considered with getting food materials into the body; now we must deal with the problem of getting waste matters out. Waste material from the cells goes into the blood stream. Carbon dioxide is given off by the lungs, while lungs, skin, and intestine help in disposing of some other waste products.

THE HUMAN KIDNEY AND ACCESSORY STRUCTURES. The main exit of waste and harmful material and the chief means of regulating the liquid contents of the blood are the kidneys. In man these are two compact, bean-shaped structures which lie, tucked out of the way, at the back of the body cavity at the small of the back. Blood is strained through the kidneys in a maze of tiny capillaries. The main bulk of the kidney consists of more than a million tiny filters (glomeruli), each attached to a much convoluted tubule; by elaborate processes of filtration, secretion, and reabsorption, waste materials, particularly urea, are removed from the blood and concentrated in the urine. Tubules from

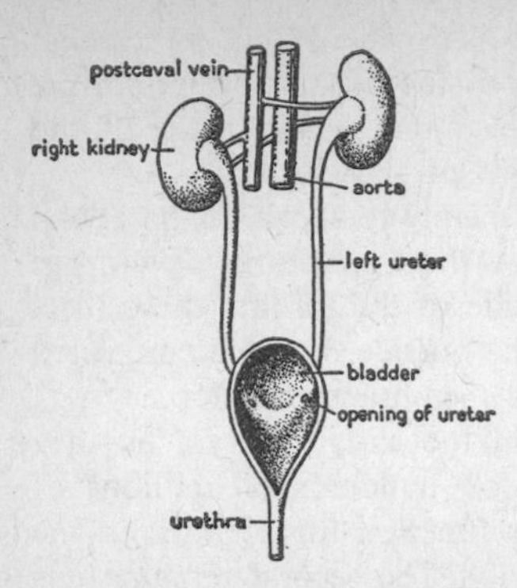

The urinary organs of man. The bladder is shown in section, and parts of aorta and post-caval vein have been added to show the blood supply of the kidneys.

the glomeruli unite to empty into a cavity at the concave side of the 'bean'.

From the kidneys, tubes a foot long (the ureters) drain the urine down into the bladder. This structure lies on the front side of the lower part of the abdominal cavity. It has readily distensible walls (the pig's bladder was, for children of a past generation, the equivalent of the rubber toy balloon) and has, in man, a maximum capacity of well over a quart. Below it the urine is drained off through a single tube (the urethra). There are two muscular stopcocks along the course of this tube, the bottom one under conscious control. In the female this tube is short and leads independently to the surface; in the male, however, it is considerably longer, is joined by the duct carrying the sperm, and reaches the surface through the penis – the male external genital organ.

THE HISTORY OF KIDNEYS. Excretory tubules are common in many invertebrates and in our early chordate ancestors. But their structure was originally quite different from that of a human kidney. In *Amphioxus* there are only a few pairs of isolated small tubules in the throat region. These do not drain waste from the blood stream. Instead, the waste collects in the liquid filling the cavities between the body organs and drains thence by the kidney tubules. Nor do the tubules unite to a common posterior opening; each one has a separate tiny opening to the surface at the far side of the body.

It is a far cry from this series of tiny separate paired pumps to a human kidney, and numerous changes have taken place. By the fish stage the tubules have been elaborated by the addition of tiny filters (glomeruli) at the top; they are gathered together in a pair of kidneys that appear as two long strips running nearly the length of the trunk along the back of the body cavity. The tubules no longer open separately to the outside but unite to empty by a pair of ducts into a pocket at the back of the body. A direct blood supply to the filters and tubules enables them to elaborate urine from the blood stream rather than from the fluid present in the primitive body cavity.

This intermediate type of kidney persists in amphibians. But in reptiles a modernized kidney appears. The old kidney apparatus – tubules, ducts, and all – is scrapped entirely for

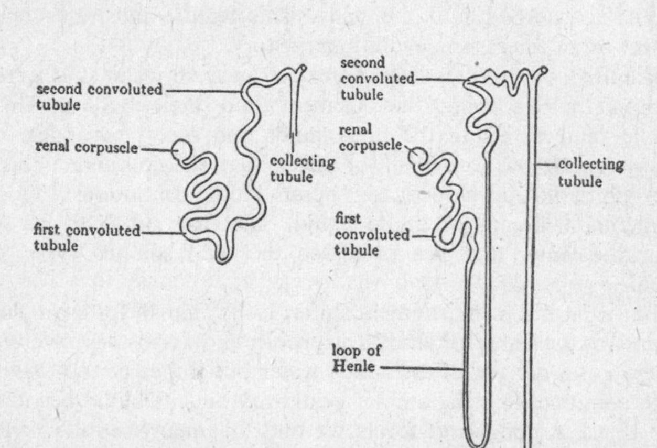

The kidney tubules of frog and man (highly magnified and semidiagrammatic). In each case there is a renal corpuscle through which blood plasma (except for contained proteins) is filtered into the tubules. In proximal and distal portions of the convoluted tubule the composition of this fluid is altered, mainly by resorption of useful materials which would be otherwise lost in the urine. The frog urine is very dilute; in man, however, much of the water is resorbed into the body, apparently by the walls of the intercalated loop of Henle, not present in the frog.

excretory purposes, and the kidney tissues become concentrated in two solid masses well to the back of the body.

If we examine, much magnified, a single kidney tubule of the generalized type seen in the frog kidney (to a total of several thousands) we find that it includes at the proximal end a filter, or glomerulus. Through this passes a convoluted blood vessel from which liquid is filtered; glomerulus and vessel together form a renal corpuscle. Beyond, a large portion of the length of the tubule is much folded, or convoluted; there is considerable reason to believe that much of the more useful portions of the liquid are reabsorbed before it passes on to the straight part of the tube and so on to the outside.

The human tubule is similar in most regards but differs in one noticeable feature. Part way along the convoluted tubule there has been inserted a long, thin loop (known as the loop of Henle, after its discoverer). While it is difficult to ascertain the functions of such small structures, it is probable that in this loop much of the water pumped into the tubule at the upper end is reabsorbed into the body. This feature illustrates one aspect of an interesting evolutionary story.

Primitive vertebrates lived immersed in fresh water and were continually absorbing that element into their bodies. This would tend to dilute the body fluids and blood to a degree too great for the well-being of the animal. To counteract this, the glomeruli developed to 'pump ship' continuously and send out a stream of dilute liquid. The frog still lives in or near the water and has preserved the old-fashioned type of tubule.

But what if the environment shifts; if the animal, for example, abandons the water for land? The problem now is just the reverse. There is no danger of too much water but rather of too little; with continual loss the animal would dry out, its blood become too thick. Among land forms we find that many reptiles have solved the problem by reducing the size of the glomerulus, thus decreasing the amount of water pumped out. The mammal has found another, if more roundabout, solution. The pump still functions as well as ever; but the mammal is an 'Injun giver', for by means of the inserted loop much of the water is taken back and effectively conserved!

REPRODUCTIVE ORGANS

Sexual reproduction is one of the oldest established features of living things; even in plants we find, just as in animals, the production of eggs and sperm and their union to commence a new generation. In many lower animals the two sexes may be combined in one animal. In vertebrates, however, separate sexes – male and female – is the almost universal rule. The two sexes may differ not only in the actual reproductive organs but in secondary characters as well. Such secondary differences are, in general, most highly developed in birds but are quite obvious in mammals such as man.

The essential functions which a system of reproductive organs must subserve include the production of the germ cells – the eggs and the sperm – mechanisms for the union of the two, and, in the case of a mammal such as man, mechanisms in the female for the protection and nourishment of the resulting embryo.

HUMAN SEX ORGANS. The primary sex glands of the female are the ovaries – small bodies attached to the back of the abdominal cavity – in which the eggs develop. Broad funnels close beside the ovaries give entrance into the paired egg tubes (oviducts) which lead down to enter the upper part of the uterus, or womb. This heavily walled sac is of fundamental importance

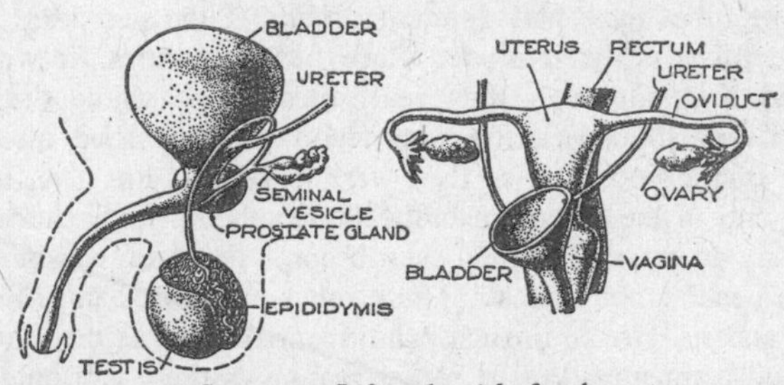

Sex organs. *Left*, male; *right*, female.

in that it forms the place of the development of the embryo. Beyond the uterus lies the vagina, developed in mammals as an aid in the internal fertilization characteristic of the group.

In the male the essential organs are the testes, which are filled with a large number of tubules in whose walls myriads of sperms come to full development. The testes originally lay, like the ovaries, in the back wall of the abdomen. But in most mammals they have descended, to be situated in a pouch – the scrotum – outside of the body cavity. This general mammalian position seems to have arisen in relation to the fact that the delicate sperms cannot develop if the temperature is too high. The heat of the interior of the human body is too much for them; in the exposed scrotum the temperature is several degrees lower.

Storage of sperms takes place in a highly coiled tube (the epididymis) lying alongside each testis. From there a tube leads up into the body and, just below the bladder, joins the urethra, which passes out into the penis.

HISTORY OF THE REPRODUCTIVE ORGANS. In the primitive vertebrates there is almost nothing of these complicated organs except the sex glands themselves. These, much alike to begin with, develop as paired ridges on the upper margin of the body cavity. Both eggs and sperm were originally shed into the cavity surrounding the organs of the body and reached the surface through pores at the back end of the body cavity near the anus and the urinary opening.

But dumping eggs and sperms pell-mell into the inside of the body is a rather inefficient system. Even in fishes there tend to develop tubes to conduct these products to the surface, and such tubes are present in all land animals.

These tubes have had different origins in the two sexes. The female tubes – the oviducts – are new structures. It will be noticed that, although they reach nearly the whole distance from ovary to uterus, the eggs technically are shed into the cavity of the body just as they were to begin with. The funnel at the end of the oviduct usually catches them, but occasionally one may go astray and may even become fertilized and develop in the general body cavity. These tubes are paired in primitive types and still are so in such primitive mammals as the duckbill and spiny anteater. But in higher mammals there is a tendency for the two to fuse posteriorly. The end portion of the fused tube forms the vagina. The more proximal uterus – place of growth of the young – is still double in many mammals but is fused into a single structure in man and his primate relatives.

The male glands, too, have acquired a duct, but in quite a different fashion. We have noted that higher vertebrates have discarded the old set of kidneys. But here, once again, we have an example of the retention of old organs for new functions. The testis originally lay in the back of the body next door to this salvageable kidney system. A part of the tubules of the kidneys forms the epididymis, and the old kidney duct has become the sperm duct. We have noted that in man the sperm duct joins the tube from the kidneys and bladder, and a union of two such functionally dissimilar structures to a common outlet seemed a bit peculiar. The fact that the testes have borrowed part of the

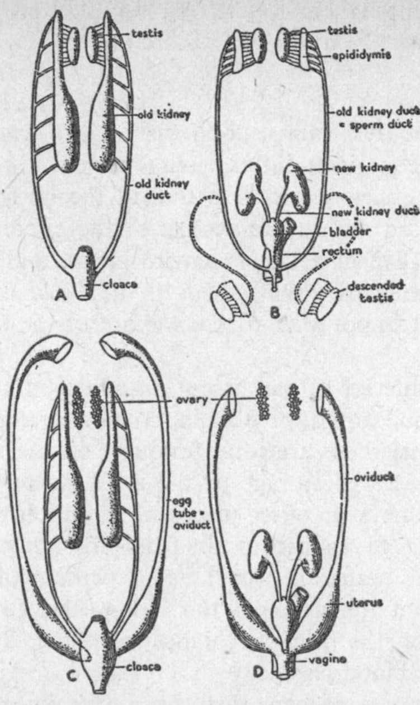

Diagrams to show the evolution of the urinogenital organs. These are ventral views, the anal or cloacal region at the bottom, *A*, *C*, male and female lower vertebrates; *B*, *D*, male and female mammalian types. In the male of primitive vertebrates the kidneys are elongated and have ducts to the cloaca without intervention of a bladder in most cases. The testes connect with the kidneys and use the same ducts. In mammals the kidneys are essentially new structures placed towards the back of the body cavity; these have acquired new ducts and a bladder. The remains of the old kidney form the epididymis, an appendix to the testis, and the old kidney duct is now the exclusive property of the reproductive system. In most mammals the testes have descended ventrally into a scrotum. This new position is indicated in broken lines. In typical mammals the cloaca disappears and the rectum is separated from the urinogenital system, whose products in the male reach the surface through a separate tube (urethra). *C*, *D*, show the transformation of the female urinogenital organs. The evolution of the kidney is similar in the two sexes. In the female, however, the genital system does not use the kidney ducts. Instead the eggs are typically shed from the ovary into the body cavity and thence pass by a funnel into an oviduct which primitively passes to the cloaca. In typical mammals, with the loss of a cloaca, the vagina develops as a separate genital outlet. Proximal to this an expansion of the oviduct forms the uterus, in which the embryo develops. In many forms (as in the diagram) the two uteri are separate; in others (as in man) they fuse into a single structure. (After Wilder, modified)

kidney system for their conducting tubes gives, of course, a reasonable explanation for this feature.

CIRCULATORY SYSTEM

THE BLOOD. The human body is mainly water. Much of this liquid is contained in the cells; however, a considerable amount – six quarts or so – is free in the body, bathing the cells, or enclosed within the vessels of the circulatory system. The cells thus live in a watery environment, and the maintenance of this internal environment in a stable condition is a matter of great importance to the welfare of the human organism.

This liquid interior of ours is not, of course, a pure 'distilled' water. The blood liquid, or plasma, contains many materials in solution. In part these are food products on the way from the intestine or places of storage to the cells, waste matter on its way to the kidneys or other places of excretion, or oxygen or carbon dioxide in transit to or from the lungs. There are, however, other materials which are a permanent part of the blood. Much of the work of the kidney has to do with the preservation of the proper balance of these dissolved constituents of the blood plasma.

Most interesting, perhaps, are the inorganic salts which are present. Of these the most common is ordinary table salt – sodium chloride – but there are also other salts, including in their composition carbon, potassium, calcium, and other elements. The proportions between the various salts are remarkably constant in man and all other vertebrates; and it is of interest that these proportions are almost exactly those found in ordinary sea water.

This fact, it has been suggested, may be explained on broad evolutionary grounds. Although the vertebrates may have evolved in fresh water, it is generally believed that their early ancestors among the very simplest animals lived in the ancient seas. In such forms all the cells were exposed to sea water and thrived only in that environment. When greater bodily complexity was attained, many of the tissues no longer lay on the surface of the body; but they required a similar saline medium for their existence, and this medium has followed them into the interior of the body through the development of a salty blood plasma. Our blood is, in a sense, an isolated pool of the early Paleozoic ocean.

The blood also includes of course, organized cellular bodies. Most common of these are the red blood cells, checker-shaped objects which in their adult stage in man have lost their nuclei. They owe their colour to their content of the complex protein haemoglobin, which is of vital importance in carrying away oxygen from the lungs and is also concerned in the return journey of carbon dioxide from cells to lungs. Also present are various types of white blood cells, including the large leucocytes and the smaller lymphocytes. The former, at least, are of great importance in the resistance of the body to bacterial invasion; the lymphocytes may play a role in the repair of injured tissues. A third type of formed elements is found in the blood platelets. These are tiny discs, much smaller than red cells, which play an important part in the clotting of the blood.

The red blood cells in a human body are to be numbered in billions. Their life-span appears to be, on the average, but a few weeks. Thus, every second of the day sees the birth of perhaps 10,000,000 of these cells in the red marrow inside the larger bones of the body and the destruction of a similar number in the spleen and liver, which are their 'graveyards'. Of the life of the white cells, much fewer in number, much less is known. The leucocytes also arise in the bone marrow; the lymphocytes arise in lymphoid tissues, discussed later.

ESSENTIAL FEATURES OF CIRCULATION. The blood is nowhere a sluggish pool of liquid. It moves; it is a transportation system.

A village has no transportation problems. The stores, the church, the school, are all close at hand. But in a great city transportation is a vital need. Just so with animals. In the simplest types each cell may gain its own food and oxygen directly or do so through the courtesy of its next-door neighbour. But in a highly complex animal means of circulation of supplies and of disposing of waste must be provided; some sort of blood system must be established.

In some invertebrate types the circulatory system is partially open. Blood may be pumped out to the tissues in closed channels but allowed to filter back through spaces between the cells. But in the blood vascular system of vertebrates the blood circulates continuously through a series of closed channels.

Four main types of channels are present in this system: heart, arteries, capillaries, and veins. The thick muscular heart is the main propulsive force in the system, driving the blood to every part of the body. The arteries have thick walls of muscles and fibrous tissue (much of it elastic in nature) and are able to withstand high pressure and carry the blood from the heart to the organs. The blood returns to the heart at a more sluggish pace through the veins, larger in diameter and with thinner walls.

The vital part of the system is the capillaries, a tiny network of vessels lying in each organ, connecting the arteries with the veins. It is only in the capillaries that the actual results of the work of circulation are attained. Only through their thin walls can pass, in one direction, the food materials needed by the cells of the body, and, in the other, the carbon dioxide and other waste materials destined to pass again from the circulation in lung or kidney. Each capillary is an exceedingly small structure; but, threading their way through every part of the body, they are, all in all, very numerous; their walls present a surface area about an acre in extent.

THE BLOOD CIRCUIT. Let us deal with the circuit of the blood from the point of view of its function as a carrier of oxygen. Leaving the tissues of any organ as a 'blue', oxygen-poor material, the blood eventually passes to one of two main lengthwise veins, the venae cavae, which enters the right side of the heart.

This structure is a double-barrelled pump, with two pairs of chambers, lying beneath the breastbone between the lungs a bit to the left of the midline of the body. It is roughly triangular in shape, the point downward, the base – at which all the vessels enter or leave – at the top. At the top are the two atria, the comparatively thin-walled outer chambers where blood collects from the veins. The venous blood from the body enters the right atrium and then descends into the right-hand member of the pair of ventricles – the main pumps of the system. Stout valves prevent a backward leakage as the thick walls of the ventricle contract and force the blood past another valve into an artery which divides to take the blood to the two lungs. Here, in passing through the complex capillary systems of these structures, oxygen is taken on in exchange for carbon dioxide.

Special veins now return the blood to the left side of the heart, where a similar passage through atrium and ventricle occurs. The walls of this ventricle, however, are considerably thicker than on the right, for this pump must force the blood to the most distant parts of the body.

Upon leaving the heart the blood enters the aorta – a large artery with very thick walls, which first runs upward and then

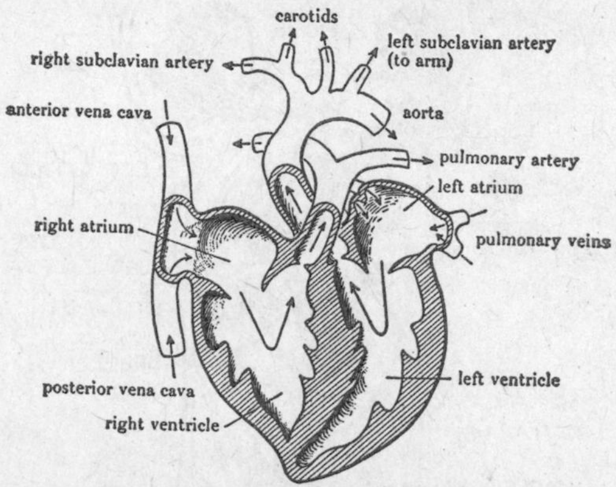

The human heart with its chambers opened from the ventral surface (modified from Jammes; semidiagrammatic). Blood from the lungs enters the left atrium (auricle) through the pulmonary veins, passes through the left ventricle, and leaves the heart via the aorta with its various branches. Blood from the remainder of the body reaches the right atrium through the two venae cavae, passes through the right ventricle, and thence reaches the lungs by the pulmonary arteries.

arches to the left side of the body. Over the course of this arch are given off the main vessels to the head and arms. The aorta itself turns downward along the back wall of the body cavity beneath the backbone and travels down to the abdomen, giving off branches to the various organs and to the legs. The blood passes to these organs, passes into their capillaries, gives up its oxygen, and begins again its double journey through the heart.

We have here described the circulation from the point of view of oxygen supply. But it is only one of its many functions; there are various special circuits. A good portion of the blood passes, for example, through the kidney on every round and not merely gives oxygen to that organ, but, as its main function there, gives off waste material such as urea and uric acid into the kidney tubules. Another specialized type of circulation is that of the blood which passes to the intestine. This does not

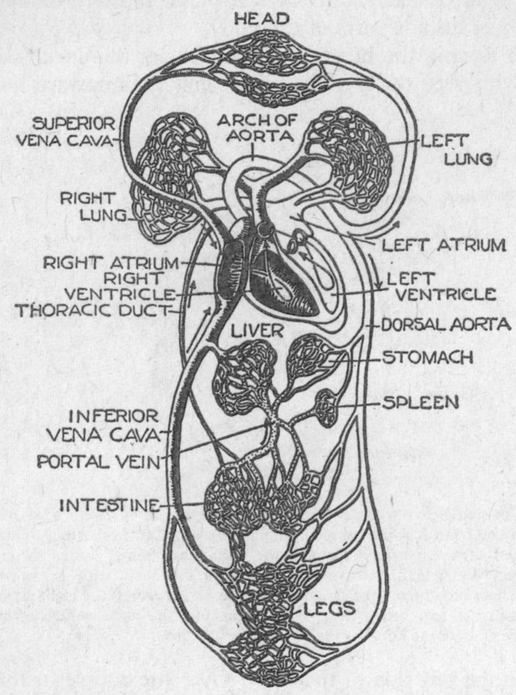

Diagram to show the circulation of the blood in man. Vessels carrying oxygenated blood light in colour; those with 'impure' blood, dark.

return directly to the heart but, charged with food, travels to the liver, where sugar is given up and transformed into glycogen (a sort of animal starch) for storage.

CIRCULATION IN FISHES. This human circulatory system is a very understandable one and one that seems quite well adapted to our needs. It is, however, quite a different one in many features from that laid down in primitive vertebrates. We shall point out the contrasts and the main steps by which our own system has evolved. The history of the venous system is an interesting one but one that we shall not discuss here; we shall confine our attention to the story of the heart and the main arteries.

The heart of a fish is a good pumping organ but a simple one. Impure blood enters the single atrium, then the single ventricle, and then is pumped forward into the throat region. Here the main throat vessel (ventral aorta) divides into a number of paired vessels. These ramify into capillary networks under the walls of the gill chambers; here oxygenation takes place. Above the gills the various vessels recombine; some blood goes to the head; the remainder, collected in a large dorsal aorta, passes back down the body beneath the backbone to be distributed to the various capillary systems in the organs.

In fish the circuit runs: organs→heart→breathing apparatus →organs; in man, organs→heart→breathing apparatus→heart →organs. How have we happened to double up the heart and add to the simple fish method of blood circulation an extra passage through this pumping structure?

COMPLICATIONS CAUSED BY THE LUNGS. The answer, of course, lies in the change in breathing apparatus. When lungs first appeared in fishes they were merely accessory breathing organs – useful in time of need but not a part of the normal system. Like any ordinary organ of the body, the blood from them passed back to the heart through the regular venous channels. Thus when, in a fish with lungs, the gills were temporarily out of operation, part of the blood from the heart went to the lung, but only a part. Further, the purified blood, when returned to the heart from the lung, mingled with the used blood from the body.

In this fashion the blood stream was always of a mixed character; the blood reaching the organs of the body was partly oxygenated but partly 'stale'; of the blood reaching the lung, part had just come back from that organ.

This is a very wasteful sort of system. In a fish it might to do tide the animal over, but it is exceedingly inefficient. And yet it was this makeshift system that the first land animals inherited and with which they began life on land. The gills had gone, but several arches led on either side from ventral to dorsal aorta. The lungs were attached to the last arch. The fresh blood from the lung went to the heart, mixed with stale blood from the rest of the body; mixed blood of this sort went more or less indiscriminately to lungs and body alike. How to do away with this wasteful type of circulation; how to regain, in this new setting, the original clear separation of fresh and stale blood, this was the 'problem' which, unsolved, would prevent efficient use of oxygen in land forms and would prevent the development of warm-blooded animals, which depend for existence upon extremely well-aerated blood.

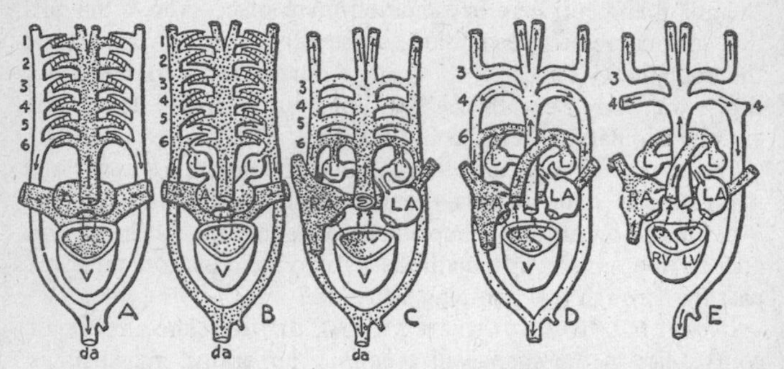

Diagrams to show the evolution of the arches in the arterial circulation from fish to mammal. The vessels of the chest and throat region are presumably seen from below, and part of the ventricle of the heart is cut away. A full stipple indicates venous (unoxygenated) blood; lighter stippling, mixed blood; absence of stippling, oxgenated (arterial) blood. *A*, atrium (or auricle) of the heart; *da*, dorsal aorta; *L*, lung, *LA*, left atrium; *LV*, left ventricle; *RA*, right atrium; *RV*, right ventricle; *V*, ventricle.

A, a primitive fish. The impure blood passes through the single atrium and ventricle, forward along the ventral aorta, and then upward on each side through the gill capillaries where CO_2 is given off and oxygen obtained. *B*, a lung-bearing fish shown at a time when the gills are assumed to be inoperative. Only the blood passing into the lungs via the sixth arch obtains oxygen; this fresh blood is mixed with venous blood in the heart. *C*, a typical adult amphibian. The gills have been abandoned, although a variable number of aortic arches are retained in their former position. The fresh blood from the lungs passes to a separate atrial chamber of the heart; however, the ventricle is still single, and, although various devices partially separate the blood streams, the body receives a mixed supply. *D*, a typical reptile. The ventricle is partly subdivided, and only a slight mixture of blood streams occurs. Of the original six pairs of aortic arches, only three persist, the third of the original series supplying the head, the fourth the body, the sixth the lungs. *E*, a mammal. The two sides of the heart are completely separated, so that no mixture of blood streams occurs. The fourth arch, carrying blood to the body, is complete only on the left side as the arch of the aorta. (Partly after De Beer)

The only 'solution' is, obviously, the development of two distinct channels. How has this been accomplished?

REDUCTION OF ARTERIAL CHANNELS. One improvement is an obvious one. With the loss of gills there is no need for a considerable number of paired arches in the throat region; these have become greatly reduced. A pair part way up the series has been retained as channels for the main vessels from the heart to the head. To the back pair the lungs are attached. These arches eventually become disconnected at their upper ends from the dorsal aorta and run to the lungs alone. An intermediate pair of arches was selected for the main supply to the body. This gives us a much simpler picture; it is this condition of the throat arteries that we find in reptiles.

One further stage leads us to the arterial condition found in mammals. A reptile has two arches on the main aorta, one on either side of the body, the two joining in their course down the back. There is no need for this duplication of service, and we find that both birds and mammals have retained but one of these two structures. But, curiously, the birds happened to have retained the vessel of the right side, while in mammals it is the left one that has been preserved as the arch of the aorta.

With this separation and reduction of arterial tubes we have now a separation of body and lung passages above the heart. Likewise, on the venous end, there soon developed a separation between the veins bearing fresh blood from the lungs and the main veins draining the body.

SEPARATION OF TWO SIDES OF THE HEART. We have now achieved a situation where we have two distinct groups of veins entering the heart and two distinct groups of arteries leading from it. But as long as the heart retains its former condition of a single pump, we are no better off. Both types of blood still mingle inside the heart, and our separation of external channels is a useless one.

But the heart, too, evolves as we proceed up the scale. There is still some mixture of blood streams in the amphibian. The two atria are separate, the lungs draining into that of the left side, the body into the right; it is only in the one great ventricle that mixing may occur. Even there, however, we find that the sorting-out process is advancing, and some reptiles have a partial cleavage of the ventricle. Finally, in birds and mammals, a complete division of the ventricle has occurred, and the two blood streams are entirely separated.

Our own double-barrelled circulatory system is quite efficient, and one would be tempted to say that it is well designed for our needs. But this is quite untrue; it is the result not of design but of a happy accident! The fish had an efficient single system. If the lung, in its early days, had happened to drain into the dorsal aorta and had thus run parallel to the gill, we would still have the old fish type of circulation. But there is no 'fore-

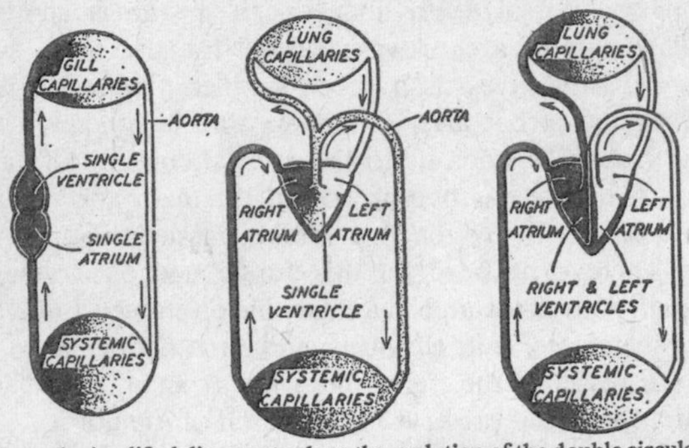

A much-simplified diagram to show the evolution of the double circulation through the heart due to the substitution of lungs for gills in higher vertebrates. In the fish the blood from the breathing organ (gills) flowed directly, via the arteries, to the body (systemic capillaries), and hence the heart was a simple pump. The lungs, however, return their blood to the heart, where it tends to mix with 'spent' blood from the body. Crosswise subdivision of the heart in birds and mammals separates the two streams. (From Carlson and Johnson, *The Machinery of the Body*)

sight' in nature; the lung, like any other ordinary organ, drained back to the heart. This led to great inefficiency, to a condition of imperfect blood aeration from which our cold-blooded land relatives still suffer. Only in birds and mammals has a successful issue resulted from this – after many millions of years of a handicapped existence.

LYMPHATIC SYSTEM. The blood flows through closed channels throughout its course. But some blood fluid escapes from these channels, and other liquids from the cells of the body never directly enter the blood stream. Such materials – the lymph – gather into numerous wandering channels found throughout the body and finally reach the veins through a small number of openings.

Largest of the lymph channels is the thoracic duct, which passes up the left side of the back wall of the body to empty into one of the veins near the heart. This duct carries not ordinary lymph but much of the food material absorbed by the intestines, particularly fats.

Along the course of the lymph vessels lie rounded masses of tissues, composed in great part of white blood cells, through which the lymph drains. Lymph nodes of this sort lie close beneath the skin in various body regions (e.g., the neck). They appear to be of importance in combating invading bacteria which may be passing through the lymph channels on their way to the general circulatory vessels. The tonsils, we have noted, consist of similar lymphoid tissue, and the spleen, graveyard of red blood corpuscles, appears to originate as lymphoid tissue also.

GLANDS OF INTERNAL SECRETION

While most of the activities of the body appear to be stimulated by the nervous system. we have become increasingly aware, in recent decades, of the fact that powerful influences on bodily activities – particularly of the internal organs – may be caused by minute amounts of internally secreted chemicals, the hormones carried about the body by the blood stream. These materials are formed in a variety of structures which are situated in various parts of the body and derived from a variety of organ systems. Despite this structural diversity, we may for convenience treat as a unit these organs of internal secretion, the endocrine glands.

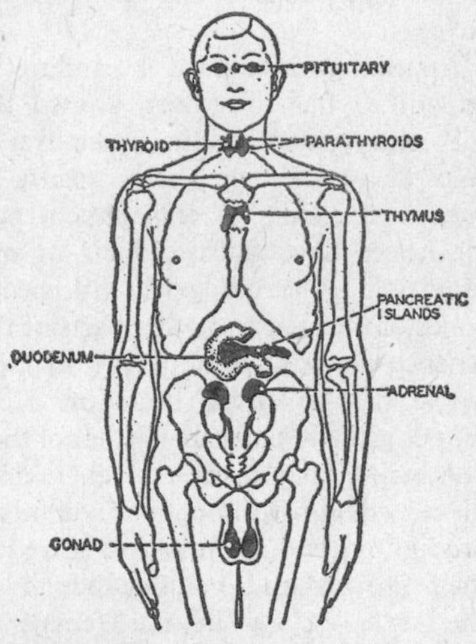

Outline sketch of the human body to show the location of the principal glands of internal secretion. (From Neal and Rand, *Comparative Anatomy*, P. Blakiston's Son & Co., Inc.)

THE PITUITARY. In the embryo of every

vertebrate a small pouch (the infundibulum) grows out from the bottom of the forebrain, and a second pocket (the hypophysis) develops upward beneath it from the roof of the mouth (cf. chap. 20). The two become associated, the connexion with the mouth is lost, and the combined structure, glandular in nature, is known as the pituitary gland. It is lodged in a small pocket in the base of the braincase behind the nose and above the back part of the mouth. Its earlier evolutionary history is obscure; perhaps it was originally a relatively unimportant gland secreting some sort of material into the mouth. In its developed form, however, the pituitary is the most important of the glands of internal secretion, not only acting directly in many ways, but also exerting a dominating influence over other endocrine structures.

Study of the pituitary hormones and their effects is currently an active field of biological work. Apparently there are a number of such secretions, and their effects are widespread. The posterior lobe of the pituitary, derived from the infundibular pouch, appears to be relatively inactive, although extracts from it have a marked effect upon smooth muscle. Much more important are the secretions of the anterior lobe, derived from the hypophysis.

A striking function of the anterior lobe is seen in its effect on growth. It has long been known that gigantism is correlated with enlargement of the hypophysis. If this enlargement takes place at an early age, an unusually large but well-proportioned individual results. If enlargement occurs at a later date, when the bones have finished their normal growth, there occurs a condition of acromegaly, with peculiar 'overgrowths' of the bones of the face and other parts of the body. On the other hand, absence or reduction of the hypophysis results in dwarfism. Apparently a normal secretion of this gland is necessary for proper growth, particularly that of the skeleton.

A second major series of functions has to do with the gonads – the sex glands – although, as will be seen, these glands themselves produce additional endocrine secretions. The pituitary stimulates their growth and maintenance, is intimately associated with the sexual cycle in the female, and stimulates the milk glands.

The pituitary, in addition, appears to exercise considerable control over other glands of internal secretion (subsequently discussed).

It definitely is known to stimulate the thyroid and appears also to have a stimulating effect on the cortex of the adrenal glands and on the parathyroids.

THYROID. The thyroid, a 'shield-shaped' gland, is a large and important gland of internal secretion, lying in the neck. This in the adult human being has no particular connexion either functionally or anatomically with the digestive system. But this gland originally functioned in eating. In little *Amphioxus* and his kind, as we have noted, the food is obtained from water drawn into the mouth and out through the gill slits. The food particles collect in the floor of the throat. Here there is situated a trough (termed the endostyle or 'internal groove') lined with cilia, which carry the food particles to the stomach.

In jawed forms with a changed eating apparatus this groove closes up and forms an internal gland. That the thyroid gland has been developed from this discarded structure is suggested by its development in man. It arises as a pocket growing out of the underside of the throat; a pit in the back of our tongue represents the place whence it started. But still better proof of this history is afforded by the lampreys. In the young lamprey the groove for food-collecting is present much as in *Amphioxus*. When the lamprey grows up, its food habits change, and the grooves become an enclosed thyroid gland. The two structures are actually identical in the same animal.

We have noted before (e.g., in the discussion of the ear) cases of marked change of function, of the re-utilization of discarded bits of animal apparatus to serve new needs. Not only in the thyroid but in other glands of internal secretion as well we find many examples of nature's economical habits.

The importance of thyroid function in man has long been known. The thyroid secretes a material of which the active portion is thyroxin, a relatively simple chemical substance which has been synthesized in the laboratory. This hormone appears to be vitally important for growth and for the maintenance of the normal metabolism of the cells of the body – their proper use of food materials for energy production and the maintenance of vital processes. This function is, it will be noted, not so distant from the former function of the endostyle in relation to food supply; and it is further of interest in this regard that the thyroid hormone, unlike most other internal secretions, can be taken by mouth and thus enter the body through the digestive tract.

A common obvious symptom of thyroid disorder is the development of a goitre – a swollen condition of the neck due to enlargement of this gland. Deficiencies in thyroid function in early life may result in the production of a type of dwarf called a 'cretin'. Thyroid diseases, curiously, appear to be more prevalent in areas covered by the Pleistocene glaciation. The thyroid hormone includes iodine in its chemical composition. The iodine must enter the body in water or food and comes originally from the soil. Apparently glacial processes denude the soil of iodine, and hence dwellers in regions once ice-covered are liable to lack a sufficient supply of this element. To compensate for this, iodine is frequently supplied artificially – in table salt, for example.

GILL-POUCH DERIVATIVES: THYMUS, PARATHYROID. In fishes the major breathing organs, the gills, develop as a series of paired pouches which grow out from the sides of the throat in the embryo and finally break through to the outside as gill slits. In higher land vertebrates the break-through never occurs, but pouches develop in similar fashion. We noted earlier that the first of the series was utilized in connexion with the ear. The other, more posterior, pouches never remain as open cavities. However, clusters of cells which form around the margins do persist and form two types of glands – thymus and parathyroid – which are to be found in the neck region of man and other vertebrates.

The thymus forms a large mass of glandular material in the human foetus and the young baby – so large, in fact, that it may cause serious trouble by interfering with breathing. It fails to grow, however, and in the adult becomes inconspicuous. It seems sure that the thymus plays some important role in early human growth; but we have as yet little concrete data as to what the exact function may be.

The parathyroids – likewise formed from cell masses derived from the gill pouches – are found in man as two pairs of little lumps of tissue embedded in the back of the thyroid gland. The presence of these little glands is essential for existence in man and other mammals, as was discovered when they were accidentally removed in operations on the thyroid. They have the power of regulating the amount of the element calcium circulating in the blood. If because of improper functioning or absence of the parathyroids calcium regulation is upset, the muscles become subject to spasms, and death in convulsion may occur.

THE PANCREATIC ISLANDS. The pancreas, as noted elsewhere, is, in the main, a gland intimately connected with the digestive system, pouring into the intestine a number of enzymes important in digestion. Most of the cells of the pancreas are obviously concerned with the formation of such substances. Long ago, however, it was noticed in microscopic sections that in the pancreas there were clusters of cells forming 'islands' among the other tissues. These islands appeared to be of a rather different nature and had no tubules connected with them to drain off secretions to the gut. It was obvious that these islands of glandular tissue, therefore, must secrete some sort of material into the blood stream and hence were of a different nature from ordinary pancreas.

In the common and frequently fatal disease called diabetes mellitus, the regulation of the sugar supply of the body is upset. Many years ago it was noted that there was a correlation between the diabetic condition and absence or diseased conditions of the pancreas. This led to the possibility that the secretion of the islands might be a substance controlling sugar metabolism. Two decades ago this secretion – insulin – was successfully isolated and has since proved of great usefulness in the treatment of diabetics.

ADRENALS. Each human kidney is capped above by a mass of tissue known, from its position, as the adrenal or suprarenal. Its tissues are glandular in nature but have no ducts, and hence the endocrine nature of the gland is apparent. It is, however, a double affair. There are two distinct types of tissue – one forming an outer layer, or cortex, the other, or medulla, an inner mass of cells. Both portions form secretions, but of entirely different natures, and their union in the form of a single structure is due to chance topographic association rather than to any real relationship.

The medulla is capable of pouring out into the blood stream relatively large quantities of a substance, well known chemically, called adrenalin (or epinephrine). This drug causes a more vigorous circulation of the blood, an increase in the power and resistance to fatigue of muscles, and other effects which tend to make the individual capable, for the time being, of greater exertions than are normally possible. This liberation of adrenalin takes place, for the most part, under stimulation by the nerves of the autonomic system, typically when the individual is emotionally excited. Although there is no proof of causal connexion, it is not improbable that the development of this adrenalin-producing gland is an adaptation for better functioning of man and his animal ancestors in situations where increased exertions in fighting or fleeing from an enemy are necessary. Under such circumstances sharp emotions are aroused, the adrenals are stimulated, and vigorous action ensues.

It is becoming increasingly apparent that the effect of many nerves upon the muscles or glands which they stimulate to activity is caused by their tips giving off minute amounts of a liquid which is identical with, or at least very similar to, adrenalin. Thus the pouring-out of adrenalin into the blood stream is to be considered as essentially a type of nervous stimulation, but one not confined to any particular structure; it is a 'shotgun' effect, acting upon almost any structure with which it comes in contact in its course about the blood stream. In this connexion it is highly interesting to note the embryological origins of the cells which compose the adrenal medulla. They do not arise in the position in which we find them in the adult. They are actually cells of the nervous tissues which, instead of remaining in the central nervous system, have wandered down into a cluster in the region near the kidneys, where there is an abundant blood supply. The adrenal medulla is thus to be regarded as a specialized part of the nervous system, adapted to give off large amounts of adrenalin rather than the minute quantities which may be excreted by ordinary neurons.

Far different in origin and function is the outer layer – the cortex – of the adrenal. The cells which compose it arise in the embryo by budding off from the wall of the body cavity not far from the position of the adult gland. The cortical function too is of a very different sort. The cortex secretes a hormone (cortin) which is essential for life; disease or absence of the cortex results in death. The exact nature of the function of this secretion is somewhat uncertain, but it appears to be concerned with the regulation of the salt content of the blood and therefore with the maintenance of a proper 'internal environment' for the living organism.

HORMONES OF THE REPRODUCTIVE ORGANS. In man and other mammals the life-processes associated with reproduction are of a complicated nature. In many forms there are cycles of reproductive activity in both sexes, and in every case there are female reproductive rhythms associated with the development of ripe eggs and the potentialities of successful initiation of the development of the young. In great measure these occurrences are under the control of internal secretions. Some influence, we have noted, is exerted by the pituitary. The sex organs themselves, however, are active centres of hormone secretion. Study of these processes is actively under way at the present time. We are far from having reached a definite stage in our knowledge of them, and we shall here merely indicate a few of the more important and well-assured findings.

In the male the testis is a centre of hormone secretion in addition to its function in sperm formation. This hormone appears to be responsible for the development of many of the features of the male which appear at puberty, including non-sexual structures as well as the reproductive organs, and contributes to the development of male sexual behaviour.

The female plays a more complex role in reproduction in mammals, and, as is only to be expected, the hormone situation is much more complicated in that sex. At least two, and possibly more, secretions are produced in the ovary. In chapter 20 it is noted that as the eggs grow they are surrounded by cells which form a follicle. The follicle cells produce a hormone termed theelin, which exerts a great influence upon the uterus. It aids the growth of this structure and its maintenance in the adult condition. It is further responsible for the periodic changes which occur in the uterus during the reproductive cycles. Apart from its influence on the uterus, this hormone appears to have effects upon the development of the milk glands and contributes to sexual behaviour.

When ripe eggs are discharged from the ovary, there follows a period in which the development of young in the uterus becomes possible. In connexion with this we find a second type of hormone is present. The follicle, when abandoned by the ripe egg, becomes a structure known as the corpus luteum, or 'yellow body', finally absorbed but long persistent. The follicle cells now surrounding it secrete a second hormone – progestin. This completes the changes in the uterine wall preparatory to possible pregnancy, makes possible the implantation and maintenance of the developing embryo in the tissues of the uterus, and, later, stimulates the enlargement of the mammary glands which result in the presence of a milk supply for the young at birth.

CHAPTER 19

The Human Body – *concluded*

Flesh and Bone

THE organ systems so far considered are of extreme importance to the physiologist and are responsible for almost all our major functional activities. We shall conclude our account of the body by a discussion of two final types of structural elements whose functions are limited in scope but which, nevertheless, are of great anatomical interest and which make up by far the greater part of our bodies – the muscles and bones.

MATERIALS

Bones and the muscles that work them are physiologically quite different types of materials. The bones are inert, supporting and protective structures; muscles are highly active – indeed, almost the only moving portions of our bodies. Yet the two are intimately related in the past history of vertebrates, in the embryonic development of our bodies and in our bodily activities, and we are thus justified in treating them together.

THE MIDDLE BODY LAYER. Primitive many-celled animals were probably (as is the case with early embryos of higher types) forms having but two layers to their bodies: inside and outside. But with growth in size there early arose a third body layer situated between the others. This middle layer has loomed large in the history of all higher animals – invertebrates as well as backboned forms. Muscles and skeletal parts are its bulkier products, but from this layer too have come the circulatory system and most of the reproductive and urinary organs, while in reality much of the substance of the skin and digestive tract is also a derivative of this middle layer of the body.

MUSCLE CELLS. Originally, we believe, every cell had the power of movement. But in this respect, as in others, increased complexity has been accompanied by a restriction of function; in most animals, as in ourselves, the power of movement is almost entirely confined to a particular type of cell, the muscle cells – long slim elements which have a power of vigorous contraction and the consequent ability to move structures to which their ends may be attached.

In vertebrates muscular tissue is of two sorts – smooth muscle and striated muscle – which differ in structure, position, and nervous connexions. Striated muscle is the type which composes the 'meat' of the body, the great muscles whose movements are, in the main, under voluntary control. The name is due to their peculiar cross-striped appearance under the microscope. Smooth muscles, on the other hand, are commonly under the control of the autonomic nervous system and are mainly found in the linings of the gut, blood vessels, and other organs. Heart muscle is of a somewhat intermediate type. The interest of the smooth muscles lies in their relation to the organs with which they are connected; we shall here concern ourselves only with the voluntary, striated muscles of the body.

EARLY STEPS IN SKELETAL DEVELOPMENT. Support was a problem obviously encountered by many-celled animals at an early date. For small sea-living animals which moved but little and were buoyed up by the water, the need for supporting structures was small. In most animals we find some type of connective tissue which fills in the interstices between various organs and body layers and helps hold them together. Such tissue generally contains numerous fibres and is thus of a rather feltlike nature, having some stiffening power. Connective tissue is still important in our own body as a sort of general 'stuffing'. Much of the skin is a dense tissue of this sort; tendons and ligaments are fibrous connective tissues.

But with size and vigorous movement of the sort that characterizes chordates has come the need for greater support and the development of skeletal structures. Among a number of nonchordate groups some sort of skeleton has developed. Almost always, however, this is on the outside of the body, as the shell of molluscs or the hardened 'skin' of a lobster or insect. Early vertebrates too developed for protection a superficial armour; but in vertebrates alone we find that the major skeletal structures are internal – buried beneath the muscles and skin.

Three types of skeletal materials have been developed by vertebrates: notochord, cartilage, and bone.

NOTOCHORD. The notochord seems to have been the first of these structures to appear. We find it already typically developed in such a primitive form as *Amphioxus*, a tough but flexible rod running the length of the body along the back below the nerve cord. The notochord helps to stiffen the body and support the various organs and also is of great use as a point of attachment for the muscles of the trunk. In the vertebrates the notochord long persisted as a functional element, and it is fully formed in the embryo of even the highest types. But in vertebrates there appear new skeletal materials which have taken over and added to the support offered by the notochord – cartilage and bone. Both these substances are formed from the connective tissues, but they differ considerably in their nature and appearance.

CARTILAGE. Gristle, or cartilage, is a translucent material formed by rounded cells which lie in the interior of its substance. It is fairly firm, but elastic and flexible, and is capable of rapid growth by expansion. It is thus a most useful material where the stresses upon it are not too great. It is a common supporting structure in lower vertebrates; in lampreys and sharks it is the only skeletal material (other than the notochord). In land forms, however, its importance has waned, and in the adult human being it plays only a minor part in the makeup of the skeleton. The ends of the ribs are composed of cartilage; there are discs of it between the joints of the backbone; the joint surfaces of the limbs are made of this material; it makes up the external ear and the tip of the nose and stiffens the windpipe. Wherever elasticity is the desideratum, we find cartilage; but in a large land dweller, such as man, it lacks the strength demanded in most parts of the skeleton.

BONE. This needed strength is found in bone, the skeletal material which is dominant in all higher vertebrates and important in even the oldest of fossil forms. Like cartilage, it is a derivative of the original connective tissues as a harder and better type of body 'filler'. Like the original connective tissue, it is basically a feltlike material containing great quantities of tiny interlacing fibres between which are irregularly branching cells. Two-thirds of its substance, however, consists of salts – mainly calcium phosphates and carbonates – laid down in this fibrous matrix. The composition of bone may thus be compared, rather roughly, to that of reinforced concrete; the fibrous reinforcements, fortunately, give the structure the elasticity necessary for it to stand up under the hard usages to which we put our skeletons.

Some bones, or portions of bones, are compact, nearly solid structures which in section are seen to be pierced by small canals carrying blood vessels. The irregular cell spaces connect, for purposes of nourishment, with these canals and with each other by tiny tubules.

Most bone, however, is not solid and compact; if it were, we would carry much unnecessary dead weight. Large bones are essentially hollow, solid at the surface, but having within them only such bony bars and braces as are necessary for the reinforcement and the propping-up of the walls. These inner portions of the bones – the marrow – are not, however, wasted in nature's economy. They have been put to use as places of manufacture

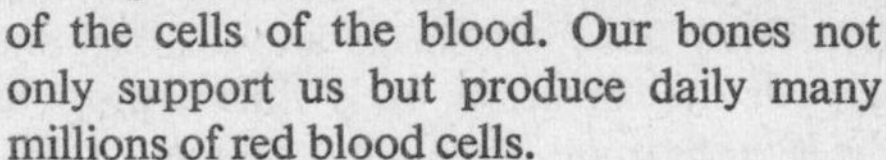

of the cells of the blood. Our bones not only support us but produce daily many millions of red blood cells.

The human thigh bone at an immature stage. (For economy of space much of the shaft has been omitted.) The two articular regions and the principal points of muscular attachment long remain as separate pieces of bone, epiphyses (*e*), between which and the shaft there remain areas of cartilage in which new bone may form. By this means the bone may grow indefinitely without disturbance in its relations to adjacent structures. When adult size is attained the epiphyses fuse with the shaft and growth ceases.

EPIPHYSES. Bone has one great disadvantage compared with cartilage; it cannot expand and can grow only by addition to the surface. This presents a problem in growth. Take, for example, the thigh bone of a child. In a boy two years old it is a small bone but about seven inches long; by the time the boy grows to manhood it must more than double in length. The bone may become stouter by adding extra surface layers; but how does increase in length take place? The bone cannot stretch; and yet we cannot merely plaster on new bone at the two ends, for these ends must remain in smoothly working articulation with the hip bones and the shin bone. The problem of growth without interference with articulations has been neatly 'solved' in man and other mammals by the development in young individuals of epiphyses – terminal pieces separate from the main portion of the bones. All the elements of the internal skeleton are first formed in the human embryo in cartilage; later the cartilage is destroyed and replaced by bone. But in this replacement process a thin film of cartilage is left separating the ends (the epiphyses) from the shaft of the bone. This film remains a growing-point; the cartilage formed here continually adds to the length of the bone; but as it is formed, the bone continually replaces it. Finally, when the adult length is attained, the cartilage is completely absorbed, and the shaft and ends of the bone fuse. Growth is over; and this growth has been accomplished without interference with the joints of the bone.

There are, in a middle-aged person, a few over two hundred separate bones in the body (half of them in the hands and feet). All in all, however, there are from embryonic days on about four times that many bones, or centres of growth, formed in the body. These gradually fuse together to form the adult number of elements. Fusion takes place at various times from embryonic life to middle age. This feature is of use in estimating the age of an individual from the skeleton.

REPLACEMENT AND DERMAL BONES. According to their method of formation, bones may be grouped in two categories: cartilage replacement bones and dermal bones. The more internal bones of the skeleton are formed first of cartilage in the embryo and are gradually replaced by bone. Such bones form the greater bulk of the human skeleton. A second series of bones are those formed in the skin – relics of the superficial armour found in the earliest vertebrates. For these dermal bones there are no cartilaginous predecessors. Such bones include a major part of the elements of the skull, the lower jaw, and the collarbone. Which is the older type of bone? The fact that cartilage appears first in the embryo, backed by the absence of bones in the lowest of living vertebrates, speaks strongly for the priority of cartilage. But we have noted that bone was present in the oldest known vertebrates, and the modern boneless forms – lampreys and sharks – are probably degenerate types descended from bony ancestors. Bone was surely a very early product of vertebrate evolution; cartilage at first may have been only an embryonic 'invention' to facilitate bone growth.

THE TRUNK

We shall, for convenience, discuss the bones and muscles of the body under three heads: those of the trunk, those of the head and throat, and, finally, the limbs.

BODY MUSCLES. The major portion of the musculature of a primitive vertebrate was that of the body and tail; it is by lateral undulations of the body that forward progression takes place. In a fish the muscles of one side of the body are relaxed, those of the opposite side tensed, causing a curvature of the body; such curves travel back down the trunk, increasing in amplitude and culminating in a powerful stroke of the tail fin. The backward pressure of successive curves upon the water forces the fish forward; it is to the trunk muscles that the major locomotor efforts of the fish are due; paired fins, even if present, are merely small steering organs. Naturally these trunk muscles are highly developed and are very bulky. They are arranged in a paired series down each side of the trunk and tail, interlocking with each other and acting upon the backbone and ribs.

THE BACKBONE AND RIBS. The development of the backbone and ribs of fishes seems to have been associated with the need of support for this powerful muscular system; the notochord and the ordinary connective tissues were not of sufficient strength. The main central part of each vertebra develops about the notochord, often as a spool-shaped structure with a rudiment of the notochord in its centre, and attaches at either side to two successive segments of the body musculature. Above the central element of each joint of the backbone is an arch and spine surrounding and protecting the spinal cord; and successive arches are joined together by interlocking connexions. A backbone lacks the flexibility of the old notochord; it is stiffer but it is stronger. Ribs project out from the backbone on either side between successive muscle segments and offer a solid point of attachment for the muscles. In some fishes there are, as extra reinforcements, two pairs of ribs and even (the shad is all too good an example) still further intermuscular bones.

REDUCED IMPORTANCE OF TRUNK AND TAIL IN LAND ANIMALS. In land forms the trunk decreases in importance as an element in locomotion; the limbs assume the main role, and the originally stout trunk musculature is reduced. The tail is no longer of importance in propulsion in land life but is generally retained; in dinosaurs, for example, it is a useful balancer. But wriggling of the body is still to some extent an aid in advancing the limbs to a forward position, and a primitive land animal still uses this means of locomotion to a considerable degree; the trunk musculature is still dominant in the tailed amphibians.

In mammals the tail is still further reduced and in general serves only as a balancer in tree life (in a few cases it has developed a prehensile power) or a handy fly-swatter. In a fish or lizard the tail is a continuation of the body; in mammals it is a mere appendage sharply marked off from the trunk. Some forms, ourselves among them, have abandoned it completely. In an average fish the tail makes up nearly half the bulk of the animal; in losing the tail we have shed a considerable portion of our original bodies.

The musculature of the trunk has become much reduced in mammals, including man. There is still a fairly well-developed set of muscles running down the back close to the vertebrae, serving to hold the head and backbone in place, and there is a thin muscular sheath over the abdomen. A fair amount of muscle connects the ribs; but these last muscles are concerned with breathing rather than bodily movement. Our trunk muscles have sadly degenerated. When one eats a fish it is the axial muscles one eats; when one eats a mammal it is leg muscles that we usually have set before us; spare ribs form one of the few exceptions.

THE BACKBONE IN LAND LIFE. But while the muscles of the trunk have degenerated, the bones are of even heightened utility. With life on land, the problem of holding the body off the ground and supporting it on the limbs becomes an important one. The backbone of a fish is almost straight. This would never do in a land animal; the weight of the trunk would cause it to cave in. The vertebrae of the trunk arrange themselves in the form of an arch, the front and hind legs forming its two piers. The organs are suspended from the arch, part of them directly by folds of skin, part indirectly through the barrel of the ribs, which tend to be bound together in the chest region by a breastbone (sternum). In fish there is no neck; the head and body move as a unit. In land animals, however, it is impractical for a creature to have to shift the whole front part of its body and legs to turn its head; a slim, easily movable neck region is developed, and the vertebrae of the neck curve upwards to give the head a bit of elevation. In mammals the first two neck vertebrae assume quite a complicated structure to afford great freedom for turning movements of the head.

In the development of man's erect posture the curvature of the backbone is further modified. It is essential that the centre of gravity be brought straight above the hips, so that maintenance of posture – fore-and-aft balance – can be accomplished without too much waste of muscular effort. This is brought about mainly by the development of a second curvature in the back. The hip region has, so to speak, been kept stationary and the chest pushed up and back. This has resulted in a backward concavity above the hips, 'the small of the back', and brings head and chest above the hip region in good balance.

In a four-footed animal the weight is distributed more or less equally between front and hind legs, and the arch of the back is fairly uniform in size throughout. In man, however, the entire weight is carried by the 'hind legs'; and it is apparent on the skeleton that the disc-like central elements of the backbone become stouter and stouter as we proceed down the spinal column to the hips, where the weight is transferred to the legs.

Parenthetically we may note that although this change to an erect posture has been accomplished successfully by the skeleton, the internal organs have in man been only imperfectly adjusted to this right-angle change in their relative position and lines of suspension. Hernias, most frequent in males, are but one obvious evidence of imperfect adjustments of our organs to our erect posture.

In a primitive vertebrate, even in many reptiles, ribs may be found on every joint of the backbone from the neck to the base of the tail. In mammals, including ourselves, ribs have become much reduced in numbers. With the decreased girth of the growing neck region, the ribs in this part of the body have tended to disappear and are represented only by stubs fused into the sides of the vertebrae. There are, in mammals, almost always exactly seven of these neck (or cervical) vertebrae. In the waist (lumbar) region, too, ribs have been done away with. In the chest, or dorsal region, however, they have been retained and are well developed, functioning in connexion with the breathing apparatus. A few short stout ribs (sacrals) are also present in the hip region binding the backbone tightly to the hip bones.

HEAD STRUCTURES

As a second great group of bony and fleshy structures we may consider those of the head and throat, first discussing the bony elements and then the muscles associated with them.

In man the skeleton of this part of the body consists of the skull, the movable lower jaws connected with it, and a few minor elements in the tongue and middle-ear region. The skull is an exceedingly complex structure, the details of which are the despair of any student of anatomy. It consists of a considerable number of bones of both cartilage replacement and dermal types fitted together in an intricate and sometimes seemingly senseless pattern. We cannot enter here into the details of its construction, but we may at least gain some idea of the reasons for its complexity if we review its history, features of which have been noted in earlier chapters.

ELEMENTS OF THE HEAD SKELETON. Let us take a long step backward to the earliest days of vertebrate history, when our ancestors were jawless and limbless types, represented today

Diagrams to show successive stages in skull formation. *A*, a primitive vertebrate with braincase and gill bars but lacking special jaw elements and dermal bones. *B*, the shark stage. Jaws have formed from gill bars. *C*, the bony fish stage; dermal bones have been added.

by the lampreys and hagfishes. These forms are somewhat specialized, and none is, we are sure, an exact duplicate of the true primitive vertebrate. For clarity we may perhaps be permitted to picture a diagrammatic primitive vertebrate head which shows the essential skeletal features as seen in a lamprey but purged of the eccentricities of that specialized living animal.

At this early stage there was no skull in the proper sense of the term, nor any jaws, upper or lower. A main element of the structure of the head was apparently a braincase – a box of cartilage or replacement bone which surrounded the brain and internal ear and protected the nostrils and eyes. A second important set of structures were the skeletal bars which stiffened the gill slits. These were, again, formed of cartilage or replacement bones; each bar included two main elements, upper and lower, on each side, the two movable on each other and turned somewhat forward at their upper and lower ends. The gill slits and their supports in many primitive vertebrates extended far forward under the head region.

A third important element of head construction lay in the presence of bony dermal armour, continuous with the scales of the body and arranged in solid plates in the skin of the head and neck region. Such armour was present in many early vertebrates; but, in order to keep the story in simple form, we have not introduced it into our figures until a later stage.

JAWS. A brainbox, a highly developed set of gill bars, and a set of dermal armour plates – these are the three basic elements from which our own skull has arisen. But it is a long road from the primitive arrangement just described to the skull structure seen in ourselves.

The development of jaws was an important step in this evolutionary process. Jaws are quite surely derived from gill bars. The original mouth was a small rounded opening on the underside near the front of the head. As it enlarged its gape, it would seem to have pushed back and crowded into the members of the gill-bar series. One or two of the foremost sets seem to have disappeared in the process (in sharks there are little nodules in the corners of the jaws which may represent them). Another pair, however, held its ground, enlarged, became associated with toothlike structures in the skin, and formed the jaws. These, in a shark, are both freely movable and are quite clearly in line with the related ordinary gill bars behind them.

FORMATION OF THE SKULL – DERMAL BONES. We now have braincase and jaws but still no complete skull. To form this we must avail ourselves of the dermal armour – the skin bones. These elements have in many fishes covered the top and sides of the head completely, have fused with the original upper jaws, on the one hand, and the braincase, on the other, and have united them into a solid structure – a true skull. These dermal bones form a solid covering, except for spaces for the eyes and nostrils. They cover over the lower-jaw region and, in fishes, the underside of the throat as well and extend back over the gill region to the shoulders. They have even invaded the mouth (which is lined with true skin). In the course of evolutionary history they have in considerable measure replaced the original braincase and jaws. The former usually lacks a roof (the dermal bones protect the top of the brain), and even the jaws, upper and lower, in many fishes consist of dermal bones, except for the actual joint between the jaws and a small region where the upper jaws join the brainbox. At the back of the head we find in bony fishes a small opening for the first gill slit (the spiracle); a wide slit farther back formed an external opening for the gills.

This is the type of skull which is found in many bony fishes today and was present in our own fish ancestors. The dermal armour and braincase were composed of a considerable number of bones arranged in definite patterns. Many of these bones can be traced down through the ages in later types to the human condition; and indeed many of the bones seen in a fish skull have been given names first applied to the same elements in man. Almost every bone present in a human skull was already formed in the skull of our Devonian fish ancestors a third of a milliard years ago. We cannot go into the details here; but an examination of the series of skulls shown in our figures will reveal that in the course of our history some of the original bones have disappeared, and the proportions of others have changed greatly, but that we still retain the essentials of the old fish scheme.

THE SKULL IN EARLY LAND ANIMALS. A great change in the skull architecture took place when our fish ancestors left the water. With the abandonment of gill-breathing, the bones covering the gill region and throat disappeared, and the dermal covering became restricted to the skull and jaws and to an isolated layer over the shoulder, represented today by our collarbone – the only skin bone in our body behind the head.

The skull pattern, however, remained much the same; and the amphibian skull figured is, except for the gill covering, almost identical with that of the bony fish seen above it. In primitive reptiles, too, there has been little change.

THE SKULL IN MAMMALS AND MAN. With the development

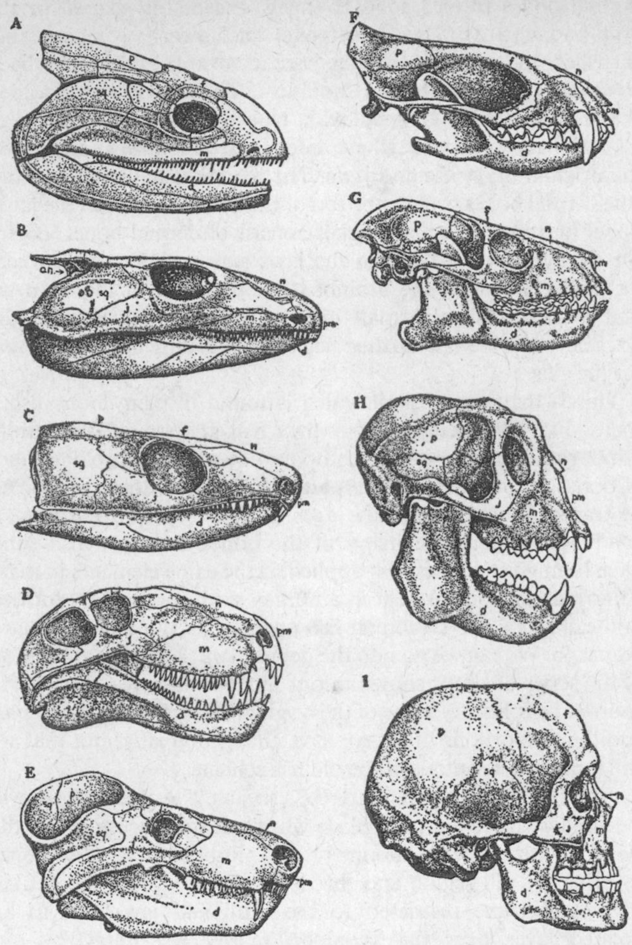

A series of figures of side views of the skull from a lobe-finned bony fish to man. These form a morphologically progressive set of stages representing the various groups through which human ancestors passed, although the genera shown may not be themselves the exact ancestors and frequently show small variations from an 'idealized' type. A few of the more prominent skull elements are labelled. *A*, a lobe-finned fish (*Osteolepis* of the Devonian). *B*, a primitive amphibian (*Palaeogyrinus* of the Carboniferous) basically similar to the last but with the front part of the skull more elongated. *on*, the otic notch in which the eardrum was of the mammal-like reptiles, further important alterations set in. A small opening in the side of the temple gave freer play to the jaw muscles; this hole becomes larger as we approach mammalian conditions, and the edge of the skull below it becomes a narrow arch – a 'handle' to the skull. Certain of the skull bones tend to drop out: this process is especially marked in the lower jaw, where six or seven bones, originally present on each side, become much reduced in size. On the roof of the mouth a partition develops to form the bony secondary palate, an essential part of our breathing apparatus. In the primitive mammal the bar behind the eye socket has dropped out, further loss of bones has occurred around the eyes, and only the expanded dentary bone remains in the lower jaw. This has formed a brand new type of jaw joint, articulating with the squamosal bone at the side of the skull, while (as noted in discussing the ear) the old jaw articulation has been taken over into the series of bones in the middle ear. A marked change is seen inside the enlarged temporal hole; the brain has enlarged in mammals, and its originally small and incomplete casing has expanded about it, the roofing bones growing down over the sides and one of the bones originally part of the upper jaw being used to fill up a gap laterally.

In the primates, leading to man, further developments have taken place. A bar – now a solid one – has been built up behind the eyes, and the face has shortened up greatly, with a small nose projecting above. The most obvious development, of course,

---

situated; this notch was present, as seen above, in the ancestral fish *C*, a stem reptile (*Captorhinus* of the early Permian), similar to the amphibian in most respects except for the elimination of the ear notch. *D*, a primitive mammal-like reptile (*Dimetrodon* of the Permian). A hole has appeared in the temple region; the teeth are becoming differentiated. *E*, an advanced mammal-like reptile (*Cynognathus* of the Triassic). The temporal opening is larger, the teeth are approaching mammalian conditions, a number of elements in skull and jaw are reduced or absent. *F*, a primitive fossil insectivorous mammal (*Deltatheridium* of the Cretaceous). There is a further loss of skull and jaw elements, the braincase is expanding, and the bar behind the orbit has disappeared. *G*, a fossil lemur (*Notharctus* of the Eocene). The post-orbital bar is re-established. *H*, a fossil monkey (*Mesopithecus* of the Pliocene). The face has shortened, the braincase much expanded, the orbits are turned well forward, and the bar behind them has become a solid partition. *I*, *Homo sapiens* (Cro-Magnon type). The face is further shortened, the braincase still more expanded, nose and chin prominently developed. Abbreviations for bony elements: *d*, dentary; *f*, frontal; *j*, jugal; *m*, maxilla; *n*, nasal; *p*, parietal; *sq*, squamosal.

is the further enormous expansion of the braincase to house the great cerebral hemispheres.

THE CONSTITUENTS OF THE HUMAN SKULL. We noted that three constituents went into the makeup of the original skull – braincase, gill bars, and dermal armour. What part have they today in our own skull?

The old braincase is still present but in much reduced condition. It forms only the more deeply concealed parts of the skull – those surrounding the base and back of the brain.

The original jaws were derived from gill bars. These had become massive, powerful structures in sharks. But today they have almost vanished. Apart from remnants in the ear and a plate in the side of the braincase they have disappeared from the skull; their place has been taken by dermal bones.

It is these latter elements which form the major architectural features of our own skull. All of its top and front, practically the entire side and even the major part of the roof of the mouth are composed of dermal bone. We have noted that the origin of this type of structure appears to have been in relation to defence against eurypterid enemies. It is curious to think that our skull today is, in great measure, a lasting memento of the struggles of our oldest vertebrate relatives against a group of crab-like creatures extinct two hundred million years ago.

FATE OF THE GILL BARS. We have, since leaving the fish stage, made no mention of the gill bars. These, very essential in fish, have naturally dwindled vastly in importance in land animals which have abandoned gill-breathing. We have noted the use that has been made of some remnants of them in the ear bones. The remaining members of the series are now represented only by small elements in the base of the tongue and in the Adam's apple.

THE THROAT MUSCLES. The ordinary muscles of the trunk come to a stop at the back of the head and the throat. The six highly specialized muscles of the eye are isolated members of this set and so are some of those of the tongue; all the other muscles of the head and throat belong to a complicated and very specialized group which was originally associated with the gill bars and, in the embryo, arises quite separately from the ordinary muscles of the body. In a fish the gills form a powerful pumping mechanism, and complicated members of this muscle series join the various gill bars with each other. When parts of this skeletal system were taken over to form the jaws, their musculature quite naturally accompanied them. Our jaw muscles, like the original jaws, were once part of the fish breathing mechanism.

In mammals generally, superficial parts of various muscle groups often become attached to the deeper layers of the dermis and are responsible for the twitching motions of the skin seen in these animals. In man most of these muscles have gone. We retain, however, a thin but effective layer of muscles beneath the skin of the head, particularly concentrated on the face and around the lips. No such muscles exist in the lower vertebrates;

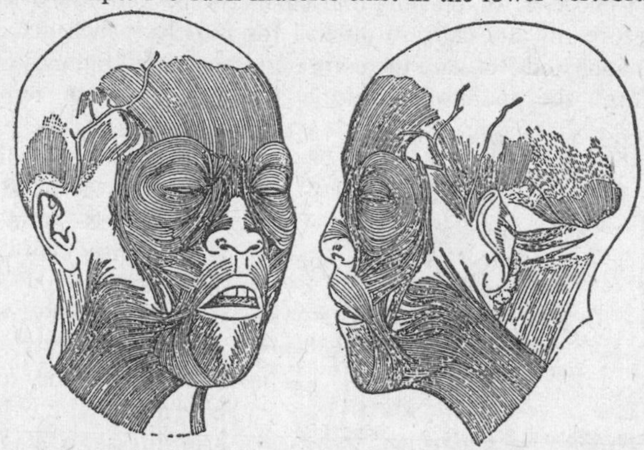

The facial muscles of man (an adult Chinese). These 'muscles of expression' are absent in forms below the mammals; they were orginally muscles which moved the bars around the fish spiracle. Note the muscles behind the ears, which in many mammals readily move that structure. (From Ernst Huber, *Quarterly Review of Biology*)

a reptile or a fish can neither smile nor frown. These muscles, too, were originally concerned with breathing. With the reduction of the gills, the muscles of the gill system still persisted in the neck. Some of them became situated just beneath the skin of that region and in mammals have migrated forward over the surface of the head to become the muscles of expression.

LIMBS

As a third main constituent of the muscular and skeletal architecture of the body we may treat of the limbs. Historically they are an outgrowth of the body. At first small appendages, they have increased in size until they, and parts connected with them, make up a vast proportion of the body's bulk. In any view of the musculature of the human body, almost all the muscles visible are limb muscles, and there are more bones in the limbs than in the rest of the body combined.

LIMB MUSCLES. To begin with, let us make a brief survey of our own limbs as one end product of the many evolutionary stories in which limbs have been concerned. Of the numerous muscular elements we shall say little. Strong muscles connect the limbs with the body. Both the upper arm and thigh have heavy muscles for opening and closing knee and elbow joints. The forearm and calf are utilized for muscles which act upon the hands and feet, and there are numerous small muscles which perform the manifold intricate motions of these terminal members of the limbs. Each of the ordinary fingers of the hand, for example, is connected with some half-dozen muscles which may move it in varying ways.

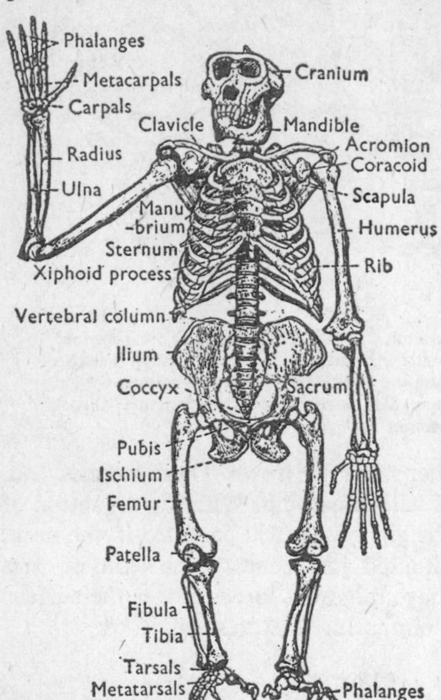

The skeleton of a gorilla with the major elements labelled. These are readily comparable with similar structures in the human skeleton in the plate opposite. (From Neal and Rand, *Comparative Anatomy*, P. Blakiston's Son & Co., Inc.)

BONES OF THE ARM. Each limb has at its base a limb girdle. In the arm this has as its main component the shoulder blade, or scapula, which is but loosely attached to the body by underlying muscles. This freedom probably owes its origin to the fact that in a four-footed animal the impact of landing on the front feet would result in violent jars to the body were there a tight connexion; the muscles formed an elastic spring which absorbed the jolts.

Below the front edge of the scapula is a tiny nubbin of bone called the 'coracoid', or crow-like process, because it is shaped like a crow's beak. This is a relic of what was, in our reptilian ancestors, a large plate of bone lying on the underside of the chest. From the scapula to the breastbone extends the collarbone, or clavicle; this is a dermal bone, an isolated relic of the armour plate which once covered the whole body of our early ancestors.

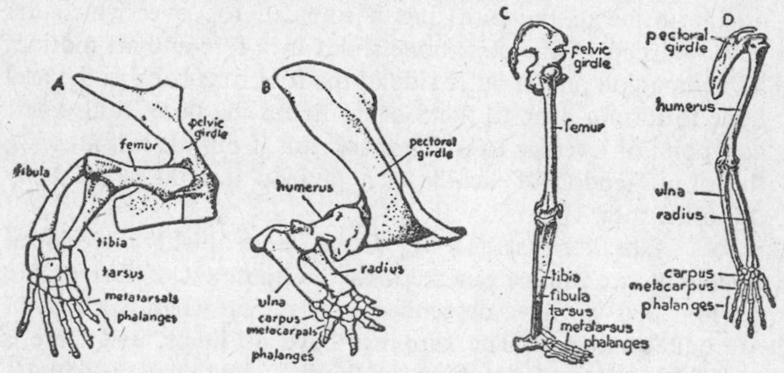

A, leg; *B*, arm of a primitive land animal; *C*, *D*, the same in man. Essentially the same elements are present, but there have been great changes in proportions.

Running from shoulder to elbow is a single stout bone – the humerus. Beyond this, a second segment, the forearm, contains two parallel elements – the radius and ulna. The former is a long thin cylinder. The head of the ulna projects above the end of the humerus and acts as a point of leverage for opening out the arm.

Below these two lies the region of the wrist, or carpus, containing some eight small bones; beyond these spread out the five fingers. At the base of each is a bone (metacarpal) embedded in the palm of the hand, while beyond lie the free joints of the fingers – two in the thumb and three in the others.

BONES OF THE LEG. The hip bones, or pelvic girdle, form a stout complex of bones fused in adults into a solid structure which is attached tightly to the base of the spine and transmits the weight of the body to the legs; its flaring sides form an area of attachment of many of the leg muscles, and its cup-shaped structure affords considerable support to the organs of the abdomen.

As in the arm, the first joint of the leg – the thigh – contains a single bony element, here termed the femur, while the second joint contains two elements – the stout shin bone (tibia) and the slim fibula (a Latin term for 'pin'). The kneecap functions in transmitting the pull of the thigh muscles over the knee to the tibia and thus opening out the leg. Corresponding to the wrist region is that of the ankle, or tarsus. Here there are some seven bones. The two upper ones are peculiarly constructed. One (that on the inside of the foot) has a rounded top over which the hollowed end of the shin bone slides in a fore-and-aft motion. Its companion on the outer side of the foot runs back as the heel bone to form a prop to the foot in the resting pose. It also acts as a point of leverage to which there runs, from the calf muscles, the stout 'tendon of Achilles'; a pull on this raises the body on to the toes.

THE LIMBS IN FISHES. If, from these highly developed structures, we retrace our steps to the humblest of vertebrates, we find that we have descended to a region where such limbs are quite unknown. The lampreys have no limbs, and there is very little trace of anything of the sort in the ostracoderms. These flattened animals seemingly kept to the bottom in locomotion, and vertically placed fins were frequently sufficient to regulate their movements. Only when vertebrates became more active did there come the problem of regulation in an up-and down direction, a need for stabilizing rudders to keep the fish on an even keel.

Seemingly it was in relation to this need that paired fins first appeared. Like the median fins, the primitive limb seems to have been a broad flap projecting out from the body but projecting to the sides rather than top or bottom. The structure seems primitively to have been that of a number of parallel horizontal skeletal bars, with their bases fused into girdles, and a layer of muscle above and below. From these bars have come eventually all limb bones; from the two simple layers of muscles covering the bars have come all the complicated muscles of our limbs. Even in our own case the muscles of the arms and legs are still for the most part obviously divided into two main sets: one leading up from the palm or sole side of the hand or foot and the other from the upper surface.

At first the motion of the limbs seems to have been merely a slight up-and-down motion of this broad-based stabilizing rudder; but in most fishes the base of the fin has become much constricted, and rotary movements are possible. Even so, the limbs of fishes are essentially steering and balancing organs rather than propulsive ones; in few cases does a fish 'row' himself along or rest upon his limbs.

Various modifications of the bones of the fin take place when the base is constricted and motility increased. One interesting type of skeletal structure is that which we have noted in the case of the crossopterygians, our own fish ancestors. In them only one bone of the fin joins the body; two bones constitute the next segment. This is the basic pattern of all land limbs; by growth of the limb and elaboration of this structure we reach the type which, with sundry modifications, is present from salamanders to men.

PRIMITIVE LAND LIMBS. In the process of change from water to land types, the two limb girdles have become considerably modified. In fish the shoulder girdle is tightly bound to the head by the dermal armour, which covers the whole front part of the body, while the pelvic girdle is small and is confined to the belly side of the body; there is no connexion with the backbone. This structure is all wrong from the point of view of a land animal. The shoulder must be freed from the head to permit of head movements without the need of shifting the front legs; and since in a land animal the hind legs must bear much of the weight of the body, they must be connected to support the backbone. In almost every land form shoulder and head are separated, and there is a good connexion between the expanded pelvic girdle and specialized sacral ribs (one in most amphibians, two or more in reptiles and higher forms).

In a primitive amphibian there was already established the essential pattern of the limbs found in man. Bone for bone, almost every human element was present in these primitive swamp dwellers which, first of all backboned animals, gained the power of leaving the water to walk on four stout limbs. Most of the changes that have occurred in the last three hundred million years or so have been changes in proportions rather than the addition of new elements.

LIMB ROTATION. The limbs of a primitive land dweller were short, and elbow and knee were directed outward. In the journey upward to the mammalian stage, length has considerably increased, and the limbs have rotated about so as to bring the knee forward and the elbow back and thus place the legs underneath the body. Many of us have done that type of 'one-two-three' exercise in which, lying prone, with arms at the sides, you touch your chin to the floor, then raise yourself on your arms. This required considerable muscular effort; yet this is just the pose in which the early land animals walked, and the turtle persistently crawls in similar fashion. Once the limbs were brought underneath the body, the bones of the limbs could carry most of the strain and the muscles could be properly put to work to move the body without wasting most of their energy for support.

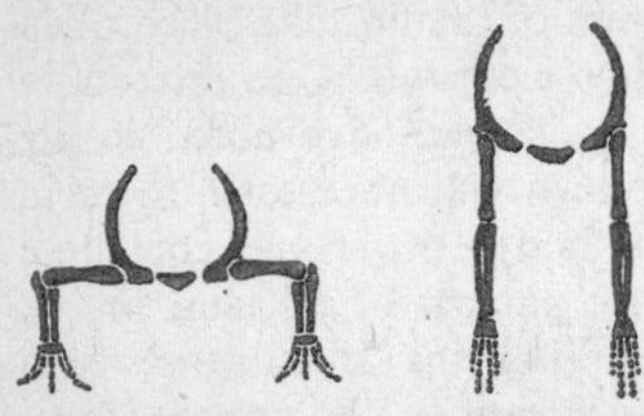

Diagrammatic sections through the bodies of four-footed vertebrates to show the contrast between the sprawling early land animals (*left*) and the erect-limbed mammalian posture.

This rotation of the limbs naturally caused considerable changes in the muscles and in the girdles from which many of the muscles spring. We shall not go into the details but may note that in this process much of the massive shoulder girdle of the reptiles went out of use and that the tiny 'crow's beak' of a coracoid in our own shoulder is a remnant of a great plate of bone which covered the chest of our reptilian ancestors.

THE HISTORY OF FINGERS AND TOES. The primitive land forms seem to have been (so to speak) a bit uncertain as to how many toes were proper and as to how many joints each should have. There may have been as many as seven toes to begin with (although the evidence is none too good); reptiles, however, had steadied down to a count of five, which (counting out from the thumb or big toe) had, respectively, 2, 3, 4, 5, and 3 joints each. This probably is related to the fact that in early reptiles, where the limbs spread widely at the sides of the body, the outer toes had to be longer to twist forward and touch the ground. In mammals, and some of the higher reptilian ancestors of mammals, the toes have been brought into line and have no more than three joints. In mammals – but not in lower vertebrate types – the thumb and big toe appear primitively to have been divergent from the others, with something of the grasping power which we have retained and improved upon in our own hands.

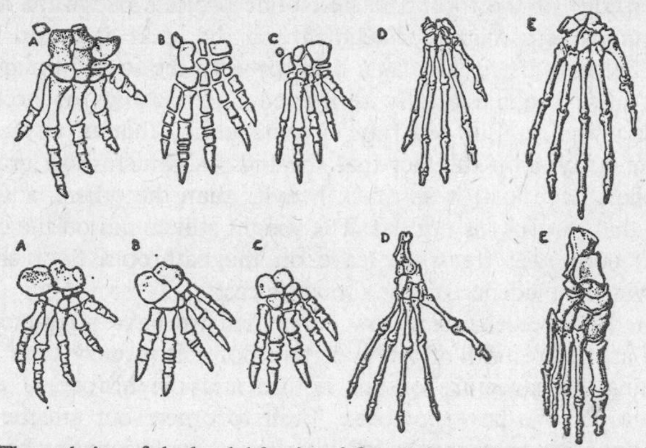

The evolution of the hand (*above*) and foot (*below*). All specimens are of the right side, with 'thumb' and 'big toe' to the *right* of the illustrations. *A*, a primitive reptile (*Ophiacodon*); *B*, *C*, mammal-like reptiles with the 'extra' toe joints reduced or absent; *D*, *Notharctus*, a lemur, representing the primitive mammalian type; *E*, man. Note the reduction in the number of joints in the toes from 2, 3, 4, 5, 3 (or 4) to 2, 3, 3, 3, 3, the specialization of the proximal ankle bones in mammals, some reduction in the number of wrist and ankle bones, and the variations in the thumb and big toe.

ARBOREAL LIFE. This grasping power and many other features in the skeleton suggest that the ancestral mammals were arboreal animals. Most later types have descended to the ground, and many forms have reduced or lost the then useless inner toes. In our own case, however, long-continued life in the trees has not only made for the retention of these toes but has preserved to us much of the primitive flexibility of the limbs of early mammals. Our whole arm structure is essentially a primitive mammalian one, and the legs, too, are essentially primitive in many ways, although the muscles and bones of the hip region have been somewhat modified in relation to the assumption of upright posture.

THE HUMAN FOOT. It is our foot, not our hand, that is the one peculiar feature of our limb skeleton. Our ape ancestors were not four-footed types but four-handed ones, and their 'hind hands' were better grasping organs than the front ones, with a widely divergent big toe opposed to the other four. Such a structure, however, is an awkward one for walking on the ground. The apes, in general, are poor walkers, resting on the outer edge of the foot. The heel bone projects backward in all mammals as a muscle attachment; in the great apes and man this becomes useful also as a back prop to the foot. In man the toes have become greatly shortened and the big toe brought back into line. But our foot is quite unlike that of any other mammal type, in the fact that the big toe (which most ground dwellers have lost) is so much heavier than the others, and the fact that our foot is not flat. The weight still comes on the outer side; every wet track we leave on the bathroom floor shows convincing evidence of our simian ancestry.

In the three chapters now concluded we have attempted to give a brief résumé of a few of the more elementary facts concerning the structure of our bodies and the history of these structures. We have not been 'built to order' but are the end result of an enormously long series of evolutionary changes. The human body bears its history indelibly stamped upon it. Many of its parts have been profoundly altered during the long history of vertebrate development; many structures have completely changed their functions; gill supports have become jaws and then accessory organs of hearing; gill pouches have become glands of internal secretion; a balancing rudder has become the human hand; a receptor for smell has become the seat of our highest mental faculties. Our body is not the result of a straightforward designing of the best possible machinery for our purposes but in many respects is such a patchwork that it seems sometimes a wonder that it functions at all.

But function it does. Our ancestors have never been perfect mechanisms; but they have been successful enough to be born, to grow, to have offspring. Our bodies are good enough to survive the test. This machinery of ours may work imperfectly, but it does work – man lives and reproduces his kind.

CHAPTER 20

The Development of the Human Body

WE marvel at the natural processes which, in the course of many millions of years, have brought about the evolution of man and many other complex animals from lowly forms of life. But a phenomenon perhaps even more wonderful than our evolutionary history is the development of the individual. A minute egg is fertilized by a microscopic sperm. Within the shelter of the mother's womb this tiny speck of protoplasm grows, divides and redivides, and gives rise to the many tissues and complex organs which make up the adult man. The evolutionary drama required aeons for its enactment of the development of man; the embryological story requires but a few short months.

EARLY EMBRYOLOGICAL BELIEFS. To the ancients, but little of this story was known. That many vertebrates, such as the frog or chick, developed from an egg was obvious, and some stages in the development could be readily observed; but it was not until about a century ago that it was discovered that a comparable, although much smaller, egg (ovum) was present in mammals.

The sperm is of fundamental importance in normal vertebrate development, activating the egg and contributing half of the hereditary factors to the new individual. This function was unsuspected in ancient times, and even today some primitive tribes are said to have no idea that the male sex has any connexion with the birth of children. The human sperm was discovered some two and a half centuries ago when the first crude microscope was invented. But even so it was long before its relation to the embryological story was placed on any certain basis.

PREFORMATION THEORY. It is obvious that at a late stage of development the young chick or young human is structurally fairly similar to the adult, although of much smaller proportions, and it was not unnatural that two or three centuries ago, before accurate observations had been made, development was generally held to be entirely a matter of increase in size. The 'germ' of the adult was thought to be fully formed and differentiated before its growth began. Some of these early theorists believed that this tiny creature was preformed in the egg. Others believed that a tiny human being was contained in the sperm which, however, need to enter the egg in order to grow properly.

Such theories, if rigidly adhered to, lead to amusing results. If we assume that the individuals of the next generation are already fully formed within the eggs of their potential mothers and that these individuals, too, were fully formed within the eggs of their maternal parents, we must logically assume that this sequence of tiny body within body must go on indefinitely. We must, accordingly, be built on the plan of one of these hollow wooden eggs with which children play; this egg contains a smaller egg, which, in turn, contains another, etc. Under this theory it was even gravely calculated how many series of successively smaller beings Mother Eve must have had within her ovary and how soon this series might become exhausted and the race ended!

A rival theory maintained that development consisted not merely of growth but of differentiation as well, and a century ago more careful observations on embryos, supplemented by the discovery that all living things were composed of cells, proved this to be the true situation. It soon became definitely accepted that each living thing springs from a single egg cell which, in the case of vertebrates, is fertilized by a sperm cell. The embryo and adult arise from these comparatively simple objects by a process of cell division and by a differentiation of cell materials. The individual arises not merely by growth but by an increasing complexity of structure.

EVOLUTIONARY CONCEPTS: THE RECAPITULATION THEORY. The invention of adequate microscopical equipment and techniques as the nineteenth century went on enabled scientists to see more fully the various stages in the embryological history of animals. An immense stimulus to this study was given by the general acceptance of the evolutionary theory in the middle of the century. It was early seen that the embryos of animals resemble one another in varying degrees and that the animals which the students of evolution believed closely related had in general the most similar developmental processes. All vertebrates, for example, have an early developmental history which follows similar fundamental patterns in forms as different, as adults, as a man and a shark; the embryo of man and other mammals resemble each other closely until a later stage in embryonic life.

Enthusiastic students went even farther with this correlation of development and evolutionary stories and developed the so-called Biogenetic Law – the theory of recapitulation. Evolution teaches us, for example, that the earliest animals were presumably one-celled forms; later there developed multicellular animals which gradually became more and more complex in structure. This evolutionary story, it was pointed out, finds a parallel in the earliest stages of the development of any of the higher animals: we originate as a single egg cell which then by division becomes multicellular and gradually increases in complexity of structure. Again, the human embryo at one stage has a good system of gill pockets like those of an embryo fish but which later disappear or are transformed into other structures. Still other features in the human embryo are suggestive of structures found in the development of the amphibian, reptilian, and primitive mammalian stages in man's ancestry.

From this basis arose the conception that the development of the individual repeats the development of the race – that ontogeny recapitulates phylogeny. The human embryo, it was said, climbs its own family tree.

This statement, however, goes too far. To take the example of gill development in the human embryo cited above: We develop pouches from the throat, in the position of the fish's gill pouches, and corresponding furrows develop on the surface of the neck; but the pouches in man never open, never assume the gill-slit structure seen in the adult fish. It is the fish embryo, not the grown fish, that the human embryo resembles.

We do not recapitulate the adult stage of any of our ancestors. An amphibian did not evolve from a fish by becoming an adult fish and then going on beyond that stage but by diverging, as an embryo, into new channels in which limbs and lungs became better developed and in which gills ceased to mature. The differences between amphibians and reptiles, between reptiles and mammals, lie almost entirely in the fact that in the evolution from one class to another embryological processes have changed. Our own embryonic development exhibits this history well. We do begin with developmental processes which are common to us and our lower vertebrate relatives, but we gradually diverge from them without attaining any previous adult stage. The human embryo repeats, but it repeats embryonic, not adult, history.

But even if we must curb an unrestricted acceptance of the biogenetic law, it cannot be doubted that it has proved of great value in the advancement of our knowledge of embryology. The recognition of the essential similarity in developmental patterns in the various vertebrate groups has aided greatly in our understandings of many curious quirks in embryonic histories which otherwise would be inexplicable. Owing very largely to the stimulus of the recapitulation theory, there has been accumulated a vast store of embryological knowledge. In almost every group of animals the painstaking study of embryos of various ages has given us the ability to describe in sequence the stages in growth and differentiation – the steps by which cell division takes place, varied tissues are established, the organs take form.

EXPERIMENTAL STUDIES. Today we can give a fairly adequate description of embryological events, just as we can, for the vertebrates at least, describe most of the major happenings in evolutionary history. But we refuse to be content with a mere description of these events; we wish to know why they happen – to seek the causes underlying them.

With evolutionary history we can do little; the books are closed on past happenings, and our lives are too short to see evolutionary events in the making. But with embryological history we are dealing with present events, and in various groups whose type of development permits of it we may deal experimentally with embryos.

We may alter an embryo or its environment from the normal in some one respect and allow it to continue its development, and, if the resultant animal differs from the normal, we may reasonable conclude that the difference is causally related to the changed conditions that we have created and thus gain some insight into the processes of growth.

When in the vertebrate embryo a cup-shaped structure which is to become the retina of the eye grows out of the front part of the brain, the skin outside of this point promptly thickens to become the lens. This is the description of the actual event. But why does the lens develop? Is its growth induced by the presence of the retina beneath, or is the lens entirely independent in its origin? We might argue the merits of these two possibilities as long as we wished, but we could not give a positive decision merely from observing normal embryos. But experimentally the question can be fairly satisfactorily answered. In many amphibians if we remove the eye cup, the lens does not form in its accustomed position; and, further, if we graft this cup into, for example, the flank of the animal's body, a perfect lens may form in the skin there. Thus we may say with confidence that in these animals the eye cup induces the formation of a lens in the skin adjacent to it.

Through many experiments of this sort, in recent decades, we have begun an analysis of the processes underlying the events of developmental history.

In the case of man, of course, such experiments are out of the question, and but little work has been done on other mammals, although techniques are currently being developed for such studies. Many other vertebrates, however – frogs, salamanders, and chickens, for cxample – yield good experimental results, and, since these forms appear to develop according to the same fundamental plan as ourselves, it is highly probable that the facts discovered from work on these forms apply in great measure to the human embryo as well.

The development of the individual obviously is resultant upon an exceedingly complex interplay of chemical and physical forces. Such work as has been done so far has been a bare beginning of the elucidation of the problems that face us. If we fully understood how any egg develops into an adult, we would have solved a majority of all biological problems. We are, today, very far from such an understanding. But science is young and work continues.

GERM CELLS. In almost all except the lowest of living things, reproduction entails the union of two cells, one derived from each of two parents, to form a single cell from which develops the new individual. In some very primitive types the two cells which thus unite are similar in appearance; in most living creatures, however, we find that the two differ markedly in size and structure.

From one parent is derived the female element, the egg, a comparatively large cell which is incapable of motion and which, besides a nucleus, contains a large amount of cytoplasm. From the other parent comes the sperm, a much smaller cell, containing little cytoplasm and consisting of a head region containing the nucleus and a long whiplash tail for propulsion – the sperm must seek the egg.

In some groups of animals the same individual may produce both sorts of sex cells; but in a majority of invertebrates and, almost without exception, in chordates one individual produces only one type or the other. Male and female sexes are thus differentiated, and the differences between the two are often marked not only in the type of reproductive cells produced and the organs which bear them but in the general architecture of the body.

The germ cells from which the human eggs and sperm arise are, from an early period in development, confined entirely to the primary sex organs (gonads) – the ovary in the female, the testis in the male; these structures were described on pages 332–6. The germ cells come into relation with other cells or organs of the body only through the blood stream, from which they derive food materials and oxygen.

This isolation of the germ cells has an important bearing on problems of heredity. In some theories of inheritance it has been claimed that characters acquired during the life of the individual and the effect of use or disuse of parts of the body can be transmitted to the offspring. If a man by hard labour develops his muscles, this type of theory holds that his children are likely to be stronger physically; if he studies long and hard, his offspring are likely to be more intellectual than would otherwise have been the case.

Such a theory seems, at first sight, eminently reasonable. But when we come to consider the actual situation, it appears untenable. Children do not arise from muscles or brains; they arise from cells in organs quite unconnected with these structures except through the medium of the blood. It is difficult to conceive of a change in other organ systems which could act at a distance upon these isolated sex cells and so change the hereditary elements contained in them as to produce equivalent changes in the next generation; and much experimental study of this problem has failed to show any evidence for the theory of the inheritance of acquired characters. Our germ cells are in great measure independent of us. The children to which they may give rise partake of the hereditary characters which the parents have inherited, but our own acts or thoughts are powerless to affect correspondingly their heritage from us.

THE EGG. At puberty the ovaries of the human female – small organs roughly the size and shape of almonds, lying in the back of the abdominal cavity – contain some hundreds of thousands of germ cells, each surrounded by a layer of smaller cells forming a spherical structure termed a 'follicle'. Most of these are doomed to degenerate and disappear; a few hundreds may become mature eggs, or ova. In general, one egg ripens each month. The tiny egg grows rapidly, but even more rapid is the growth of the follicle as a whole; there develops within it a liquid-filled cavity, the egg adhering to one margin. Approaching maturity, the follicle may be as much as an inch in diameter and cause a large swelling on the outer wall of the ovary. The development of the follicles seems to be so timed that one ripens monthly at a period which appears to be, on the average, about two weeks after the onset of menstruation. When mature, the follicle bursts (a process termed ovulation), and the egg is liberated into the body cavity but is caught up into the funnel of the oviduct, or egg tube, and slowly passes down within that structure towards the uterus.

During the growth of the follicle the egg has grown to be about ·15 mm. (one one-hundred-and-sixtieth of an inch) in diameter, being thus barely visible to the naked eye. (In some vertebrates, such as birds, the egg contains a large amount of yolk and is thus extremely large by comparison.) The egg contains a nucleus and a very considerable amount of protoplasm containing some yolk material, the whole contained in a thin membrane and a tough capsule.

Under the microscope the human egg seems to have a simple type of cell structure. This apparent simplicity is, however, deceptive; experimental work on various invertebrate and lower vertebrate types shows that the egg alone, if properly stimulated chemically or physically, is capable of initiating the development of a new individual even when not fertilized by a sperm.

During the ripening of the egg the nucleus divides twice, three of the four nuclei so produced splitting off and leaving the egg with bits of protoplasm as tiny cells which soon degenerate. The nuclei of the germ cells are of prime importance as the carriers of

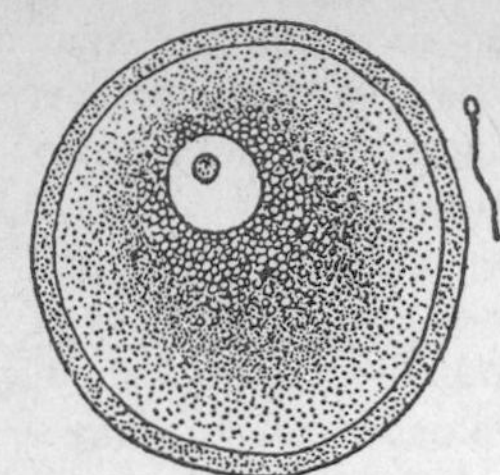

A human egg and sperm drawn to the same scale. Highly magnified (about 300 times natural size).

hereditary factors into the new generation, and these divisions, into the details of which we need not go here, seem to constitute a process of preparing the egg nucleus for a later union with that of the male germ cell. A comparable process of nuclear reduction goes on in the development of the sperm.

THE SPERM. The male germ cell, the sperm, is of a very different character. There is very little cytoplasm; the cell consists essentially of an oval head, mainly filled by the nucleus, and a long 'tail' – a whiplike propulsive organ. The male sex cell is much smaller than the egg. Its length is about one-third of the egg's diameter, but since this length is mainly the slim tail, its bulk is such that it would take some eighty-five thousand sperm to equal the egg in volume. This lack of size is more than compensated for in numbers, for, in contrast with the slow production of ripe eggs, many millions of mature sperm may be present at one time.

Sperm are formed along the margins of numerous tiny tubules in the testes. They are stored in immense numbers in the coiled epididymis adjacent to that structure and, when discharged through the ductus deferens, are carried in a viscous fluid secreted by the prostate and other glands lying along the course of this tube.

REPRODUCTION AND SOCIAL ORGANIZATION. In most vertebrates reproduction is a definitely periodic activity, the production of mature sex cells, sexual intercourse, and gestation taking place only at long intervals – frequently at one particular season of the year; but in the higher primates, man included, sexual activity is constant. This fact has probably had much to do with man's social evolution. Most vertebrates are highly individualistic and in most cases (disregarding the incompletely organized herd or flock grouping which is found here and there throughout the phylum) tend to congregate only during the breeding season. But in the primates, since the breeding season extends the year round, the association of members of the two sexes has likewise become permanent, and family life has been established. In a monkey cage at the zoo we frequently witness the family group established, a mature male, the 'old man' of the family, presiding over the activity of his wife or wives and their offspring. This is a simple type of social organization but one which may have been the principal, if not the only, social unit among our Paleolithic ancestors not so many thousands of years ago and one upon which have seemingly been established higher 'superfamily' units – clan, tribe, nation.

PATHS OF EGG AND SPERM. Once each month, as has been said, a ripe egg cell usually enters the upper end of the oviduct and begins a slow journey down that tube. Its chance of developing into an embryo depends upon its encountering a sperm during this journey. The life of the egg, if not thus fertilized, is comparatively brief. Exact knowledge is wanting in the case of man, but in some mammals which have been carefully studied it is found that the possible period of fertilization varies from a few hours in some cases to a day or two in others. Probably the viability of the human egg is somewhere between these figures; sexual union must occur close to the time of egg release if fertilization is to occur.

The sperms received in the vagina travel actively upward through the uterus into the oviducts – a distance of several inches, a long journey for such tiny objects. It is probable that their maximum span of life within the female reproductive tract is a matter of but one to three days.

FERTILIZATION. Fertilization is accomplished if one single sperm of the millions released during a sex act reaches and penetrates an egg at the upper end of the oviduct. The tail of the sperm is abandoned; the head, containing the nucleus, enters the substance of the egg, and developmental processes begin.

The sperm serves several functions in the developmental process. The most obvious feature is the fact that the nuclei of the sperm and egg unite to form a nucleus which, through repeated divisions, comes to be present in every cell of the embryo. Much observational and experimental work has conclusively shown that the nucleus is responsible for the carrying of hereditary factors, and the union of nuclei in the fertilized egg is the mechanism which brings about biparental inheritance.

Normally, but a single sperm of the many that may be present in the oviduct can penetrate an egg. It appears that the entrance of one sperm causes chemical changes at the surface of the egg which wards off others. Such a mechanism is a necessity if normal development is to occur; the entrance into the egg of additional sperm nuclei is found to lead to abnormalities in development.

But the sperm has a more immediate effect upon development than the carriage of hereditary factors. As soon as it touches the egg – even before its entrance – the sperm activates it, 'awakens' it from its previous passive state, and the initial stages in development are at once begun. It would appear that the egg, seemingly so simple, is really a complex mechanism, all 'set' to develop into an embryo, 'wound up', and only needing some stimulus to trip a lever and start the developmental processes at work. This activating effect of the sperm is something quite apart from its function as a bearer of paternal hereditary factors. In experiments on various animals, development has been successfully initiated by other types of stimuli. Eggs have been induced to develop into fatherless embryos by the use of various chemicals, or even by pricking them with a needle.

TWINS. In the higher primates, man included, but a single offspring is ordinarily produced at one time. In many other mammal groups, however, a litter of several offspring is the rule; and even in man the production of twins is not infrequent (once in about eighty-five births), and occasionally higher numbers are reported; six seems to be the maximum.

Twins are of two quite different types. More commonly, they appear to be due to the fact that two eggs have been released from the ovary and fertilized at the same time, the resultant embryos growing quite independently. Ordinary twins of this sort may have received quite different combinations of paternal and maternal hereditary characters and may differ in sex as well as in many physical and mental characters; there is no reason why they should resemble each other more than any two children of a family born separately.

Quite different in origin are identical twins. Such twins are always of the same sex and are always strikingly similar in physical and mental characters, except in so far as they have been differently affected by postnatal environmental factors. Identical twins arise, we believe, from a single fertilized egg which at some early stage of its development into an embryo has become divided into two parts, each of which develops separately. Coming thus from a single egg and single sperm, it is obvious that they will have exactly the same heritage of parental characters and hence may be expected to be remarkably similar.

CLEAVAGE OF THE EGG. During the first few days after fertilization the human egg travels from the upper part of the oviduct down this tube towards the uterus, where the growing embryo is destined to remain. During this time occur the earliest

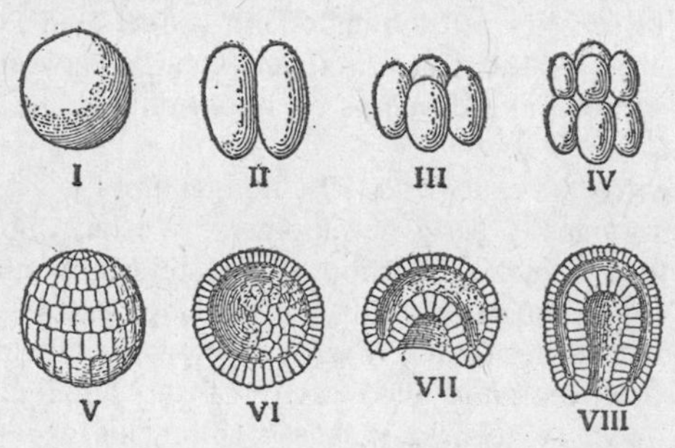

A series of stages in the early development of *Amphioxus*. Successive cleavages result in the formation of a hollow sphere, the blastula (*V*), seen in section in *VI*. This sphere folds in to form the gastrula (*VIII*), with an outer layer of ectoderm and inner layer of endoderm. (After Hatschek)

stages in embryonic development. The fertilized egg cell divides in two, the two cells into four, etc. The process is comparatively slow; very likely each successive cell division may take as much as a day for its accomplishment. But, as anyone who has ever worked out a problem in geometric progression knows, the increase in cell numbers soon becomes a rapid one.

EARLY DEVELOPMENT IN PRIMITIVE FORMS. The early embryonic history of man and other mammals is complicated by the fact that within a short time the embryo becomes embedded in the tissues of the maternal uterus, and a number of peculiar features in our early development are due to this situation. We may perhaps understand our own story better if we first consider the early development of such a primitive type as *Amphioxus*, where the egg is shed into the open sea and no such complications occur.

In this little marine chordate the fertilized egg divides into two cells, into four, etc., until over one hundred cells are present, arranged in a hollow sphere something like a raspberry or mulberry in shape. Then on one side the cells begin to push inward, just as one may push in one side of a soft, hollow, rubber ball, until the embryo becomes a sac with an inner and an outer layer of cells.

Such an early embryo is called a gastrula – a 'little stomach' stage in development. The internal cavity is destined to become the cavity of the digestive tract of the adult, the outer surface of the sac is destined to form (among other things) the skin. The inner cell layer is termed the endoderm ('inner skin'), the outer cell layer is termed the ectoderm ('outer skin'); between the two, at a later stage, there develops an important middle layer, the mesoderm.

EMBRYONIC MEMBRANES. The human embryo has no such simple history in its early development. We have noted in an earlier chapter that the evolution of the land egg in our reptilian ancestors was associated with the development of accessory embryonic structures (p. 80). The embryo proper was surrounded by the protective liquid-filled cavity of the amnion. The gut extended down to form a yolk sac embracing a considerable mass of yolk for the nutrition of the embryo. A third cavity, the allantois, grew out from the hind end of the gut towards the surface to function as a receptacle for waste liquid and also as an embryonic lung, blood vessels in its walls carrying the oxygen down to the growing body. Surrounding all these structures was a spherical outer wall – the chorion.

EARLY HUMAN DEVELOPMENT. These embryonic membranes have all been retained in man and other mammals, although there have been changes in conditions and functions. The human embryo becomes embedded in the wall of the uterus within a few days after development begins; and since these accessory structures must begin to function early, their necessarily rapid development has been, it would seem, responsible for radical differences between the early development of a primitive chordate and that of man.

The cleavage of a mammalian egg, as shown in photographs of the rabbit's egg, takes place, at first, in a fashion similar to that of *Amphioxus*, forming, as in that animal, a compact cluster of cells.

But from that point on, resemblance ceases. The cell mass soon divides into two portions, a hollow sphere of cells and, attached to it at one side, an inner cell mass. The outer sphere of cells represents the beginning of the chorion. The embryo is soon to

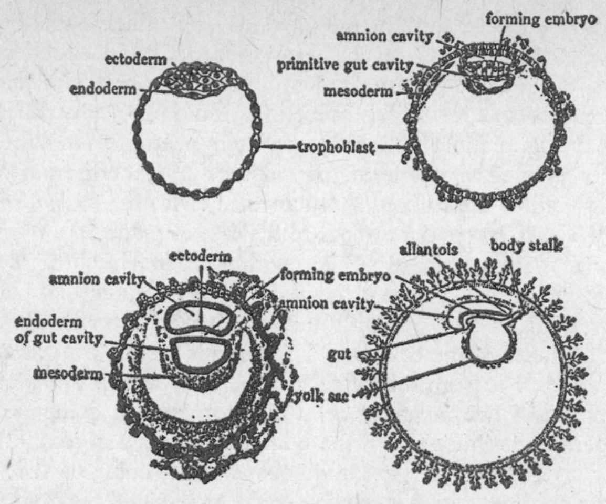

Diagrams to show early stages in the formation of the embryo and its membranes. These are all sections made vertically through the long axis of the developing embryo. *Upper left*, a very early stage comparable to the last of the series of photographs of mammalian eggs. An outer layer of trophoblast has been thrown out to come into contact with the walls of the uterus, while the remaining inner cell mass has barely begun differentiation into ectodermal and endodermal components. *Upper right*, somewhat more advanced. A double layer of cells represents the forming embryo; above this there has begun the formation of the amnion cavity; below, the formation of the cavity of the gut plus yolk sac. *Lower left*, mesodermal tissues (stippled) are now widespread, and amnion and gut cavities are larger. With the addition of mesodermal tissues to the trophoblast, the outer membrane is termed the chorion; this has begun to send out processes into the surrounding uterine tissues. The embryo at this stage is comparable to that seen in dorsal view at the left of the second text figure following (p. 393). *Lower right*, a more advanced stage. The embryo is rounding up, and the amniotic cavity extends downward in front of the expanding head. The gut cavity is beginning to pinch off from the yolk sac, while the allantois is growing out from the gut towards the surface along the body stalk by which alone the embryo is now connected with the chorion. In this outer membrane the development of processes (villi) which interweave with maternal tissues to form the placenta is now far advanced. (Arey, *Developmental Anatomy* [copyright, W. B. Saunders Co.])

become embedded in the walls of the uterus; and this outer layer must form rapidly to effect a union with the maternal tissues about the sac in which the embryo develops. From the inner cell mass alone develop the embryo and the remaining embryonic membranes.

Having thrown off this outer sphere as (so to speak) an advance guard for entrance into the uterine tissues, the inner mass of cells proceeds to form a gastrula with ectodermal and endodermal layers. But the complications of embryonic membrane formation have caused this process to occur in a fashion radically different from the simple infolding seen in a more primitive animal. The amnion is lined by ectoderm, the yolk sac by endoderm; and these two structures are formed simultaneously with the formation of the two germ layers concerned. In the case of man and a number of other mammals there develop within the inner cell mass two cavities: that lying above is the cavity of the amnion, that below, the yolk sac, continuous with the primitive gut. Between the two the remainder of the cell mass is spread out in the form of a flat oval plate. It is from this plate that the body arises. The plate is composed of two layers of cells. The top layer is composed of ectoderm, continuous with the lining of the amnion cavity. The lower layer is endoderm, continuous with the lining of the yolk sac. At one end (which is to become the hind end of the body) the plate remains connected with the outer sphere of cells. Into this, the body stalk, there grows out a tube, the allantois, from the hind end of the endodermal sac.

This, then, is the topography of a human embryo after some two to two and a half weeks of existence: a flat oval disc about ¼ mm. (one one-hundredth of an inch) across; a layer of ectoderm above, facing the cavity of the amnion; a layer of endoderm below, facing the yolk sac (and future digestive tube); a stalk connecting the disc with the outer lining of the cavity in which these structures lie.

MOTHER AND EMBRYO. Within a period variously estimated at from three days to a week, the early human embryo enters the uterus and soon becomes embedded in the maternal tissues lining that organ.

Primitively the egg developed outside the body of the mother. But retention of the embryo within the womb has potential advantages – protection and nourishment. Even in a number of fishes, amphibians, and reptiles the eggs are retained within the mother's body until they hatch. They are there protected against any of the dangers to which they would otherwise be exposed. Among the mammals we have noted that two primitive types still lay eggs; the vast majority, however, retain the embryo within the uterus.

But development of the embryo within the uterus is a more difficult problem in mammals than in reptiles or sharks. These forms have large eggs which contain a considerable amount of yolk. The embryo can, by utilizing this material, attain a considerable size before birth. In mammals, however, the egg is very small and there is little food for the embryo. Some other source of food supply is necessary; and the one available source is the food materials contained in the blood stream of the mother. Some mechanism is needed by which these food materials can be furnished to the embryo within the uterus.

The marsupial's early development takes place within the mother's body; but the problem of affording nourishment to the embryo has not been adequately 'solved'. In higher mammals, however, there is present an efficient placenta. This structure is formed by close union of maternal and embryonic tissues. Through it food and oxygen can be transferred to the embryo from the mother in exchange for waste materials and carbon dioxide; a long, unhurried period of development within the uterus is rendered possible.

MENSTRUATION. Periodically the uterus is prepared for the reception of an embryo through the phenomena of the menstrual cycle. The membrane lining this organ is in a state of constant change. When an egg is released from the ovary there occur definite changes – a thickening of the walls, associated with the possible reception of a fertilized egg. If, however, none arrives, the greater part of this thickened mass of tissues is sloughed off (menstruation), the cycle begins anew, and the uterus again makes ready for an embryo.

It is during the period when the lining is beginning to thicken and becomes 'receptive' that the egg, if fertilized, reaches the uterus. This, it appears, is not a matter of chance; the rupture of the ripe egg from the follicle is closely related to the changes in the uterine walls. The empty follicle develops into a large body termed the corpus luteum ('yellow body'). This body sends into the blood a hormone which stimulates the uterus to further activity.

DEVELOPMENT OF THE PLACENTA. When the tiny embryo reaches the uterus it lodges against the soft vascular walls of that organ and bores its way into these receptive maternal tissues. Menstruation ceases and the uterine lining remains thickened throughout the months of pregnancy. When the embryo first enters the uterine linings it is so small that it causes no alteration in the appearance of the womb. Within a few weeks, however, growth of the embryo and its membranes causes the region of the wall containing the embryo to bulge out into the cavity of the uterus. Soon further growth occludes this cavity altogether, and, by the time of birth, the uterus as a whole has been expanded to many times its original size.

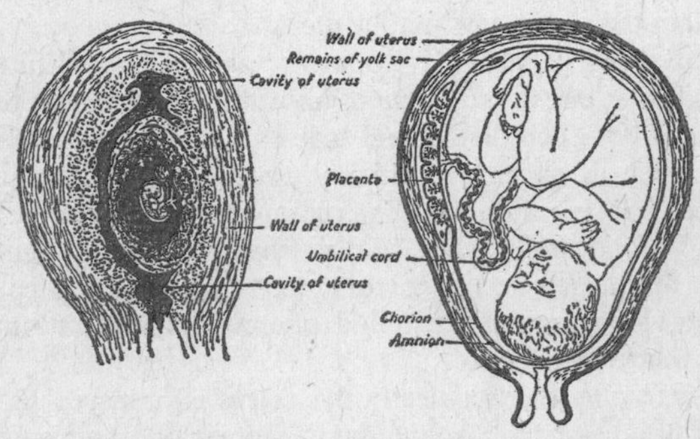

Sections through the uterus at two stages of development to show the relations of the embryo to the uterine tissues. *Left*, after about 3 or 4 weeks' growth. The fertilized ovum has sunk into the wall at the right of the section and is surrounded by uterine tissues but does not completely fill the uterus. Within the maternal tissues can be distinguished the outer envelope of the embryo (chorion); internal to this a space with the young embryo enclosed by the amnion and with the yolk sac also visible.

Right, the foetus shortly before birth. The embryo and its membranes have grown so that they fill the entire cavity of the distended uterus. A portion of the wall has become the placenta (for exchange of materials between mother and foetus). The yolk sac is now only a vestige. The amnion cavity has expanded so that it entirely surrounds the foetus except for the umbilical cord. (After Thompson and Ahlfeld, from Arey, *Developmental Anatomy* [copyright, W. B. Saunders Co.])

The embryo, we have noted, early gave off an outer sphere of cells. This gives rise to the chorion, which comes into close contact on every side with the maternal tissues surrounding the embryo. Outside of the chorion lie maternal blood vessels containing blood rich in food and oxygen. Within, on the embryo's side, blood vessels arise along the body stalk which, by transfusion through the intermediate membranes, take up food and oxygen from the mother's blood and transport them to the growing embryo. In some mammals this exchange of blood-contained materials may take place over the entire periphery of the embryonic sac. But in others, including man and all other primates, except the lemurs, this function is concentrated in a circular area around the region where the body stalk is attached. This area is made up of a thick mass of closely connected embryonic and maternal tissues. At birth it is not unlike a pancake in shape and size, and to this fact is due the Latin term, *placenta*, applied to it. It is shed at birth.

'PRENATAL INFLUENCE'. It will be noted that the blood of the mother does not enter the body of the embryo; that individual develops its own circulatory system, its own blood. The only connexion between the two is a transfusion of materials in solution through permeable membranes. The mother has little influence over the embryo once development has begun; she protects and nourishes the unborn young, but, beyond the possibility of causing it to be poorly nourished or injured physically, she has no control over its destinies.

The frequently repeated stories concerning prenatal influence of the mother upon the nature of the unborn young are thus almost entirely without foundation in fact. Much reading of Ibsen by the expectant mother will not tend towards the production of an intellectual giant; eating strawberries to excess is not the cause of strawberry marks on a child. Either activity might impair the embryo's food supply because of parental indigestion but could not otherwise affect it.

ORGANIZATION OF THE EMBRYO. When we left the embryo proper at an age of two weeks or so to discuss the future history of the membranes by which it had become surrounded, we left it in a very unhuman condition. It was then simply a flat, oval, two-layered disc of cells, the future outside of the body facing upward towards the amnion cavity, the future inside opening widely downward into the yolk sac.

An adult human being is a three-dimensional bilaterally symmetrical animal; but this early embryo is essentially a two-dimensional affair with at first almost no indication of orientation – no sides, no front or back to it at all.

Soon, however, orientation and organization begin on this simple disc, and the development of bodily shape and structure are under way. Of fundamental importance in this process is the development of a structure known as the primitive streak, with the primitive node (or knot) at its front end. This appears towards the end of the third week of development as a band of thickened tissue on the part of the embryonic disc adjacent to the body stalk. The primitive streak marks out the longitudinal axis of the body; the front end of the embryo develops from the area beyond the primitive node; the hind end develops at the opposite end of the disc, towards the body stalk.

The primitive streak appears to be of vital importance in the further history of the embryo. In some way, not well understood, this region acts as a centre of growth, appears to determine the position and order of appearance of various regions and organs, and serves as an 'organizer' of the early embryo. In front of the primitive-streak region there appears – in order from front to back – the whole anterior portion of the body: first the head region and then the greater part of the trunk. The streak itself fails to grow, gradually diminishes in relative size, and eventually disappears; but its influence long continues, and the back portion of the body and the tail grow out from this same region. The early appearance of the head and upper part of the trunk gives these regions a considerable 'head start' in their growth, and throughout prenatal life and early childhood the upper portions of the body are ahead of the lower part in their development.

THE GERM LAYERS. The primitive streak appears to be an active agent in the differentiation of tissues. We have seen that the early embryo consists of two types of tissue – ectoderm and endoderm. With the appearance of the primitive streak further differentiation occurs. The adjacent portions of the ectoderm fold downward in this area and spread out laterally and anteriorly between ectoderm and endoderm to form the third great germ layer – the mesoderm.

This division of the embryo into three primary layers was discovered more than a century ago, and the germ-layer conception has played an important part in the history of the science of embryology. Every structure in the later embryo and adult can be traced back to components arising from one or more of these germ layers.

From the ectoderm – the outer cell layer of the embryo – arises, as might be expected, the outer layer (epidermis) of the skin and such structures as hair and sweat glands. But also from this primitive outer layer comes the entire nervous system. Such an

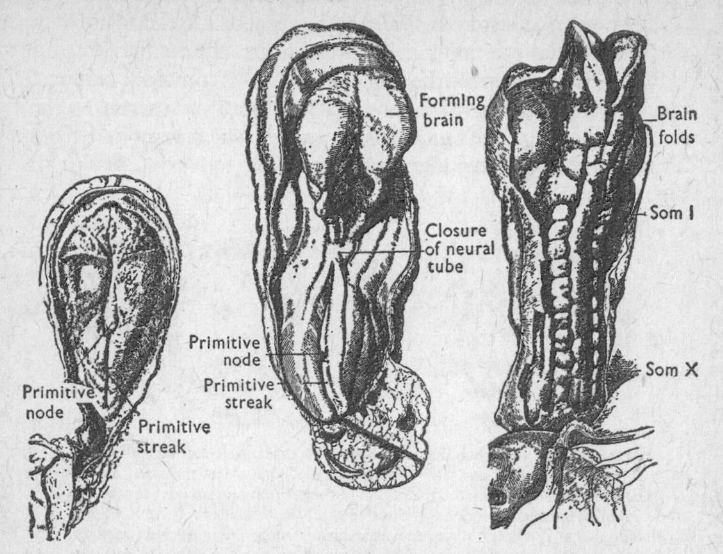

Young human embryos seen from the upper surface and much enlarged. *Left*, a very early stage, with an age somewhat less than three weeks from fertilization of the egg. The amnion has been cut off from over the top of the embryo; the yolk sac lies beneath and projects at the front end (above). At the lower end of the figure is the body stalk connecting the embryo with the outer membranes. On p. 387, the figure at the lower left is a vertical section through an embryo of approximately this age. At this stage the embryo appears to be little more than a flat disc, an oval 'pancake' with the future surface of the body above and the future lining of the gut on the under surface. There is little evidence of organization at this stage except for the important 'organizing' region of the primitive streak with the primitive node at the front.

Centre, a somewhat older embryo, between three and four weeks old. The primitive streak and node now occupy only a small part of the back of the embryonic area, for growth in front has been rapid. Neural folds are growing up in front to form the brain and spinal cord and have already closed into a tube at one point.

Right, a still later embryo, about four weeks old. The neural tube has closed except at the ends, forming the spinal cord and brain. On either side is a row of somites of mesoderm which give rise to trunk muscles. By this stage the body is beginning to round up and gain a definite three-dimensional shape rather than being a flat disc. In the plates are shown top and side views of an embryo of this age and following this a series of side views illustrating the later development of body form. (Carnegie Institution, Department of Embryology Publications, after Heuser, West, and Corner, respectively) embryological origin might be expected on historical grounds, for we have every reason to think that the nervous elements were derived, in primitive many-celled animals, from the skin.

From the endoderm – the inner cell layer – is formed, of course, the lining of the digestive tube. In addition it gives rise to the essential parts of the numerous structures which grow out from it: liver, pancreas, bladder, lungs, and the endocrine glands in the neck region.

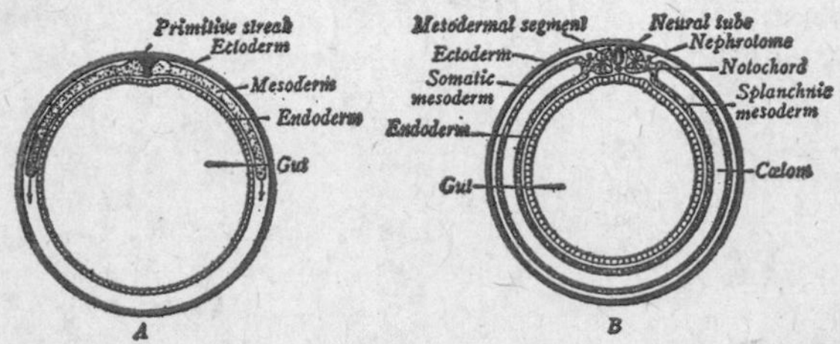

Diagrammatic cross-sections of embryos to show the relationship of the three germ layers and the development of the mesoderm. In *A* the mesoderm is forming from the region of the primitive streak and spreading laterally between ectoderm (primitive skin) and endoderm (primitive gut lining). In *B*, a later stage, the mesoderm is differentiating into various components. The structures seen here are comparable to those seen in actual photographs of embryos, as in the last of the accompanying plates. Ventrally the mesoderm has split to form the body cavity (coelom); splanchnic and somatic are terms to indicate the layers of mesoderm bordering this cavity internally (around the viscera) and externally towards the body wall. Higher up the mesoderm forms the primitive kidney structures (nephrotome), while the 'mesodermal segment' or somite gives rise to muscle, connective tissues, and skeletal materials. Between the somites the ectoderm has meanwhile folded off the neural tube; below this the notochord has formed independently. (After Bryce and Prentiss, from Arey, *Developmental Anatomy* [copyright, W. Saunders Co.])

The mesoderm is slow to develop in early embryonic life. But once started, its growth is rapid, and it soon bulks much larger than either of the other two germ layers. The mesoderm begins as a 'filler-in' between ectoderm and endoderm and quite naturally is found to give rise to the connective tissues of the adult body. From it, too, arise those more specialized types of 'fillers', cartilage and bone, and the notochord, prominent in embryonic life.

Early in embryonic life we find that the mesoderm of the trunk has assumed a very definite arrangement in paired segments (somites) down the body. The upper parts of the somites form thick blocks of tissue down either side of the back; from these blocks come the muscles of the body and limbs. More laterally the mesoderm gives rise to the greater part of the urinary and genital organs. The ventral part of the somites forms the lining of the body cavities, in which the organs of the chest and abdomen are situated. From mesoderm, too, arise the blood vessels and the blood cells.

Flesh, blood, and bone – these three mesoderm derivatives in themselves make up the greater part of the bulk of the body. But in addition other structures derived to begin with from ectoderm or endoderm are eventually composed mainly of mesodermal derivatives. In the skin the superficial portion is ectodermal, but the greater part of its thickness is connective tissue, derived from the mesoderm. The stomach and intestine are lined with endoderm, but most of the bulk of these organs is due to the thick layers of connective tissue and smooth muscles with which they are surrounded, and both these elements are mesodermal derivatives. Our structure (except for the nervous system) may perhaps be compared to that of a house. The ectoderm is the paint on the outside; the wallpaper and the floor varnish correspond to the endoderm. All the rest – timbers, clapboards, flooring, plumbing, laths, and plaster – is mesoderm.

DEVELOPMENT OF EXTERNAL BODILY FORM. Once the primitive streak is in evidence, the embryo rapidly takes shape, and the flat plate soon becomes a three-dimensional body. This change in form is essentially due to the rapid growth of the materials forming the disc. Growth is very rapid at the front end, and soon the head region bulges forward beyond the original limits of the embryonic area; much slower to develop is the tail region at the back. Lateral growth results in a downward curving of the sides of the disc and the production of side walls to the body. This expansion of the embryo may be roughly compared to the blowing of a soap bubble, which, when it grows, must swell out in every direction above the mouth of the pipe.

As the embryo grows and assumes form and finally comes to have not only a back but sides and even a ventral surface, the amnion increases also in dimensions, until, long before birth, it forms an almost complete spherical covering for the entire embryo. At first, in the disc stage, the entire lower surface of the embryo (the primitive endoderm) connects freely with the empty yolk cavity – gut and yolk sac are one. But the growth of the yolk sac fails to keep pace with the growth of the embryo. We may compare the yolk sac to the bowl of the pipe, with the bubble – the embryo – expanding above it. The digestive tract grows forward and backward above the yolk sac, and the increasing disparity in size results in a gradual separation of these two structures, although for some time they are connected by a tube – the yolk stalk.

The body stalk, along which runs the allantois and the vital blood vessels connecting embryo and placenta, persists throughout embryonic life. But as the body expands and the amnion grows down about it, the body stalk is crowded together with the yolk stalk into a slim cylindrical structure – the umbilical cord. This, in all late stages, forms the only connexion from the body of the embryo through the liquid-filled amnion cavity to the surrounding structures.

By the end of a month or so, the body, now about 2·5 mm. (one-tenth of an inch) in length, has assumed a recognizable shape – recognizable, that is, as the embryo of a vertebrate of some sort, although there is little to tell us that we are dealing with a man rather than, for example, a monkey or a pig. It is the head that has grown the fastest, and a bulging brain region and prominent gill furrows are the most striking features. Behind the head, formation of the trunk is taking place rapidly, segment after segment making its appearance. Down the back paired swellings mark the position of the muscle blocks. The primitive streak still persists at the back end of the growing embryo but is now comparatively insignificant in size.

During the second month the embryo becomes recognizable not merely as a vertebrate but as definitely human in character. The body now has grown to the length of about 2·5 cm. (an inch). The head is still enormous, but beneath the swollen braincase there is a recognizable face: eyes, nostrils, jaws, and ears have put in an appearance, and the gill region has shrivelled up (except for the ear fold). Stages in the developing face are shown in an accompanying plate. Limbs have budded forth as tiny paddles and by the end of the second month are essentially human in shape, although short. A tail had sprouted bravely out but by this time is already on the wane. Internally development has been rapid, and many organs are already close to the structure which they have at birth.

The remaining seven months of prenatal development are mainly a matter of growth rather than of the appearance of new features. At two months the human embryo weighs but 2 gm., that is, but one-fifteenth of an ounce. Before birth it must grow, and grow enormously, to reach a birth weight some two thousand times as great.

THE NERVOUS SYSTEM. At two weeks the human embryo is an almost featureless disc; at two months its structures are almost fully formed. A volume in itself would be required to describe adequately the many complex processes of differentiation and organization which go on within the embryo during this period of six weeks or so. Here we shall attempt only to sketch out briefly a few of the more striking examples of organ development.

The rapid development of the brain and spinal cord is an obvious feature of early human embryonic history. These structures arise from the ectoderm along the midline of the body. The brain region is earliest to develop. In front of the primitive streak there runs forward a thickened band of cells which rapidly develops into a groove – the neural groove. The outer edges of this structure rise up into prominent folds which eventually meet above to form an enclosed canal. Behind the brain region the long spinal cord is formed in similar fashion. The front and hind ends of this hollow tubular structure remain open to the surface for some time but close during the fifth week of development; the walled-off interior develops into the liquid-filled cavities of the brain (ventricles) and the cavity of the spinal cord in the adult.

The brain and spinal cord grow out above the notochord, and experimental work on amphibian embryos shows that that ancient chordate structure exerts, curiously enough, a profound influence on the development of the nervous system. If a piece of notochord is transplanted to a position beneath the skin on the underside of an amphibian, a brain will arise in the skin of the belly!

The size of the neural tube is particularly great in the future brain region, the first portion of the nervous system developed in the embryo. So rapid is this growth that the head region not only pushes forward from the original disc area but bends down sharply at the front end of the embryonic area. By the fifth week the three major divisions of the brain can be clearly recognized. The forebrain is bent sharply down upon the rest of the brain, and with continued brain growth further bending of the brain tube is visible. By the middle of the second month there has begun the great growth of the cerebral hemispheres particularly characteristic of man.

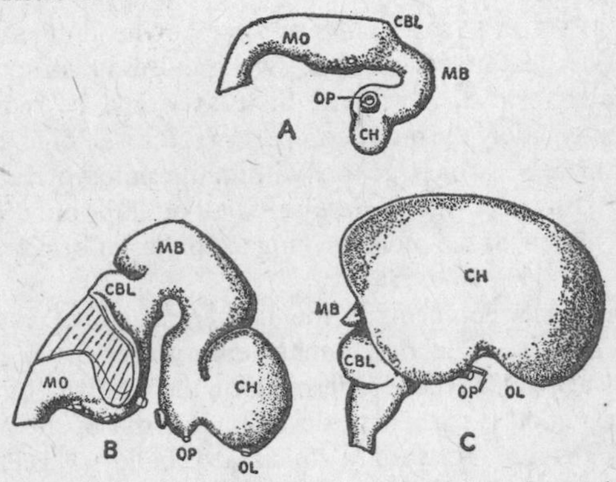

Early stages in brain development. *A*, embryo about five weeks old (×·57); *B*, about seven weeks old (×2·6); C, about twelve weeks old (×3). The anterior end of the body is at the *right*; in each figure the brain is cut off at the lower left, where it connects with the spinal cord. The brain begins as a simple tubular structure, but complexities appear at an early stage. At five weeks the forebrain is sharply twisted on the rest of the brain; later, further bending occurs. In the brain stem the midbrain, cerebellum, and medulla are early distinguishable. The most obvious change during growth is the great expansion of the cerebral hemispheres which grow greatly backward and downward to cover most of the brain stem in a fashion which parallels the phylogenetic history discussed in chapter 17. *cbl*, cerebellum; *ch*, cerebral hemispheres; *mb*, midbrain; *mo*, medulla oblongata; *ol*, olfactory region of brain; *op*, in *A* indicates the developing eye cup, in *B* and *C*, the optic nerve. In *B* the developing pituitary is seen beneath (i.e., at the left) of the forebrain. (After Bartelmez; data from Hochstetter)

From the nerve cord grow out the motor fibres of the nerves of the body. The sensory cells arise from the ectoderm immediately at the side of the developing cord, sending one fibre into the cord and another outward to join the motor fibres and form the spinal nerves. How the nerve fibres attain their proper connexions with their proper end organs is not a settled problem. Do the motor nerves merely grow out 'blindly', following the course of least resistance, until they encounter the muscles which they are to control? Or is there some chemical or physical influence which the muscles exert upon the growing nerve fibres? Perhaps both factors play a part in nerve growth.

THE EYE. The development of the eye is closely connected with that of the brain; indeed, the retina is shown by its development to be actually a budded-off portion of the brain itself.

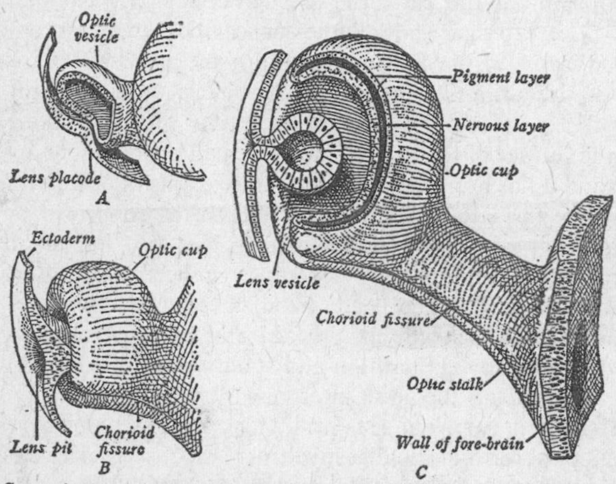

Stages in the early development of the eye (during the fifth week). *A*, the optic vesicle is budded off from the brain (*right*); the skin outside is thickening to form the lens. *B*, *C*, further stages in the infolding of the optic cup and lens formation. The optic vesicle folds inward on itself. The outer fold, toward the brain, forms merely a pigmented layer; the infolded portion forms all the sensory and nervous elements of the retina. The lens buds off from the skin to form first a hollow sphere and later a solid structure. The chorioid fissure, a cleft at the bottom of the cup, allows mesodermal tissues, including blood vessels, to enter the inner part of the eyeball. Later, around lens and retina, further layers of mesodermal tissue gather to form chorioid, iris, sclera, and cornea. (After models by Mann, from Arey, *Developmental Anatomy* [copyright, W. B. Saunders Co.])

On either side of the forebrain there grows out a hollow, clublike projection. As this structure grows out towards the surface, the outer wall of its spherical end portion folds inward, giving a two-layered cup. This cup is destined to develop into the retina and the underlying pigmented layer.

While much of the eye structure is derived from the mesoderm, lens and cornea are also ectodermal derivatives. Opposite the developing optic cup part of the skin thickens, folds in, and separates off as the embryonic rudiment of the lens. In some vertebrates, as we have said, lens formation is known to be directly due to the stimulation afforded to the ectoderm by the proximity of the optic cup; whether this is the case in man is unknown.

THE EAR. We have, in earlier chapters, noted some points in the evolutionary history of the human ear. The embryonic development of the ear structures gives a closely comparable story. The external and middle-ear cavities are formed from the rudiments of the first gill opening; the ear ossicles arise as part of the primitive jaws (malleus, incus) and first gill bar (stapes). In a shark the internal ear cavity retains a connexion with the surface of the head through a small duct (endolymphatic duct) and it has been suggested that the ear was once a skin sense organ like the lateral line canals. This seems confirmed by the development of this structure in man. The first indications of the internal ears are paired thickenings of the skin on either side of the back part of the head. From these thickenings develop pits which sink beneath the surface and become rounded, enclosed cavities. By elaboration and subdivisions of these cavities arise the canals of the adult internal ear.

THE PRIMITIVE DIGESTIVE TRACT AND ITS DERIVATIVES. The simplest form of the digestive tract is that seen in an embryo two weeks or so in age. The endoderm has the shape of the lining of a large sac. Its upper portion forms the bottom surface of the embryonic disc. Below, it is completely merged with the comparatively large yolk sac.

In our reptilian ancestors this sac was distended with yolk from which the embryo derived its nourishment. In mammals the yolk is reduced, but the sac persists; the embryo is curiously conservative in its retention of this structure. In the absence of the evolutionary theory we would be at a loss to explain the development in the human embryo of this comparatively useless structure. It was pointed out, in our discussion of the biogenetic law, that it is not past adult forms but past embryonic history that the embryo repeats; and there is no better example of this than the presence of the yolk sac in man – the development of an organ which was never present in any adult ancestor of ours but which was an important factor in the embryonic life of our reptilian forefathers.

At an early stage of development the allantois grows out from the back part of this primitive gut sac into the body stalk. Present in reptiles and birds as an embryonic bladder and

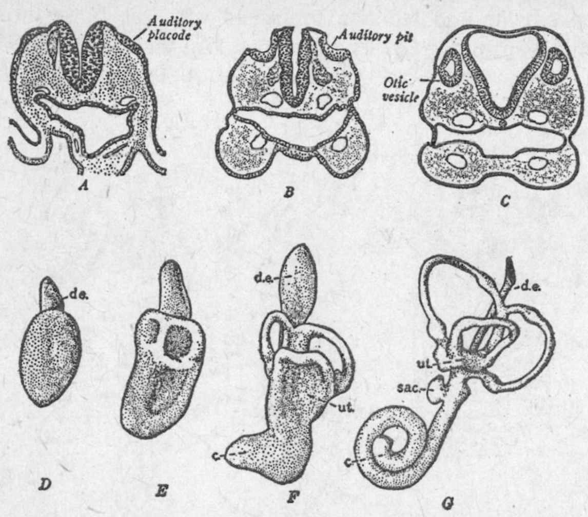

The development of the internal ear. Early stages, occurring at about 4–5 weeks of embryonic life, are shown in *A–C*, sections across the back part of the head regions of embryos. In the *centre* of *A* is seen the thick neural groove which in *C* has folded together to form the hindbrain. At either side a thickening of tissue (placode) marks the beginning of internal ear development. This tissue develops into a pit and then into a hollow sphere (otic vesicle), seen in section.

In *D–G* the fate of this vesicle is pursued. Here the vesicle is represented in solid form, as if dissected out from the head. By complicated subdivisions it becomes the system of sacs and canals containing the important endolymph liquid of the internal ear; the walls surrounding these cavities include the sensory cells associated with hearing and balance. *de*, endolymphatic duct; *ut*, utriculus, with which the semi-circular canals connect; *sac*, sacculus, from which the cochlea grows out; *c* ,cochlea. (*A–C* from Arey, *Developmental Anatomy* [copyright, W. B. Saunders Co.]; *C–F* after His and Bremer)

breathing organ, it is mainly of importance in ourselves because of the blood vessels in its walls which carry blood between embryo and placenta. Its cavity is never of large size and eventually disappears.

With downward growth of the side walls of the body and the eventual formation of the umbilical cord as the only connexion between the embryo and the surrounding structures, the single original endodermal sac becomes gradually pinched nearly in two. The lower portion of the definitive yolk sac is relegated to the outside and remains connected with the body through a slim tube running the length of the cord and connecting with the small intestine. Even this connexion usually disappears about the sixth week.

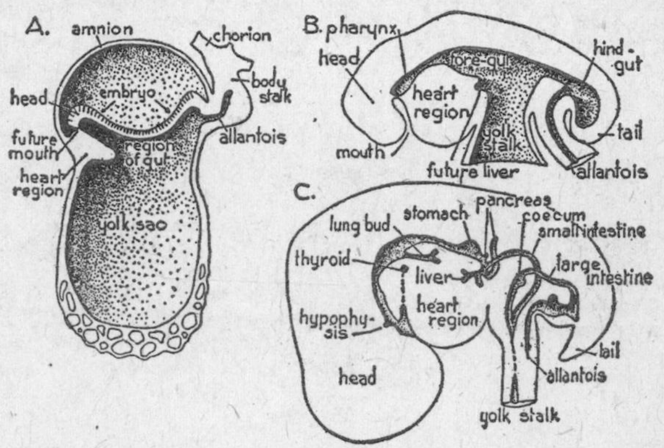

Sections taken lengthwise through human embryos to show early stages in the differentiation of the digestive tract; the head (*left*). *A*, an early stage in which the embryo is merely a flattened disc comparable to the left-hand specimen on p. 393; 2½ weeks old. The gut is nearly completely continuous with the yolk sac; the allantois is growing out into the body stalk. *B*, at about four weeks, comparable with the right-hand specimen on p. 393. The gut and yolk sac are fairly well separated, and the first rudiment of the liver is present. *C*, about five weeks old. The digestive tract is completely separated from the yolk sac, and the various portions of the tract are readily distinguishable, although simple in structure; lungs, thyroid, and hypophysis are budding off from the upper end of the gut; the mouth has opened (the anal opening appears much later). (Mainly after Arey, simplified)

The upper portion of the original cavity elongates with the increase in length of the embryo and becomes a simple tubular digestive tract. In this tube there gradually appear the beginnings of differentiation into the various adult digestive organs: pharynx, oesophagus, stomach, intestines (small and large). But, since the digestive organs play no part in the nourishment of the body until after birth, they remain of comparatively small size in the early embryo.

To begin with, the digestive tube has no connexion with the

outside of the body. The mouth cavity develops as a pocket from the outside of the head. The membrane separating it from the throat breaks during the fifth week; the anal opening develops a month later.

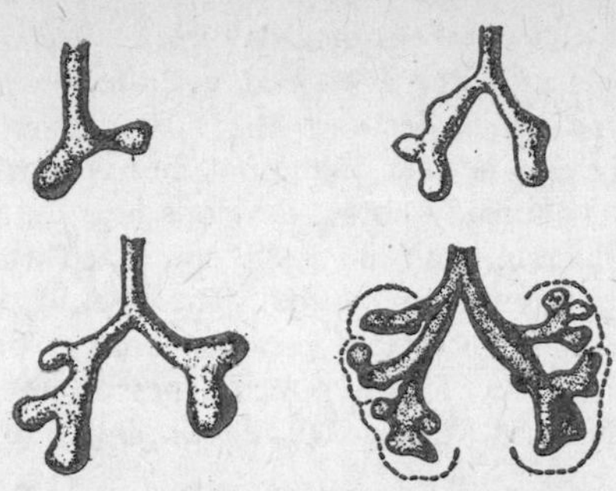

A series of stages in the early development of the lungs, as seen in front view. The lung begins (as seen in the next figure) as a bud from the underside of the pharynx, this representing the adult trachea. Soon the bud divides into two portions, representing the bronchi leading to the two lungs. By numerous further subdivisions, only a few of which are indicated in the figures, the complicated adult condition is reached. The stages figured are at embryonic ages of five to seven weeks. (After Heiss and Ask-Upmark from Arey, *Developmental Anatomy* [copyright, W. B. Saunders Co.])

Out from the rudimentary digestive tract there sprout, in several regions, hollow tubules which, coming into contact with surrounding mesodermal tissues, grow to become important adult organs. The liver and pancreas, closely associated with digestive processes, are formed in this fashion. The lungs, too, begin from a tubular outgrowth from the digestive tract, in the region of the pharynx. First develops a single tube, the rudiment of the windpipe. This forks into the two bronchi, one for each side, which, dividing repeatedly, finally assume the complex structure of the adult lung.

A second median outgrowth from the floor of the throat is the thyroid gland. Historically, we have noted, this structure was originally a digestive organ. In the early embryo it begins as a simple pocket growing down from the underside of the pharynx. Only later does it lose its connexion with the digestive tract and become an organ of internal secretion.

THE GILL REGION. Interesting processes are those seen in the development of the pharyngeal or gill pouches. Man never uses these fish structures for actual breathing purposes, but his early embryo begins an ambitious development of gills along the lines seen in fish embryos. A series of pouches – four pairs in man – grows out from the sides of the pharynx, and depressions corresponding to them develop on the outer surface of the neck.

The two sets of structures, however, never meet; open gill slits are never developed, and the surface depressions (except for that which becomes the tube of the external ear) soon fade away. The fate of the pouches is interesting. The first one, we have already noted, develops into the cavity of the middle ear, which in adult life is still connected with the throat by a narrow tube (eustachian tube). The second pair of pouches becomes inconspicuous (the palatine tonsil comes from this region). The third and fourth pouches persist, in part, but become highly modified. Instead of developing into breathing organs, they

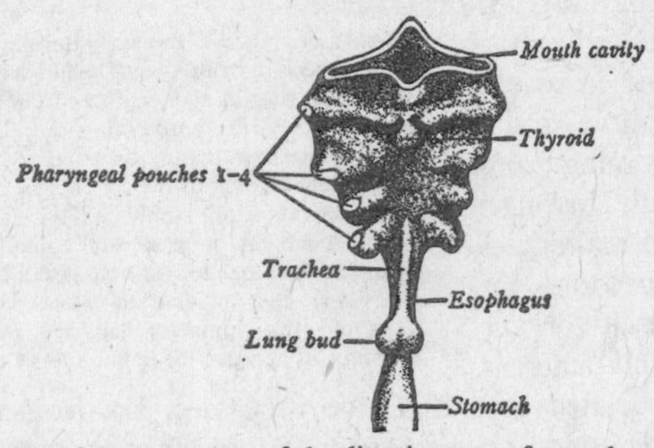

Front view of the upper part of the digestive tract of an embryo about five weeks old (×30). The gill pouches are well developed; the thyroid and lungs are budding off from the under wall of the throat. (After Prentiss and Arey)

lose their connexion with the digestive tract and develop into glands. From parts of the third and fourth pouches develop the parathyroid glands – small but important organs of internal secretion lodged in the adult in the sides of the thyroid gland. From other portions of these pouches develop the thymus glands, which are large and apparently of great importance in late foetal life and infancy.

ORIGIN OF THE CIRCULATORY SYSTEM. Many organs and organ systems function but little during embryonic development; their careers consist entirely of growth towards adult conditions. Not so, however, with the circulatory system. No more in the embryo than in the adult can the cells of the individual live without supplies of food and oxygen; and the blood must obtain these materials from the mother, via the placenta, and bring them to every part of the developing body.

The materials from which blood vessels and blood cells arise are derived from the middle body layer. Blood vessels early develop in the body stalk and the lining of the yolk sac; and by the time the embryo is three weeks old, still exceedingly tiny in size, blood vessels have appeared within the embryo proper.

THE HEART. As a pumping organ, the heart is a highly necessary feature in early embryonic life. This structure has appeared (by a fusion of two paired blood vessels) by the end of the fourth week. It is a simple, rather fishlike heart which receives blood from the veins in a pocket called the sinus venosus, passes it to a single atrium, then to the single ventricle and thence through a bulblike termination into the aortic vessels. At first the heart is a fairly straight tube, with the atrium lying below the ventricle. In the adult this position is, however, reversed; the atria lie above and to the back of the ventricles. This process soon becomes apparent in the human embryo; the ventricle twists, in a S-shaped curve, down in front of the atrium, and, at about a month's age, the adult position is attained. The four serial chambers, too, tend to be reduced. The venous sinus becomes incorporated into the atrium, and most of the terminal bulb is taken over into the ventricle.

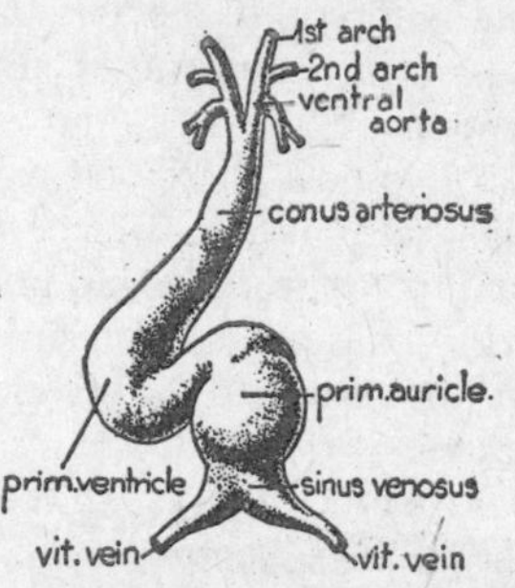

An external view of the human heart at an early stage in development. There are four chambers forming a single tube. Blood is collected from the veins into a venous sinus, thence passes through the single atrium (auricle) and ventricle to the arterial cone, from which it reaches the aortic arches. The ventricle is already looping downward; later it lies below the atrium. The venous sinus becomes absorbed into the atrium, the cone is in great measure absorbed into the ventricle, and these two remaining portions of the heart divide into two to form the adult structure. (After *Contributions to Embryology*, Carnegie Institution of Washington)

The early embryonic human heart, like that of an adult primitive vertebrate, forms a single series of structures, whereas in the adult man we have a complete separation of the two sides, with two atria and two ventricles. This separation is, of course, related to the presence of lungs and the need for separating the blood going to and from these organs from the body circulation.

No such separation is necessary in the embryo; the lungs are not functioning, and very little blood passes through them. The beginning of separation, however, soon becomes apparent. The two ventricles become completely separated by the end of the second month. The atria have partially separated by that time, but the separation remains incomplete until birth, an oval opening allowing blood to pass freely between the two cavities. This is an obvious necessity, owing to the lack of function of the embryonic lungs. In the adult the only blood received in the left atrium is that which comes from the lungs. But, as has been noted above, almost no blood flows through the lungs in the embryo. If the two halves of the heart were completely separated, one half of the embryo's heart would be almost empty.

Almost all the blood enters the embryo's heart through the right atrium into which flow the great veins from the body (and placenta). The gap in the wall enables half of this blood to cross over to the left side and permits the pumping function of the heart to be divided between the two powerful ventricles.

AORTIC ARCHES. In the adult fish the blood, passing up the throat in a ventral trunk, the aorta, divides into a series of paired channels which pass up into the gills; from the gills the aerated blood is collected in the dorsal aorta to be distributed to the body. In land animals, with the substitution of lungs for gills, these channels become much reduced and modified. The development of the aortic arches in the human embryo presents a picture highly comparable to this evolutionary history.

At an early stage in human development there is but a single arch on either side, curving up the side of the neck and running back down the dorsal region to the body. This first aortic arch lies in front of the region where the gill pouches are developing. Somewhat later three other arches, the second to fourth of the series, appear, running up between successive gill pouches, and eventually a last member of the series, a pulmonary arch, appears behind the last gill pouch. From this last a small branch runs back to the lung, but practically all the blood in this arch continues until birth to flow on upward to the dorsal aorta.

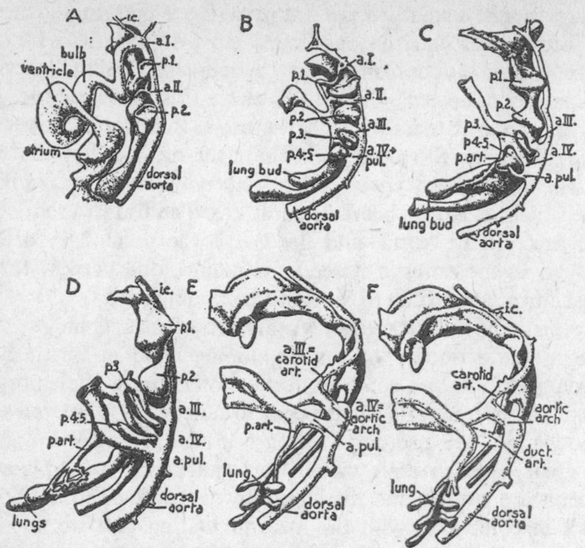

To show the development of the blood vessels of the throat, the aortic arches. A series of embryos seen from the left side, with the skin of the throat removed. The outline of the anterior part of the digestive tract, including gill pouches, is shown in darker shading. In *A* the heart is included; in others only the aortic trunk leading from it. If the complete embryo were shown, the brain would lie above the structures figured, the notochord and nerve cord would lie to the right, close beside the dorsal aorta. *A*, a four weeks' old embryo 3 mm. long. The first aortic arch is formed, the second forming. Two throat pouches are present. *B*, four and one-half weeks, 4 mm. long. The first three arches formed, the remaining two are forming; the pouches are all developed, the lung bud is beginning. *C*, five weeks, 5 mm. long. The first two arches have dropped out, the third and fourth are functioning, the last still in process of formation. There is a well-developed lung bud and the pulmonary artery is forming. *D*, six weeks, 11 mm. long. The last arch is formed. *E*, six and one-half weeks, 14 mm. long. The third arch has lost connexions with the dorsal aorta to become a vessel supplying the head only (internal carotid artery). *F*, a diagram to show the further changes which occur after birth; the distension of the pulmonary artery and the closure of the upper portion of the last arch. *a. I–IV*, aortic arches; *a pul.*, last (pulmonary) arch; *duct. art.*, connexion of pulmonary arch with dorsal aorta (ductus arteriosus); *i.c.*, internal carotid artery; *p. art.*, pulmonary artery, *p.* 1–5, gill pouches. (*A–E* from *Contributions to Embryology*, Carnegie Institution of Washington)

While the lower arches have been developing, the upper ones have been degenerating. The first two soon disappear entirely. The third ceases to connect with the others and becomes merely a comparatively small vessel transporting blood to the head. The fourth arch and the pulmonary now do almost the entire job of taking blood from heart to body. At their roots they become disconnected, the fourth arch arising from the left ventricle, the last from the right ventricle. Both these arches are paired to begin with; but soon the right members of the pair dwindle, and presently we are left with only two great trunks – those which leave the heart in adult life. The fourth arch is the adult arch of the aorta, and the last is the pulmonary artery, although in the embryo it sends its main blood current to the dorsal aorta rather than to the non-functioning lung.

CIRCULATORY CHANGES AT BIRTH. Great changes take place in the economy of the developing child at birth. Both oxygen and food had come from the mother; now the embryo's own digestive tract and lungs begin to function. Correlated with these changes are profound changes in the circulatory system. The great blood vessels which bore nutriment from placenta to foetus are cut off, and the blood flow is confined to the body.

It is in connexion with the lung circulation that we find the greatest and most startling changes in blood flow. At birth, when the lungs begin to function, the two previously small pulmonary arteries leading to them distend with blood; the upper end of the pulmonary arch soon closes, and, in consequence, all the blood from the right ventricle, from which the pulmonary trunk alone arises, now flows to the lungs. From the lungs the heart now receives for the first time a full flow of blood into the left atrium. This chamber had formerly been filled by blood from the right atrium through a gap in the wall. This gap now closes; the two sides of the heart are completely separated, and the adult circulation is established. These changes take place in an exceedingly short time after birth. Occasionally, however, the gap in the heart partition fails to close, oxygenated and oxygenless blood streams mix, and a 'blue baby' results.

POSTNATAL DEVELOPMENT. The study of embryology in a narrow sense ceases with birth; but development is even then far from completed. At that time many structures, such as teeth and reproductive organs, are still present only in a rudimentary form, and the bodily proportions at birth are markedly different from those of the adult. Processes of growth or reduction continue throughout life, although most growth is over by the time majority is reached, and little degeneration usually takes place until late in the normal life-span. We may roughly divide a normal life-period into (1) infancy – between the stage of the newborn babe and the assumption of the erect posture; (2) childhood – ceasing at puberty, the beginning of potential sexual activity, usually somewhere between twelve and sixteen years; (3) adolescence, to about majority; (4) adult life; (5) a final adult period of old age and senescence, ending in death.

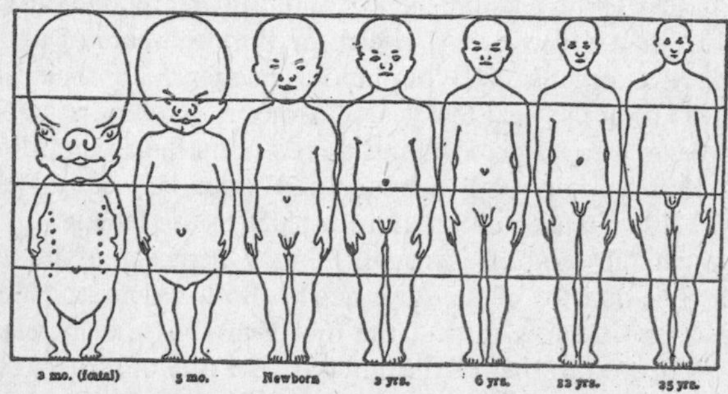

Figures illustrating the changes in proportion during prenatal and postnatal growth. The trunk remains nearly constant in relative size throughout. The head, and particularly the brain, grows enormously in early embryological stages. In later periods there is little brain growth, and hence the head is relatively smaller, while, on the other hand, the legs, very short at first, grow enormously. (From Scammon after Stratz, in Morris, *Human Anatomy*, P. Blakiston's Son & Co., Inc.)

Marked changes in proportions occur during the earlier portions of this life-cycle. We have noted the rapid rate of growth of the brain and head in the embryo; and indeed the whole upper part of the body grows rapidly in the early stages, while the lower parts grow but slowly. The head in the foetus is enormous; at two months, it constitutes almost half the body length, and even in an infant the head is relatively large. Most head growth is over early in childhood, and the adult head is smaller proportionately. The arms early obtain their growth. The trunk persistently remains at a figure of about half the bulk of the body and about three-eighths of its length. The legs are the slowest parts of the body in their development; even in a fairly late foetus they constitute but about one-fourth of the body length, while in the adult the legs account for about half our stature.

Differences in growth rates are marked in many of the organ systems. Of major features, the brain shows the greatest growth before birth and the slowest in later years. Some 15 per cent of the weight of the newborn babe is brain; the adult brain is but one-fortieth of the body weight. On the other hand, the muscles, which constitute well on toward half the weight of the adult man, constitute but a quarter of the bulk of the babe. Remarkedly retarded in their growth are the genital organs. At birth they are in a rudimentary condition and remain dormant for more than a decade. At twelve or thirteen years of age the reproductive organs have but about one-tenth of their adult weight. During the next few years, however – the age of puberty – they begin a rapid growth, and there occurs the assumption of adult conditions in both primary and secondary sexual characters; these changes occur more rapidly in the female.

At birth the infant has roughly but 5 per cent of its adult weight, one-quarter of its adult height. Both weight and height increase considerably during the first year, but the increase is slight compared to that of the embryo. The rate of growth slows considerably before birth; but, even so, the rate during the last prenatal month would, if continued, result in an adult a thousand million times as large as the sun!

At puberty begins a new period of growth in both height and weight, particularly the former. This acceleration begins and ends more rapidly in girls than in boys; growth is practically completed in females at about eighteen years, in males at about twenty.

OLD AGE. In nature the success of a species or an individual is measured solely by its success in reproducing itself. Any features in the race or the individual which enables it to survive through the reproductive period mean more offspring; but features which tend to preserve the individual beyond the period of reproduction or care of the young will have no effect upon the success of the species as measured by its numbers. In consequence, we find in general among animals that when the reproductive period is over life soon ceases for most individuals. Degeneration sets in; bodily processes slow down. We see, in nature, few old animals. With stagnation of activities and feebleness, the procurement of food becomes a difficult problem, and a violent death from enemies or rivals soon occurs.

In man, as well as other animals, decline sets in as sexual activities cease. In women the potentialities for reproduction usually cease abruptly in the late forties; in men sexual activities decline somewhat more slowly. Human society affords many safeguards to the old not found in nature, but, even so, a person who has reached in health an age of fifty has on the average but twenty more years of life to expect.

Our body wears away – our complex machinery, with so many essential and irreplaceable structures, tends to break down, to repair injuries more slowly. Our skin shrinks but little and becomes wrinkled as the fat beneath it tends to be used up and not replaced, and the underlying muscles wither. The bones for the most part retain their contours but tend to lose the lime salts which form their main bulk and become brittle and easily fractured. The teeth, irreplaceable after the permanent set, often begin to go at an early age, and many of us, in a state of nature, would soon perish from lack of nourishment.

Many of our cells seem potentially immortal; if, for example, tissues are taken from a young animal and kept in artificial cultivation, they may live indefinitely. The life of a chicken is normally but a few years; but cells taken from the heart of an embryonic chick and kept in artificial food mediums in glass dishes are still alive, as this is written, after several decades and show no signs of degeneration. Our own cells, for the most part, do not die because of any individual fault, but because the complicated system of which they are a part breaks down.

One great source of cell death – and consequent body death – lies in the circulatory system. It is upon the blood that the cells depend for oxygen and food; once this supply is cut off the individual cell soon dies. In older persons there is often a hardening of the walls of the arteries (sclerosis), which may result in a cutting-down of the blood supply to some essential structure. Even more serious is the fact that a heightened blood pressure results from the restricted blood space in the less elastic arteries. This may result in the bursting of blood vessels, particularly unfortunate in the case of the brain because of injury to brain areas and the consequent impairment of mentality or of nervous control over body activities.

In civilized communities the old may be well cared for. They may be carefully nourished, kept from undue exertion, protected in great measure from disease. Sooner or later, however, the machine breaks down, vital activities cease, death occurs. Nature has done with the individual – cares nothing for it as soon as it has ceased to reproduce. Each one of us must die; the race goes on.

APPENDIX 1

A Synoptic Classification of Vertebrates

In the brief classification given below a number of minor groups have been omitted, and subdivisions of major groups have been made only where necessary for the purposes of the present volume. Generic names (in italics) are in general given only for forms mentioned in the text or illustrated; many forms just as important as those listed are, in consequence, omitted. Common names and, in the case of fossils, times of geologic occurrence are given in parentheses.

Class Agnatha (jawless vertebrates)

Order Osteostraci. *Cephalaspis* (Silurian, Devonian)
Order Anaspida. *Birkenia* (Devonian)
Order Heterostraci. *Thelodus* (Silurian)
Order Cyclostomata. *Petromyzon* (lamprey), *Lethenteron* (brook lamprey)

Class Placodermi (archaic jawed fishes)

Order Arthrodira. *Dinichthys* (Devonian)
Order Acanthodii (spiny sharks). *Climatius* (Devonian)

Class Chondrichthyes (sharklike fishes)

Order Cladoselachii (primitive sharks). *Cladoselache* (Devonian)
Order Elasmobranchii (sharks, skates, and rays.) *Scyllium* (smooth dogfish), *Squalus* (spiny dogfish), *Cetorhinus* (whale shark), *Carcharias* (sand shark), *Carcharodon* (fossil shark), *Sphyrna* (hammerhead), *Raja* (skate)
Order Holocephali (chimaeras). *Chimaera*

Class Osteichthyes (higher bony fishes)

Subclass Actinopterygii (ray-finned fishes)
Order Chondrostei. *Cheirolepis* (Devonian paleoniscid), *Acipenser* (sturgeon), *Polyodon* (paddlefish), *Polypterus* (bichir)
Order Holostei. *Lepidosteus* (gar pike), *Amia* (bowfin)
Order Teleostei. *Clupea* (herring), *Scomber* (mackerel), *Anguilla* (eel), *Prionotus* (sea robin), *Ostracion* (trunkfish), *Mola* (sunfish), *Chilomycterus* (globe fish), *Hippocampus* (sea horse), *Phyllopteryx*

(Australian sea horse), *Limanda* (flounder), *Cyprinus* (carp), *Amiurus* (catfish), *Salmo* (salmon and trout), *Toxotes* (archer fish), *Chauliodus*, *Melamphis* (deep-sea fishes), *Anableps* (four-eyed fish), *Remora* (shark sucker), *Naucrates* (pilot fish), *Electrophorus* (electric eel), *Periophthalmus* (mudspringer)

SUBCLASS CHOANICHTHYES (fishes with internal nostrils)

SUPERORDER CROSSOPTERYGII (lobe-finned fishes). *Osteolepis*, *Eusthenopteron* (Devonian), *Latimeria*

SUPERORDER DIPNOI (lungfishes proper). *Dipterus* (Devonian), *Scaumenacia* (Devonian), *Epiceratodus*, *Protopterus*, *Lepidosiren*

CLASS AMPHIBIA

ORDER LABYRINTHODONTIA (primitive amphibians). *Diplovertebron* (Carboniferous), *Eryops* (Permian), *Buettneria* (Triassic)

ORDER URODELA (salamanders, newts). *Necturus* (mud puppy), *Siren*, *Cryptobranchus* (hellbender), *Amblystoma* (spotted and tiger salamanders and axolotl), *Lyphlotriton* (blind salamander), *Pseudotriton*, *Eurycea*, *Amphiuma*

ORDER ANURA (frogs, toads). *Rana* (common frogs), *Bufo* (common toad), *Hyla* (tree toad), *Pipa* (Surinam toad), *Dendrobates* (South American poison toad)

ORDER APODA (or Gymnophiona) (wormlike forms). *Ichthyophis*

CLASS REPTILIA

SUBCLASS ANAPSIDA

ORDER COTYLOSAURIA (stem reptiles). *Seymouria* (Permian), *Bradysaurus* (pareiasaur, Permian)

ORDER CHELONIA (turtles). *Testudo* (tortoises), *Trionyx* (soft-shelled turtle), *Dermochelys* (leatherback), *Eretmochelys* (loggerhead), *Chelone* (green turtle), *Archelon* (Cretaceous), *Eunotosaurus* (Permian), *Chelydra* (snapping turtle)

SUBCLASS ICHTHYOPTERYGIA

ORDER ICHTHYOSAURIA. *Merriamia* (Triassic), *Ichthyosaurus* (Jurassic), *Ophthalmosaurus* (Cretaceous)

SUBCLASS SYNAPTOSAURIA

ORDER SAUROPTERYGIA (plesiosaurs, etc.). *Plesiosaurus*, *Thaumatosaurus* (Jurassic), *Elasmosaurus* (Cretaceous)

SUBCLASS LEPIDOSAURIA

ORDER EOSUCHIA (ancient two-arched reptiles)

ORDER RHYNCHOCEPHALIA. *Sphenidon* (tuatera)

ORDER SQUAMATA

SUBORDER LACERTILIA (lizards). *Varanus* (monitor lizard), *Clidastes* (Cretaceous, mosasaur), *Heloderma* (Gila monster), *Ophiosaurus* (glass 'snake'), *Phrynosoma* (horned 'toad'), *Neoseps* (small-legged lizard), *Anguis* (blind worm), *Draco* (flying dragon), *Chameleo*

SUBORDER OPHIDIA (snakes). *Python*, *Naia* (cobra), *Hydrus* (marine snake), *Crotalus* (rattler), *Agkistrodon* (copperhead and water moccasin), *Micrurus* (coral snake), *Zarhynchus* (king cobra), *Eunectes* (anaconda)

SUBCLASS ARCHOSAURIA (ruling reptiles)

ORDER THECODONTIA (ancestral forms). *Ornithosuchus*, *Euparkeria* (Triassic), *Mystriosuchus* (Triassic, phytosaur)

ORDER CROCODILIA. *Steneosaurus* (Jurassic), *Geosaurus* (marine crocodile, Jurassic), *Crocodilus*, *Alligator*, *Gavialis* (Indian gavial)

ORDER PTEROSAURIA (flying reptiles). *Rhamphorhynchus*, *Pterodactylus* (Jurassic), *Pteranodon* (Cretaceous)

ORDER SAURISCHIA ('reptile-like' dinosaurs)

SUBORDER THEROPODA (bipeds). *Compsognathus*, *Allosaurus* (Jurassic), *Struthiomimus*, *Tyrannosaurus* (Cretaceous)

SUBORDER SAUROPODA (quadrupeds). *Brontosaurus*, *Diplodocus*, *Apatosaurus*, *Camarasaurus*, *Brachiosaurus* (all Jurassic)

ORDER ORNITHISCHIA ('birdlike' dinosaurs)

SUBORDER ORNITHOPODA (bipeds). *Camptosaurus* (Jurassic), *Trachodon*, *Corythosaurus*, *Parasaurolophus*, *Lambeosaurus* (these four are Cretaceous duckbills)

SUBORDER STEGOSAURIA. *Stegosaurus* (Jurassic)

SUBORDER ANKYLOSAURIA (Cretaceous armoured dinosaurs). *Ankylosaurus*, *Palaeoscincus*

SUBORDER CERATOPSIA (horned dinosaurs, Cretaceous). *Triceratops*, *Protoceratops*

SUBCLASS SYNAPSIDA (forms leading towards mammals)

ORDER PELYCOSAURIA (Permian and Carboniferous). *Dimetrodon*, *Edaphosaurus*, *Casea*, *Ophiacodon*

ORDER THERAPSIDA (mammal-like reptiles, Permian and Triassic). *Cynognathus*, *Kannemeyeria*

CLASS AVES (birds)

SUBCLASS ARCHAEORNITHES (archaic birds). *Archaeopteryx*, *Archaeornis* (Jurassic)

SUBCLASS NEORNITHES (more advanced birds). *Ichthyornis*, *Hesperornis* (Cretaceous, toothed birds), *Diatryma* (Eocene), *Phororhacos* (Miocene), *Dinornis* (moa, Pleistocene), *Aepyornis* (Pleistocene 'elephant bird' of Madagascar), *Struthio* (ostrich), *Rhea*, *Casuarius* (cassowary), *Dromaeus* (emu), *Apteryx* (kiwi) *Aptenodytes* (penguins), *Pluvialis* (golden plover), *Gallus* (fowls), *Tympanuchus* (heath hen), *Didus* (dodo)

CLASS MAMMALIA (mammals)

SUBCLASS PROTOTHERIA (egg-laying)

ORDER MONOTREMATA. *Ornithorhynchus* (duckbill), *Echidna* (spiny anteater)

ORDER MULTITUBERCULATA (an archaic extinct group of doubtful position)

SUBCLASS METATHERIA (young born alive, placenta usually undeveloped or poor. The first three orders are Jurassic fossil forms; their embryology is unknown, and hence their position uncertain, although they presumably belong here)

ORDER PANTOTHERIA (Trituberculata). (Probably ancestors of later types of mammals)

ORDERS TRICONODONTA, SYMMETRODONTA

ORDER MARSUPIALIA (pouched mammals). *Didelphys* (opossum), *Dasyurus* (Australian 'cats'), *Sarcophilus* (Tasmanian 'devil'), *Thylacynus* (Tasmanian 'wolf'), *Paragalia* (bandicoot), *Phalanger* (Australian 'squirrels'), *Petaurus* (flying phalanger), *Phascolarctus* (koala, or Australian 'bear'), *Phascolomys* (wombat), *Macropus* (kangaroo), *Petrogale* (wallaby), *Cladosictis*, *Prothylacynus* (carnivorous, Miocene of South America)

SUBCLASS EUTHERIA (Monodelphia) (placental mammals)

ORDER INSECTIVORA (insect-eaters, archaic placentals). *Erinaceus* (hedgehog), *Talpa* (mole), *Sorex* (shrews), *Deltatheridium* (Cretaceous), *Tupaia* (tree shrew)

ORDER CARNIVORA (flesh eaters)

SUBORDER CREODONTA (archaic flesh-eaters). *Sinopa*, *Oxyaena* (Eocene), *Hyaenodon*, *Andrewsarchus* (Oligocene)

SUBORDER FISSIPEDIA (land carnivores)

FAMILY VIVERRIDAE (civets). *Herpestes* (mongoose), *Viverra* (civet), *Genetta* (genet)

FAMILY HYAENIDAE (hyenas). *Hyaena*

FAMILY FELIDAE ('cats'). *Dinictis* (Oligocene cat), *Felis* (most living felids), *Acinonyx* (cheetah), *Hoplophoneus* (Oligocene sabretooth), *Smilodon* (Pleistocene sabretooth)

FAMILY MUSTELIDAE (weasel group). *Mustela* (weasel), *Martes* (marten), *Mephitis*, etc. (skunks), *Meles*, *Taxidea* (badgers), *Gulo* (wolverine), *Lutra* (otter), *Enhydris* (sea otter)

FAMILY CANIDAE ('dogs'). *Cynodictis* (Oligocene), *Canis* (dog, wolf, jackal), *Vulpes* (fox)

FAMILY PROCYONIDAE (raccoon group). *Procyon* (raccoon), *Nasua* (coati), *Ailurus* (panda), *Ailuropoda* (giant panda)

FAMILY URSIDAE (bears). *Ursus* (most bears), *Thalarctos* (polar bear)

SUBORDER PINNIPEDIA (marine carnivores)

FAMILY OTARIIDAE. *Eumetopias* (sea lion), *Callorhinus* (fur seal), *Mirounga* (elephant seal)

FAMILY ODOBAENIDAE. *Odobaenus* (walrus)
FAMILY PHOCIDAE. *Phoca* (Atlantic seal)

ORDER CONDYLARTHRA (primitive ungulates). *Phenacodus* (Eocene)

ORDER DINOCERTA (uintatheres). *Uintatherium* (Eocene)

ORDER PERISSODACTYLA (odd-toed ungulates)

FAMILY EQUIDAE (horses). *Eohippus, Orohippus* (Eocene), *Mesohippus, Miohippus* (Oligocene), *Parahippus, Merychippus* (Miocene), *Hipparion* (Miocene-Pliocene), *Equus* (Pleistocene-Recent)
FAMILY TAPIRIDAE *Tapirus* (tapirs)
FAMILY RHINOCEROTIDAE *Hyracodon, Baluchitherium* (Oligocene), *Teleocerus* (Miocene), *Rhinoceros*, etc. (living forms)
FAMILY TITANOTHERIIDAE (titanotheres, Eocene-Oligocene)
FAMILY CHALICOTHERIIDAE. *Moropus* (Miocene)

ORDER ARTIODACTYLA (even-toed ungulates)

SUBORDER SUINA (piglike forms)

FAMILY SUIDAE (swine), *Sus* (pigs), *Phacochoerus* (wart hog), *Babirussa. Tayassu* (peccary)
FAMILY HIPPOPOTAMIDAE. *Hippopotamus, Choeropsis* (pygmy hippo)
FAMILY ENTELODONTIDAE (giant hogs). *Archaeotherium* (Oligocene), *Dinohyus* (Miocene)

SUBORDER PROTOSELENODONTIA (primitive ruminants). *Oreodon* (Oligocene)

SUBORDER TYLOPODA (camels). *Oxydactylus* (giraffe-camel, Miocene), *Camelus* (camels), *Auchenia* (llama)

SUBORDER PECORA (ruminants)

FAMILY TRAGULIDAE (chevrotains, water deer). *Tragulus, Synthetoceras* (Pliocene)
FAMILY CERVIDAE (deer family). *Megaceros* (Pleistocene 'Irish elk'), *Cervus* (red deer, American 'elk'), *Odocoileus* (Virginia deer), *Capreolus* (roe deer), *Alces* (moose), *Rangifer* (reindeer, caribou)
FAMILY GIRAFFIDAE. *Giraffa* (giraffe), *Okapia* (okapi)
FAMILY ANTILOCAPRIDAE. *Antilocapra* (prongbuck)
FAMILY BOVIDAE (cattle group). *Bos* (cattle), *Bison, Ovis* (sheep), *Capra* (goats), *Ovibos* (muskox), and many other genera of antelopes, etc.

ORDER HYRACOIDEA (conies). *Hyrax*

ORDER PROBOSCIDEA (elephant group)

FAMILY MOERITHERIIDAE (archaic proboscidians). *Moeritherium* (Eocene-Oligocene)
FAMILY MASTODONTIDAE, etc. (mastodons), *Phiomia* (primitive mastodon, Oligocene), *Triplophodon* (Miocene), *Mastodon* (Pleistocene)
FAMILY ELEPHANTIDAE (mammoths and elephants). *Mammonteus* (woolly mammoth), *Elephas* (Asiatic elephant), *Loxodonta* (African elephant)

ORDER SIRENIA (sea cows). *Halicore* (dugong), *Manatus* or *Trichechus* (manatee), *Rhytina* (Stellar's sea cow, extinct)

ORDER NOTOUNGULATA (major group of extinct South American ungulates). *Protypotherium, Astrapotherium, Nesodon* (Miocene), *Toxodon* (Pleistocene)

ORDER LITOPTERNA (extinct South American ungulates). *Thoatherium* (Miocene)

ORDER PYROTHERIA (extinct South American parallels to elephants). *Pyrotherium* (Oligocene)

ORDER RODENTIA (rodents, gnawing animals)

SUBORDER SIMPLICIDENTATA (with one pair of upper 'chisels')

INFRAORDER SCIUROMORPHA. *Aplodontia* (mountain beaver), *Sciurus* (squirrels), *Tamias* (chipmunk), *Citellus* (ground squirrels), *Cynomys* (prairie dog), *Marmota* (woodchuck), *Castor* (beaver), *Castoroides* (giant beaver, Pleistocene), *Geomys* (pocket gopher), *Dipodomys* (kangaroo rats)

INFRAORDER MYOMORPHA. *Mus* (house mouse), *Rattus* (house rats), etc.

INFRAORDER HYSTRICOMORPHA (mainly South American). *Cavia* (guinea pig), *Chinchilla*, *Erithizon* (American porcupine), *Hystrix* (Old World porcupine), *Synetheres* (Brazilian porcupine), *Coenodon* (tree porcupine), *Hydrochoerus* ('water pig' or capybara)

ORDER LAGOMORPHA DUPLICIDENTATA (gnawing animals with an extra pair of upper 'chisels'). *Lepus* (hares), *Oryctolagus* (common rabbit), *Sylvilagus* (cottontail)

ORDER CHIROPTERA (bats)

SUBORDER MICROCHIROPTERA (ordinary bats). *Vespertilio* (common bats), *Desmodus* (vampire)

SUBORDER MEGACHIROPTERA (fruit bats or 'flying foxes'). *Pteropus*, etc.

ORDER CETACEA (whales)

SUBORDER ARCHAEOCETI (extinct archaic whales). *Zeuglodon* (Eocene)

SUBORDER ODONTOCETI (toothed whales). *Physeter* (sperm whale), *Phocaena* (porpoise), *Kogia* (pygmy sperm whale), *Globicephalus* (blackfish), *Hyperoodon* (beaked whale)

SUBORDER MYSTACOCETI (whalebone whales). *Balaenoptera* (rorquals, including blue whale), *Balaena* (right whales)

ORDER EDENTATA (South American edentates)

SUBORDER LORICATA (armoured forms). *Tatusia* or *Dasypus* (nine-banded armadillo), *Stegotherium* (Miocene armadillo), *Propalaeohoplophorus* (Miocene glyptodon), *Glyptodon* (Pleistocene), *Periodon* (giant armadillo)

SUBORDER PILOSA (hairy forms). *Myrmecophaga* (giant anteater), *Choloepus*, *Bradypus* (tree sloths), *Megatherium*, *Mylodon*, *Megalonyx* (giant ground sloths, Pleistocene), *Hapalops* (Miocene ground sloth)

ORDER TUBULIDENTATA. *Orycteropus* (aard vark)

ORDER PHOLIDATA. *Manis* (pangolin)

ORDER PRIMATES

SUBORDER LEMUROIDEA. *Lemur* (ordinary lemurs), *Galago* ('bush baby'), *Perodicticus* (potto), *Loris* (slow lemur), *Notharctus* (Eocene)

SUBORDER TARSIOIDEA. *Tarsius*, *Tetonius* (Eocene).

SUBORDER ANTHROPOIDEA (monkeys, apes, men)

INFRAORDER PLATYRRHINI (South American monkeys)

FAMILY CEBIDAE. *Cebus* (common 'organ-grinder's monkey' or capuchin), *Ateles* (spider monkey)

FAMILY HAPALIDAE (marmosets). *Hapale*, *Callithrix*

INFRAORDER CATARRHINI (Old World forms)

FAMILY CERCOPITHECIDAE (Old World monkeys). *Parapithecus* (Oligocene), *Cercopithecus* (small African monkeys), *Macacus* (macaques, rhesus monkey), *Papio* (baboons, drill, mandrill), *Semnopithecus* or *Pithecus* (langurs), *Nasalis* (proboscis monkey)

FAMILY SIMIIDAE (great apes). *Propliopithecus* (Oligocene), *Hylobates* (gibbon), *Simia* (orang), *Dryopithecus*, etc. (Miocene-Pliocene), *Australopithecus*, *Plesianthropus* (Pleistocene), *Gorilla*, *Anthropopithecus* (chimpanzee)

FAMILY HOMINIDAE. *Pithecanthropus*, *Sinanthropus*, etc. (Pleistocene), *Homo*

APPENDIX 2

Phylogenetic Charts of the Vertebrates

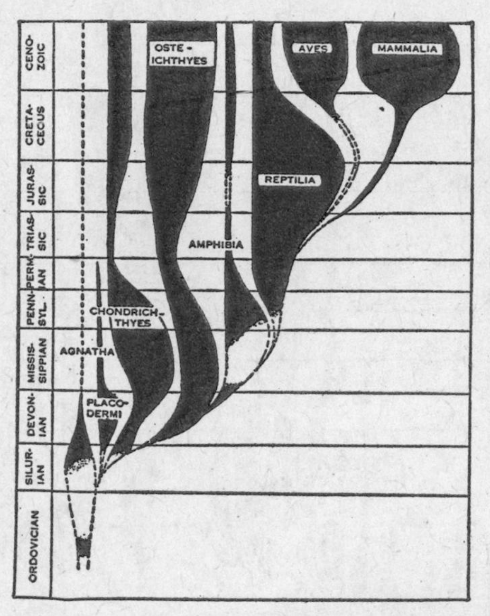

A family tree showing the times of appearance and relative abundance at various eras of the vertebrate classes.

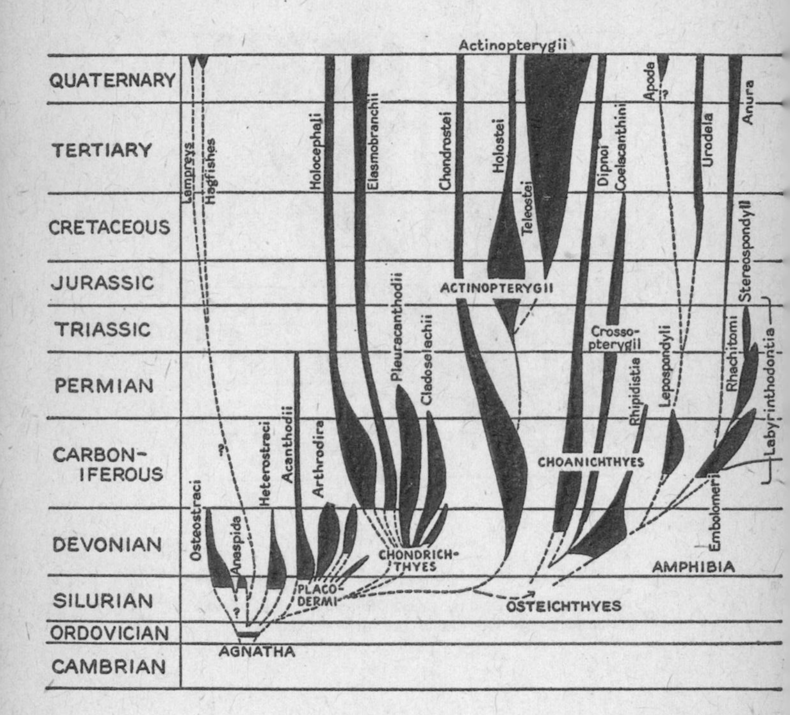

A family tree of the vertebrates giving their evolutionary history in detail. All recognized orders of vertebrates are

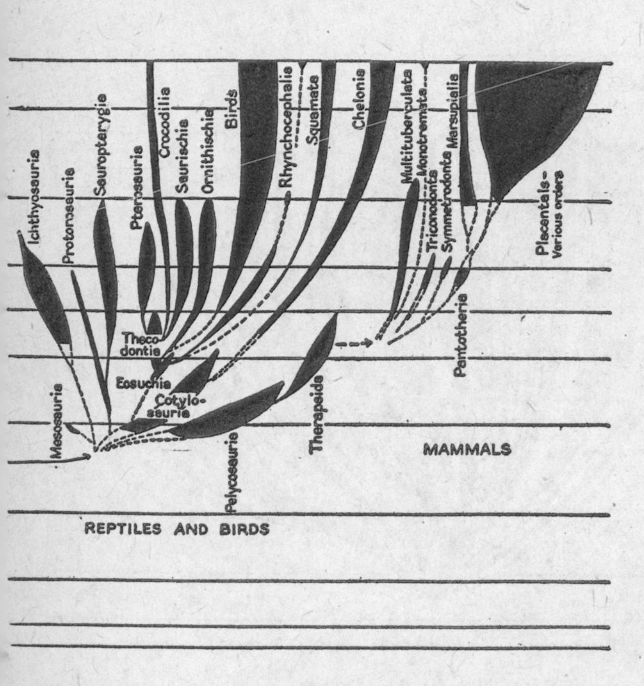

indicated except in the case of the birds and mammals; several orders not otherwise mentioned are included.

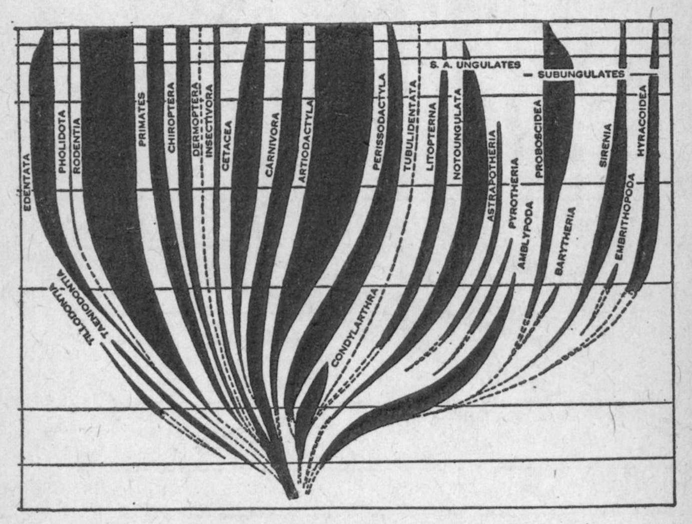

The distribution in time of the orders of placental mammals.

Index to Volumes One and Two

Numbers in italics refer to the plates. Generic and specific names of animals are printed in italics

MORE ABOUT PENGUINS AND PELICANS

Penguinews, which appears every month, contains details of all the new books issued by Penguins as they are published. From time to time it is supplemented by *Penguins in Print*, which is a complete list of all books published by Penguins which are in print. (There are well over three thousand of these.)

A specimen copy of *Penguinews* will be sent to you free on request, and you can become a subscriber for the price of the postage – 25p for a year's issues (including the complete lists) if you live in the United Kingdom, or 50p if you live elsewhere. Just write to Dept EP, Penguin Books Ltd, Harmondsworth, Middlesex, enclosing a cheque or postal order, and your name will be added to the mailing list.

Some other books published by Penguins are described on the following pages.

Note: *Penguinews* and *Penguins in Print* are not available in the U.S.A. or Canada

A PELICAN CLASSIC

THE ORIGIN OF SPECIES

Charles Darwin

The Origin of Species is at the root of man's present attitude to himself and the universe: no one book since the *Summa* of Thomas Aquinas has made a comparable impact. Written for the general public of the 1850s, it remains, in the words of Dr Burrow's helpful and entertaining introduction, 'easily the most readable and approachable of the great revolutionary works of the scientific imagination'.

PELICAN CLASSICS

We all know by name the books which have changed history. They lie in almost every library, as monumental as the Pyramids or the Great Wall of China, and as seldom visited. In fact many of these great works can be read with profit today by any intelligent reader. The books may be old but their arguments often find an echo in modern thinking.

The Pelican Classics will present some of the most influential books in philosophy, religion, science, history, politics, and economics in new editions for a modern audience, and each work will be prefaced by a critical introduction assessing its significance for its contemporaries, its effect on succeeding generations, and its relevance today.

THE THEORY OF EVOLUTION

John Maynard Smith

All living plants and animals, including man, are the modified descendents of one of a few simple living things. A hundred years ago Darwin and Wallace, in their theory of natural selection, or the survival of the fittest, explained how evolution could have happened, in terms of processes known to take place today. This book describes how their theory has been confirmed, but at the same time transformed, by recent research, and in particular by the discovery of the laws of inheritance.

After stating the problem and Darwin's answer to it, the author describes what can be learnt from laboratory experiments, and then gives the evidence that evolutionary changes are taking place today in wild populations. Later chapters discuss the origins of species, and the special problems which arise in studying the origins of major groups of animals and plants. The book ends by contrasting evolutionary and historical changes, and considers the relative importance of the two processes in the origin and future development of human society.

HUMAN HEREDITY

Cedric Carter

Such ideas as aristocracy, hereditary rights, and good breeding have for years been out of favour. It remains true, nevertheless, that the difference between one man and another is due as much to breeding as to background.

In this study of heredity a past secretary of the Eugenics Society, now working for the Medical Research Council, outlines our present knowledge about the subject and takes a look into the future. Wherever material environment improves, heredity differences become more and more important. Better education and more efficient health services, by eliminating needless wastage, are already beginning to underline inequalities in genetic endowment. For, clearly, men are not born equal.

MAN AND ENERGY

A. R. Ubbelohde

It is the control and use of 'dead' energy – whether from coal, oil, or uranium – which is the distinctive mark of modern civilization. The machine (powered by men or animals) is comparatively ancient. It was not until about A.D. 1700 that men began to move slowly forward from the employment of wind and water as prime movers towards the use of steam and atomic energy. With unlimited power now at our command, Utopia has yielded to Tektopia in human dreams. Technical perfection, however, is accompanied by such threats as dislocation of labour and total destruction in war.

The Professor of Thermodynamics at the Imperial College of Science and Technology surveys in these pages the shifting relationship between man and energy, in history and in the new era. The growth of man's power is illustrated with many woodcuts and drawings, and his final chapters on the science of thermodynamics, with its two famous laws, explain very lucidly the theoretical advances which have allowed men to enslave the energy latent in matter.

THE NERVOUS SYSTEM

Peter Nathan

The nervous system enables us to move, to be aware of things, and to collect our impressions together. From all we have remembered we then make decisions and perform work, whether it is the handling of implements or the creation of art or music. The same nervous system provides us with simple and primitive reflexes and also enables us to avoid being bound by reflex reactions. It controls our bodies, our glands, breathing, heart, bowels, and bladder. It makes us stay awake or makes us sleep, and when we sleep it makes us dream. When the nervous system is upset, we get pins and needles in the finger-tips, numbness, paralysis, epilepsy, migraine, and shingles.

The Nervous System explains the whole field of nerves both to general readers and to those with scientific training. It covers subjects as diverse as memory, how the brain affects behaviour, how we see, hear, smell, balance, imagine, how messages are sent along the nerves, and how the nervous system has some resemblance to computers. By clear exposition, witty analogies and examples culled from the whole animal kingdom, Dr Peter Nathan shows that this all-embracing subject can be made comprehensible to everyone who has ever asked questions about the mind, the brain, psychology, psychiatry ... or the nervous system.

MICROBES AND MAN

John Postgate

Life on earth, as we know it, could not exist without microbes. These microscopic creatures, which live in seas and rivers, soil and dust, the food we eat and the air we breathe, and even in and on ourselves, are far from being exclusively the carriers of disease.

A professor of microbiology explains in this new Pelican how microbes keep our terrestrial biochemistry moving and influence our food supplies at every stage, from the growth of crops to their preparation, consumption, and digestion; how, aeons ago, they laid down coal and mineral deposits, on which heavy industry depends today; how they function in the corrosion and deterioration of materials and in the disposal of wastes; how they play their part in light industry – for example in wine-making, producing antibiotics and synthetic hormones, even in laundering.

Though in some senses primitive, microbes are the most versatile of living things: they provide, too, some insight into the sorts of creatures that existed when life began on this planet ... and could exist elsewhere in the universe. Moreover, as Professor Postgate makes clear, our knowledge of the life processes of microbes forms the basis of modern cell biology.

CHANGING MAN'S BEHAVIOUR

H. R. Beech

Since Pavlov's famous work on the conditioning of dogs and Watson's 'Little Albert' experiments of nearly fifty years ago, many psychologists have formed the conclusion that abnormal behaviour may be the results of faulty learning rather than of deep-seated conflict, as taught by Freud. A direct attack upon symptoms is, in their opinion, therefore justified.

This radical departure from the traditional psychotherapeutic viewpoint has led to the rapid growth of a completely new style of active and dynamic treatments called 'behaviour therapy'. The powerful and compelling ideas involved threaten not only to challenge existing notions about the nature and treatment of psychological disorders, but to change and shape our way of thinking about human behaviour in the widest context.

Dr Beech outlines the nature and development of behaviour therapy in this Pelican and shows how patients in Britain and America are today being treated by these methods on a large scale. The techniques themselves are described in detail and their use is illustrated by numerous references to a wide range of clinical problems including alcoholism, homosexuality, sexual fetishes, irrational fears, and many other forms of psychological disturbance.

This book introduces to the general reader a new approach which may well resolve, by its speed and efficiency, the classic objections to orthodox psychotherapy – time, money, and limited effectiveness.

A DICTIONARY OF BIOLOGY

M. Abercrombie, C. J. Hickman, M. L. Johnson

5th Revised Edition

In this dictionary the authors' aim is to explain biological terms which a layman may meet when reading scientific literature; to define the terms which a student of biology has to master at the beginning of his career – the thousand or so words which so grimly guard the approaches to the science; and to provide a reminder for the professional biologist reading outside his own narrow field. The entries are not restricted to a bare definition: some information about most of the things named is given, so as to convey something of their significance in biological discussion.

The authors have tried, as it were, to interpret a foreign language as it is actually used. It would be wrong to rely on etymology as a guide to correct usage. The meaning of a Greek root may be unequivocal, but biologists are not talking Greek: they are using a living language, and the proof of the meaning is in the speaking.